ELSEVIER'S DICTIONARY OF HYDROGEOLOGY

In Three Languages
English . French . German

COMPILED AND ARRANGED ON
AN ENGLISH ALPHABETICAL BASIS BY

HANS-OLAF PFANNKUCH

Associate Professor, Department of Geology and Geophysics,
University of Minnesota, Minneapolis, U.S.A.

ELSEVIER PUBLISHING COMPANY
AMSTERDAM/LONDON/NEW YORK
1969

DISTRIBUTION OF THIS ELSEVIER DICTIONARY
IS BEING HANDLED BY THE FOLLOWING
TEAM OF PUBLISHERS:

for the U.S.A. and Canada:
AMERICAN ELSEVIER PUBLISHING COMPANY, INC., NEW YORK

for Great Britain:
ELSEVIER PUBLISHING COMPANY, LTD., BARKING, ESSEX

for all remaining areas:
ELSEVIER PUBLISHING COMPANY, AMSTERDAM

Standard Book Number 444-40717-0

Library of Congress Card Number 67-19852

To my father
Johannes Pfannkuch

PREFACE

Hydrogeology, in its older and more restricted definition, deals with the occurrence and movement of ground water within the subsurface environment and its interrelation with the geological framework. It represents, however, only part of the hydrologic cycle which is the logical basis for all integral water resources planning. The modern hydrogeologist has to be thoroughly familiar with all aspects of the hydrologic cycle that directly influence the ground water situation. He has furthermore to be knowledgeable in ground water exploration, drilling and development techniques, as well as in the increasingly qualitative laboratory and analytical methods. In water resources planning and development, the hydrogeologist has to assume the role of the integrating generalist besides that of the specialist in his own field in order to bring together intelligently all pieces of information and to fit them into their proper place.

The aim of this dictionary is to cover the range of words and technical terms occurring in the field of hydrogeology proper, geohydrology, which deals with the analytical methods of hydromechanics in the geological and related laboratory context, ground water exploration through geophysical methods, aquifer development and exploitation through well-drilling and completion methods. Those parts of the hydrological cycle that have a direct bearing on the ground water situation are included, such as hydrometeorology, surface hydrology, hydrogeochemistry, and water quality. In recent years many new analytical tools, computer methods and laboratory procedures have been introduced or adapted from other fields in an interdisciplinary approach to the subject matter. It is only appropriate that the most frequently used terms be included.

The entries have been chosen from the English literature as cited in the bibliography and checked against the standard works in French and German. Terms were selected on the basis of their relevance and representativity in the principal categories and also according to frequency of appearance in the hydrogeological literature when they came from borderline and overlapping disciplines. In most cases an English definition is given to facilitate use and comprehension as well as to avoid ambiguities. Both standard works and specialized treatises of the subject matter were used as sources and reference. The English spelling is according to the American usage and follows Webster, the French Larousse, and the German Duden, with the exception of using ss instead of the β for typographical reasons.

The dictionary is intended for the hydrogeologist, hydrologist, earth scientist engineer and water resources planner, who have to keep up with the scientific and trade literature in the respective languages. Furthermore, it will be useful for those authors and information analysts who have to translate titles and abstracts of scientific articles in the field for the purpose of information dissemination and retrieval.

Although great care has been taken in selecting, defining and finding the equivalent French and German terms, certain omissions, ambiguities and errors are bound to occur in a dictionary of this scope. The author appreciates and encourages all suggestions, comments and criticisms pertaining to this dictionary. Last but not least, the help of Mrs. Marilyn Clarke for typing the manuscript, the author's wife for keeping the file, and Dr. Richard Davis for reading and discussing parts of the manuscript are gratefully acknowledged.

Saint Paul, 1969   Hans-Olaf Pfannkuch

BIBLIOGRAPHY

Andreae, H.: *Neue hydrometrische Verfahren*, pp.202, Oldenbourg Verlag, München, 1966.

Brinkmann, R.: *Abriss der Geologie: Allgemeine Geologie*, Band I, pp.286, Enke Verlag, Stuttgart, 1956.

Castany, G.: *Traité Pratique des Eaux Souterraines*, pp.657, Dunod, Paris, 1963.

Chow, Ven Te (editor): *Handbook of Applied Hydrology*, pp.1453, McGraw-Hill, New York, 1964.

Dadone, R.: *Notions sur les Diagraphies dans les Sondages*, Réf. 3030, Institut Français du Pétrole, pp.53, Ed. Technip, Paris, 1959.

Davis, S.N. and DeWiest, R.J.M.: *Hydrogeology*, pp.463, Wiley, New York, 1966.

DeWiest, R.J.M.: *Geohydrology*, pp.366, Wiley, New York, 1965.

v. Englehardt, W.: *Der Porenraum der Sedimente*, pp.207, Springer Verlag, Berlin, 1960.

Goguel, J. (editor): *La Terre*, pp.1735, Encyclopédie de la Pléiade, Librairie Gallimard, Paris, 1959.

Houpeurt, A.: Production *Etude des Roches Magasins*, Tome I, Réf.1093, Institut Français du Pétrole, pp.143, Ed. Technip, Paris, 1956.

Houpeurt, A.: Production *Mouvement des Fluides dans les Gisements d'Hydrocarbures - Essai des Puits*, Tome III, Réf. 2703, Institut Français du Pétrole, pp.229, Ed. Technip, Paris, 1958.

Keilhack, K.: *Lehrbuch der Grundwasser - und Quellenkunde*, pp.545, Geb. Bornträger, Berlin, 1912.

Keller, R.: *Gewässer und Wasserhaushalt des Festlandes*, pp.520, B.G. Teubner Verlagsges., Berlin, 1961.

Kettner, R.: *Allgemeine Geologie: Der Bau der Erdkruste*, Band I, pp.412, VEB Deutscher Verlag der Wissenschaften, Berlin, 1958.

Leliavsky, S.: *An Introduction to Fluvial Hydraulics*, pp.257, Dover Publ., New York, 1966.

Linck, G. and Jung, H.: *Grundriss der Mineralogie und Petrographie*, pp.290, Gustav Fischer, Jena, 1935.

Lynch, E.J.: *Formation Evaluation*, pp.422, Harper & Row, New York, 1962.

Maull, O.: *Handbuch der Geomorphologie*, 2nd edn., pp.600, Verlag F. Deuticke, Wien, 1958.

Meinzer, O.E.: *Outline of Ground-Water Hydrology*, U.S. G. S. Water Supply Paper 494, pp.71, U.S. Govt. Printing Office, Washington, D.C., 1923.

Meinzer, O.E.: *The Occurrence of Ground Water in the United States*,
U.S. G. S. Water Supply Paper 489, Reprint 1959, pp.321, U.S. Govt.
Printing Office, Washington, D.C., 1923.

Meinzer, O.E. (editor): *Hydrology*, pp.712, Dover Publ., New York, 1942.

Muskat, M.: *The Flow of Homogeneous Fluids Through Porous Media*, pp.763,
J.W. Edwards, Ann Arbor, Michigan, 1946.

Nahrgang, G.: *Zur Theorie des vollkommenen und unvollkommenen Brunnens*,
pp.43, Springer Verlag, Berlin, 1954.

Roche, M.: *Hydrologie de Surface*, pp.430, Gauthier-Villars, Paris, 1963.

Schoeller, H.: *Arid Zone Hydrology - Recent Developments*, pp.125, UNESCO,
Paris, 1959.

Schoeller, H.: *Les Eaux Souterraines*, pp.642, Masson & Cie., Paris, 1962.

Thurner, A.: *Hydrogeologie*, pp.350, Springer Verlag, Wien, 1967.

Todd, D.K.: *Ground Water Hydrology*, pp.336, 6th printing, Wiley, New York,
1967.

Tolman, C.F.: *Ground Water*, pp.539, 1st edn., McGraw-Hill, New York, 1937.

Twort, A.C.: *A Textbook of Water Supply*, pp.422, American Elsevier,
New York, 1964.

Vollmer, E.: *Encyclopaedia of Hydraulics, Soil and Foundation Engineering*,
pp.398, Elsevier, Amsterdam, 1967.

Wechmann, A.: *Hydrologie*, pp.535, Oldenbourg Verlag, München, 1964.

Wundt, W.: *Gewässerkunde*, pp.320, Springer Verlag, Berlin, 1953.

Dictionaries

American Geological Institute, *Dictionary of Geological Terms*, pp.545,
2nd edn., Dolphin Reference Book C360, Doubleday & Co., New York,
1962.

Ketchian, S., Desbrandes, R., Dupuy, M., Pfannkuch, H.O.: *Dictionnaire
Pétrolier des Techniques de Diagraphie, Forage et Production*, pp.334,
Ed. Technip, Paris, 1965.

Meinck, F. and Möhle, H.: *Dictionary of Water and Sewage Engineering*,
pp.449, Elsevier, Amsterdam, 1963.

Moltzer, J.: *Elsevier's Oilfield Dictionary*, pp.162, Elsevier, Amsterdam, 1965.

Visser, A.D.: *Elsevier's Dictionary of Soil Mechanics*, pp.359, Elsevier,
Amsterdam, 1965.

Office of Water Resources Research, *Water Resources Thesaurus*, pp.237,
U.S. Govt. Printing Office, Washington, D.C., 1966.

Duden, *Rechtschreibung der deutschen Sprache und der Fremdwörter*, 13. Aufl.,
Duden Verlag, Wiesbaden, 1952.

Petit Larousse, 22 tirage, pp.1798, Ed. Larousse, Paris, 1966.

Webster's Seventh New Collegiate Dictionary, G. & C. Merriam Co., Springfield,
Massachusetts, 1967.

CONTENTS

Preface vii
Bibliography ix
Language Indication and Abbreviations xii
Basic Table 1
French Index 137
German Index 151

LANGUAGE INDICATION – LANGUES – SPRACHEN

f French   français   Französisch
d German   allemand   Deutsch

ABBREVIATIONS

f	feminine	*mpl*	masculine plural
fpl	feminine plural	*n*	neuter
m	masculine	*npl*	neuter plural

BASIC TABLE

A

1   ABANDONED WELL
f   puits *m* abandonné
d   aufgelassene Bohrung *f*

2   ABLATION
wearing away of ice or snow
surfaces through evaporation
f   ablation *f*
d   Ablation *f*

3   ABOVE GROUND
f   de surface
d   oberirdisch; über Tage

4   ABSOLUTE ATMOSPHERE
10^6 dynes per cm^2
f   atmosphère *f* absolue;
atmosphère physique
d   absolute Atmosphäre *f*,
physikalische Atmosphäre

5   ABSOLUTE HUMIDITY
moisture content by weight per unit
volume of air
f   humidité *f* absolue
d   absolute Feuchtigkeit *f*

6   ABSOLUTE POROSITY
porosity established by taking into
account all interconnected and non-
connected or isolated void volumes
f   porosité *f* absolue
d   absolute Porosität *f*

7   ABSOLUTE PRESSURE
f   pression *f* absolue
d   Absolutdruck *m*

8   ABSORBING WELL
recharge well, infiltration well
f   puits *m* de recharge
d   Versickerungsbrunnen *m*

9   ABYSS
extremely great depth
f   abîme *m*; gouffre *m*
d   Schlund *m*; Abgrund *m*

10   ACCESSORY MINERAL
mineral constituents of a rock
occurring only in very small
amounts
f   minéral *m* accessoire
d   Begleitmineral *n*

11   ACCLIVITY
ascending slope
f   pente *f* ascendante
d   ansteigender Hang *m*

12   ACCRETION
land addition by sediment deposition
of a stream
f   remblaiement *m*; exhaussement *m*
d   fluviatile Akkumulation *f*;
Aufschüttung *f*

13   ACCUMULATED PRECIPITATION
f   précipitations *f pl* cumulées
d   Niederschlagssumme *f*; Niederschlagsfülle *f*

14   ACCUMULATION
building of new land by addition of
sedimentary deposits
f   accumulation *f*
d   Anhäufung *f*, Akkumulation *f*

ACCUMULATION, moisture see 2062

15   ACIDITY
property of water with a pH below 4.5,
caused by presence of mineral
acids; expressed in equivalent
amounts of calcium carbonate
f   acidité *f*
d   Azidität *f*; Säuregrad *m*

16   ACIDIZING OF WELLS
improving well yield by pumping
acids to clean walls or create
solution channels
f   traitement *m* acide de puits
d   Säurebehandlung *f* von Brunnen

17   ACID MINE DRAINAGE
acid waters originating from
surface or underground mine
workings
f   effluent *m* acide (venant d'une
mine)
d   saure Grubenwässer *n pl*

18   ACOUSTIC LOG
log measuring speed of sound in
rocks to determine porosity
f   diagraphie *f* sonique
d   Geschwindigkeitslog *n*

19 ACOUSTIC RESISTANCE
product of wave velocity and rock
density indicating the reflective
power of a boundary between two
strata
f résistance *f* acoustique
d Schallhärte *f*

20 ACRE-FOOT
amount of water which would cover
1 acre to a depth of 1 ft (326.000
gal.)
f mesure *f* de volume anglo-
américaine (1230m)
d Anglo-Amerikanisches Hohlmass
n (1230m)

21 ACTIVE GLACIER
glacier in active stage of growth
and movement
f glacier *m* actif
d aktiver Gletscher *m*

22 ACTIVE WATER
water with corrosive properties
f eau *f* active; eau *f* corrosive
d Aktivwässer *npl*; korrosive
Wässer *npl*

23 ACTIVITY COEFFICIENT
f coefficient *m* d'activité
d Aktivitätskoeffizient *m*

24 ADAPTER
f pièce *f* d'ajustage
d Passtück *n*

25 ADIABATIC
property of thermodynamic process
with no heat exchange
f adiabatique
d adiabatisch

26 ADJUSTED STREAM
stream flowing parallel to strike
of underlying beds
f rivière *f* subséquente
d subsequenter Fluss *m*

ADJUSTMENT, zero see 3028

27 ADJUSTMENT CURVE
f courbe *f* d'ajustage
d Ausgleichskurve *f*

28 ADSORPTION
f adsorption *f*
d Adsorption *f*

29 ADVECTION
phenomenon of cool air mass
intruding and interrupting evaporation and causing condenstion due to
heat loss
f advection *f*
d Advektion *f*

30 AERATION
introduction of air into water or
other liquid
f aération *f*
d Belüftung *f*

31 AERIAL PHOTOGRAPH
f photographie *f* aérienne
d Luftbildaufnahme *f*

32 AEROBIC
property of aquatic forms of life
existing only in presence of oxygen
f aérobique
d aerobisch

33 AGGRADATION
land addition through sediment
deposition
f remblaiement *m*
d Akkumulation *f*, Aufschüttung *f*

34 AGGRADING RIVER
river actively elevating its bed by
deposition of sediments
f rivière *f* remblayante
d akkumulierender Fluss *m*

35 AGGREGATE
grain mixture held together loosely
f agregat *m*
d Aggregat *n*

AGGREGATE, soil see 2589

36 AGGRESSIVE
quality of waters that attack metals
and concrete chemically by
dissolution
f agressif
d angreifend; aggressiv

37 A-HORIZON
topmost eluviated horizon of a soil
profile
f horizon *m* éluvial
d A-Horizont *m*; Eluvialhorizont *m*;
Auslaugungszone *f*

AIR, compressed see 332

38   AIR CONTENT
     f   indice *m* d'aération
     d   Porenluftgehalt *m*

39   AIR DRILLING
     drilling with air as drilling fluid
     for the transport of cuttings
     f   forage *m* à l'air
     d   Bohren *n* mit Luftspülung

40   AIR-DRY
     state of equilibrium between
     moisture held in porous sample and
     atmosphere
     f   sec à l'air
     d   lufttrocken

41   AIR HAMMER
     percussion drilling tool
     f   marteau *m* pneumatique
     d   Presslufthammer *m*

42   AIR LIFT
     method of lifting liquid column in
     a well by introducing air at the
     bottom
     f   air-lift *m*
     d   Lufthebeverfahren *n*

43   AIR LINE
     cable suspended above the stream
     water level (in discharge
     measurements)
     f   câble *m* exondé
     d   Luftseil *n*

44   AIR PRESSURE
     f   pression *f* d'air
     d   Luftdruck *m*

45   AIR RELEASE VALVE
     f   clapet *m* à échappement d'air
     d   Luftauslassventil *n*

46   AIR SEPARATING TANK
     tank in which desorbed gases are
     separated from the liquid and
     evacuated by pumping
     f   séparateur *m* d'air
     d   Luftabscheider *m*

47   AIR-VENT
     hole allowing passage of air during
     filling operations of closed
     reservoirs
     f   trou *m* d'aération; trou *m*
          d'échappement
     d   Entlüftungsöffnung *f*

48   ALBEDO
     ratio of reflected radiation to total
     radiation on a natural surface

     f   albedo *m*
     d   Albedo *n*

49   ALGAE CONTROL
     control of growth of micro-organisms
     in water bodies
     f   mesures *f pl* contre les algues
     d   Algenbekämpfung *f*

50   ALGAL LIMESTONE
     limestone formed by calcium
     secreting algae
     f   calcaire *m* d'algues
     d   Algenkalkstein *m*

51   ALGONKIAN
     geologic period of the Pre-Cambrian
     era
     f   Éocambrien *m*
     d   Algonkium *n*

52   ALKALI FLAT
     salt covered or heavily saline
     depression in arid environment
     f   salina *f*; chott *m*
     d   Salzpfanne *f*

53   ALKALI METAL
     f   métal *m* alcalin
     d   Alkalimetall *n*

54   ALKALINITY
     the property of water to neutralize
     acids expressed as calcium carbonate
     equivalents
     f   alcalinité *f*
     d   Alkalinität *f*

55   ALLOCHTHONOUS
     said of material originating from
     a different locality than the one
     where it is deposited
     f   allochtone
     d   allochthon; angeschwemmt;
          nicht bodenständig

56   ALLUVIAL APRON
     fan-like plain of glacial outwash
     deposit
     f   cône *m* d'alluvions
     d   Sandr *m*; alluviale Gletscher-
          ablagerung *f*

57   ALLUVIAL CHANNEL
     channel bed composed of
     unconsolidated alluvial material
     f   chenal *m* alluvial
     d   alluviale Rinne *f*

58   ALLUVIAL FAN
     fan-like deposit of detrital

material from steep mountain slopes
f éventail *m* d'alluvions; cône *m*
d'alluvions
d alluvialer Schuttfächer *m*

59 ALLUVIAL FAN DEPOSIT
f dépôt *m* d'éboulis
d Fanglomerat *n*

60 ALLUVIAL PLAIN
plain formed by the deposition of
water borne sediments
f plaine *f* alluviale
d alluviale Aufschüttungsebene *f*

61 ALLUVIAL VENEER
very thin cover of water borne
sediments
f pellicule *f* alluviale
d dünner Schuttmantel *m*

62 ALLUVIUM
sedimentary deposits of streams
in relatively recent time
f alluvion *m*
d Alluvium *n*

63 ALTERNATING CURRENT
f courant *m* alternatif
d Wechselstrom *m*

64 ALVEOLAR
of a honeycomb shape; of certain
erosional patterns resulting in
cellular structure
f alvéolaire
d wabenförmig

65 AMMETER
current meter
f ampèremètre *m*
d Strommesser *m*, Ampèremeter *n*

66 AMORPHOUS SILICA
silica with no definite crystalline
structure
f silice *m* amorphe
d amorphe Kieselsäure *f*

67 AMORTIZATION
f amortissement *m*
d Stossdämpfung *f*

68 AMPHIBOLE;
HORNBLENDE
silica mineral
f amphibole *m*; hornblende *m*
d Hornblende *f*; Amphibol *n*

69 AMPLITUDE
half distance between the two

extreme points of a wave phenomenon
f amplitude *f*
d Amplitude *f*; Schwingungsweite *f*

70 ANALOG
physical or mathematical systems
obeying similar differential equations
with similar boundary conditions
as prototype such as network analogs,
electrolyte tanks etc. in ground
water flow problems
f modèle *m* analogique
d Analogmodell *n*

ANALOG, conductive-liquid see 342
-, conductive-sheet see 343

71 ANALOG SOLUTION
f solution *f* analogique
d analogische Lösung *f*; Analoglösung *f*

ANALYSIS, chemical see 284
-, complete see 330
-, core see 388
-, frequency see 388
-, morphometric see 2078
-, physical see 2225
-, sieve see 2543
-, statistical see 2643

72 ANCHOR ICE;
GROUND ICE
ice temporarily attached to the
bottom of a river
f glace *f* de fond; glace *f* profonde
d Grundeis *n*

73 ANDESITE
basic volcanic rock
f andésite *m*
d Andesit *m*

74 ANEMOMETER
apparatus to measure wind speeds
f anémomètre *m*
d Windmesser *m*

75 ANGLE OF CONTACT;
WETTING ANGLE
angle between liquid phase and solid
boundary measured through liquid
phase
f angle *m* de contact
d Randwinkel *m*; Kontaktwinkel *m*

76 ANGLE OF INCIDENCE
in seismic reflection method angle
between the incident seismic ray and
the normal to the surface of
reflection such as boundaries between

geological formations of different
acoustic properties
f   angle *m* d'incidence
d   Einfallswinkel *m*

77 ANGLE OF REFLEXION
in seismic reflection method angle
of the reflected ray with respect
to the normal to the reflecting
surface
f   angle *m* de réflexion
d   Reflexionswinkel *m*

78 ANGLE OF REFRACTION
in seismic refraction method angle
of the refracted ray with respect
to the normal of the refracting
surface
f   angle *m* de réfraction
d   Brechungswinkel *m*

79 ANGLE OF REPOSE
natural slope of unsupported granular
material
f   angle *m* de repos
d   Böschungswinkel *m*

80 ANGULAR
property of unconsolidated grains
with sharp edge
f   anguleux à arêtes vives
d   kantig; eckig

81 ANGULAR UNCONFORMITY
unconformity with marked
difference in dip of the superimposed
series
f   discordance *f*
d   Diskordanz *f*

82 ANHYDRIDE
anhydrous calcium sulfate, $CaSO_4$
f   anhydrite *m*; sulfate *m* de calcium
    anhydre
d   schwefelsaurer Kalk *m*; Anhydrit *n*

83 ANISOTROPIC
property of aquifer systems displaying different hydrological
properties in different directions
f   anisotropique
d   anisotropisch

84 ANNUAL FROST ZONE
top layer of ground subject to annual
freezing and thawing
f   zone *f* du gel annuel
d   jährliche Gefrierzone *f*

85 ANNUAL MEAN
mean value taken over all events

occurred during a year such as
precipitation, river stages, water
table levels
f   moyenne *f* annuelle
d   Jahresdurchschnitt *m*

86 ANNULUS
annular space between drill pipe
and casing or between casing and
walls
f   espace *m* annulaire
d   Ringraum *m*; Annulus *m*

87 ANOMALY
deviation from normally expected
findings, especially in exploration
geophysics an indication of change
in subsurface environment (i.e.
gravity-anomaly)
f   anomalie *f*
d   Abweichung *f*; Anomalie *f*

ANOMALY, gravity see 880

88 ANTECEDENT PRECIPITATION
    INDEX
index based on amount of previous
precipitations
f   indice *m* de saturation
d   Vorwetterbeiwert *m*

89 ANTECEDENT-SOIL MOISTURE
degree of water saturation in the soil
prior to a precipitation event
f   teneur *f* antécédente d'eau
    dans le sol
d   vorhergehender Bodenwasser-
    gehalt *m*

90 ANTECEDENT STREAM
stream having established its course
before occurrence of orogenic events
altering general drainage pattern
f   rivière *f* antécédente
d   antezedenter Flusslauf *m*

91 ANTECEDENT VALLEY
valley established before
occurrence of orogenic movement
f   vallée *f* antécédente
d   antezedentes Tal *n*

92 ANTICLINAL VALLEY
valley established along the axis
of an eroded anticline
f   vallée *f* anticlinale
d   Satteltal *n*

93 ANTICLINE
upfolded stratum

f   anticlinal *m*
d   Sattel *m*

94   APATITE
phosphorite mineral
f   apatite *m*
d   Apatit *m*

95   APPARENT RESISTIVITY
f   résistivité *f* apparente
d   scheinbarer spezifischer
    Widerstand *m*

96   APPROACH SEGMENT
part of hydrograph curve before
onset of precipitation
f   segment *m* non-influencé de
    l'hydrogramme
d   unbeeiflusster Kurvenast *m*

97   APPROPRIATION
f   concession *f*
d   Verleihung *f*

98   AQUEDUCT
conduit to convey water, usually
above ground
f   aqueduc *m*
d   Aquädukt *m*

99   AQUICLUDE
impermeable rock stratum storing
but not transmitting ground water
f   aquiclude *m*
d   Grundwasserstauer *m*

100   AQUIFER
geological subsurface formation
containing and transmitting ground
water
f   couche *f* aquifère; milieu *m*
    aquifère
d   Grundwasserleiter *m*

AQUIFER, artesian see 113
-, coastal see 314
-, leaky see 1147
-, tilted see 2790

101   AQUIFER STORAGE
gas storage in an aquifer
f   stockage *m* de gaz dans une
    couche aquifère
d   Gasspeicherung *f* im Wasser-
    träger

102   AQUIFUGE
rock neither storing nor transmitting water
f   aquifuge *m*
d   Grundwassersperre *f*

103   AQUITARD
semi-confining stratum permitting
some groundwater flow at a very
low transmission rate
f   aquitard *m*
d   begrenzt durchlässiger Grund-
    wasserstauer *m*

104   ARAGONITE
instable orthorhombic carbonate
mineral, $CaCO_3$
f   aragonite *m*
d   Aragonit *n*

105   ARCHEAN
geologic period or the Pre-Cambrian
era
f   Infracambrien *m*
d   Archaikum *n*

AREA, drainage see 548
-, intake see 1048
-, overbank see 2153
-, wetted see 3009

106   AREA ELEVATION DISTRIBUTION
surficial distribution of elevations
for a given area
f   répartition *f* hypsométrique
d   Höhenverteilung *f*

107   AREA OF INFLUENCE
area over which effects of well
drainage are perceptible
f   aire *f* d'influence
d   Absenkungsfläche *f*; Einwirkungs-
    fläche *f*

108   ARGILLACEOUS
property of rocks containing clay
in non-negligible proportions
f   argileux
d   tonhaltig

109   ARGILLACEOUS LIMESTONE
limestone containing a considerable
portion of clay
f   calcaire *m* argileux; marle *m*
d   toniger Kalkstein *m*; Mergel *m*

110   ARID
property of dry climates and regions
with a net deficiency of moisture
f   aride
d   arid; trocken

111   ARITHMETIC MEAN
f   moyenne *f* arithmétique
d   arithmetisches Mittel *n*

112 ARRIVAL TIME
time interval for first seismic
wave to arrive at geophone
f instant *m* de la première
   arrivée
d Zeitdauer *f* bis zum Anfangs-
   einsatz

113 ARTESIAN AQUIFER
confined aquifer where piezometric
surface rises above top of aquifer
bed
f couche *f* aquifère artésienne
d artesischer Grundwasserleiter *m*

114 ARTESIAN SPRING
water flowing under artesian pressure
pressure with piezometric surface
above ground surface
f source *f* artésienne
d artesische Quelle *f*

115 ARTESIAN WELL
free flowing well
f puits *m* artésien
d artesischer Brunnen *m*

ARTESIAN WELL, flowing see 756

116 ARTIFICIAL DISCHARGE
discharge of ground water through
pumping of wells
f exutoire *m* artificiel
d künstliche Grundwasserspende *f*

117 ARTIFICIAL RECHARGE
artificial replenishment of an
aquifer
f recharge *f* artificielle
d künstliche Grundwasserneubildung *f*

118 ATMOMETER
instrument to measure intensities
of evaporation
f atmomètre *m*
d Atmometer *n*; Verdunstungsmesser *m*

119 ATMOSPHERE
gaseous envelope of earth containing
and transporting air and water in
vapor and condensed form

f atmosphère *f*
d Atmosphäre *f*

ATMOSPHERE, absolute see 4

120 ATTRITION
wearing away of rocks by friction
f attrition *f*; usure *f*
d Abrieb *m*

121 AUGER
rotary drilling device where the
dry cuttings are removed continuously
by helical grooves on the drill pipe
f tarière *f*
d Erdbohrer *m*

122 AUGITE
silica mineral; pyroxene
f augite *m*
d Augit *n*

123 AUTOCHTHONOUS
of sedimentary material originating
and deposited at about the same
location
f autochtone
d autochthon; bodenständig

124 AVAILABLE WATER
water available to plants in soil
zone as defined by the interval
between field capacity and wilting
point
f eau *f* disponible (pour les
   plantes)
d nutzbare Kapazität *f*; ausnutzbares Wasser *n*; pflanzennutzbares Wasser *n*

125 AVALANCHE
snow or ice mass sliding or rolling
rapidly down a mountain slope
f avalanche *f*
d Lawine *f*

126 AZONAL SOIL
soils without distinct layering in
horizons
f sol *m* azonal
d azonales Bodenprofil *n*

B

127 BACKFLOW
f reflux *m*
d Rückfluss *m*

128 BACKGROUND NOISE
level of intensity of signals due to
normal activities other than the
specific signal emission of especial
importance in the interpretation of
geophysical data
f bruit *m* de fond
d Störgeräusch *n*

129 BACKPRESSURE
f contrepression *f*
d Gegendruck *m*

130 BACKWASHING METHOD
method of well development by
repeated flushing
f méthode *f* de lavage par contre-
courant
d Rückspülungsmethode *f*

131 BACKWASH WATER
f eau *f* de rinçage
d Spülwasser *n*

132 BACKWATER
accumulated water above normal
level of a water course due to
impoundment at a point downstream
f eaux *fpl* de remous
d Rückstau *m*; Rückstauwasser *n*

133 BACKWATER CURVE
water surface profile in stream or
channel above constriction or
impoundment
f courbe *f* de remous; courbe *f* de
retenue
d Rückstaukurve *f*; Staukurve *f*

134 BAILER
cylindrical container with bottom
valve for the clearing of drill
cuttings from the bottom hole
f cuiller *f*
d Sandpumpe *f*; Sandlöffel *m*;
Schmandlöffel *m*

BAILING LINE see sand line

135 BALL VALVE
f clapet *m* à billes
d Kugelventil *n*

136 BANK
ascending slope bordering a river
(or lake)
f rive *f*; berge *f*
d Ufer *n*

BANK, high see 931

137 BANK EROSION
erosion of a river bank
f érosion *f* de la rive
d Ufererosion *f*; Seitenerosion *f*

138 BANK STORAGE
river water having infiltrated river
banks during a high flow period and
being retained in temporary storage
f emmagasinement *m* dans la rive
d Uferspeicherung *f*; Uferfiltrierung

139 BAROGRAPH
pressure recorder
f barographe *m*
d Barograph *m*; Druckscheiber *m*

140 BAROMETER
indicator of barometric pressure
f baromètre *m*
d Barometer *n*

141 BAROMETRIC EFFICIENCY
ratio of water level change to
atmospheric pressure change in a
well
f coefficient *m* barométrique;
efficacité *f* barométrique
d barometrischer Wirkungsgrad *m*

142 BAROMETRIC PRESSURE
f pression barométrique *f*;
d barometrischer Druck *m*

143 BARRIER
geological formation or part of a
formation having become impervious
to ground water movement due to
facies change
f barrière *f*
d Barriere *f*

BARRIER, fresh-water see 792
-, groundwater see 894
-, hydrologic see 973
-, permeability see 2206

144 BARRIER SPRING
subsurface barrier forcing water to
rise to surface and discharge as
spring
f source *f* de débordement
d Stauquelle *f*

145 BASAL COMPLEX
crystalline igneous or metamorphic
rocks underlying sedimentary
series
f socle *m*
d Urgebirge *n*; kristalliner Grundkomplex *m*

146 BASAL CONGLOMERATE
conglomerate deposited on an
erosion surface; conglomerate at
bottom of a new sequence of layers
f conglomérat *m* basal
d Basalkonglomerat *n*

147 BASALT
lava belonging to gabbro family
f basalte *m*
d Basalt *m*

148 BASE-EXCHANGE
f échange *m* de base
d Basenaustausch *m*

149 BASE FLOW;
BASE RUNOFF
sustained fair weather runoff
f flot *m* de base; débit *m* de base
d Trockenwetterkurve *f*

150 BASE LEVEL
lowest level of erosion by a stream
f niveau *m* de base
d Erosionsbasis *f*

151 BASE LEVEL OF EROSION
lowest theoretical level of surface
to be achieved by erosion
f niveau *m* de base d'érosion
d Erosionsbasis *f*

152 BASE LINE
arbitrary line from which deflec-
tions of self potential are read;
shale line
f ligne *f* de base (des marnes)
d Basislinie *f*

153 BASE LOAD
f charge *f* normale
d Grundlast *f*

154 BASE PLATE
plate to seal off bottom of well
f plaque *f* de base
d Fussplatte *f*

BASE RUNOFF see
base flow

155 BASE WIDTH
width of the hydrograph determined
by a line parallel to the time axis
cutting through the points where the
rising limb starts and where
recession curve ends
f temps *m* de base
d Basisbreite *f*

156 BASIN
hydrogeographic unit receiving
precipitation and discharging
runoff in one point
f bassin *m* versant
d Becken *n*

BASIN, closed see 309
-, drainage see 549
-, experimental see 691
-, groundwater see 895
-, infiltration see 1024
-, intermontane see 1064
-, settling see 2516

157 BASIN CHARACTERISTICS
physiographic geologic and ecologic
characteristics of a basin
f caractéristiques *m pl* du bassin
d Beckeneigenschaften *f pl*

158 BASIN METHOD
recharge method by spreading water
in shallow basins
f méthode *f* par bassins d'infiltration
d Sickerbeckenmethode *f*

159 BASIN MOUTH
point at which runoff leaves a basin
f exutoire *m* du bassin
d Münduhg *f* eines Entwässerungsgebietes

160 BASIN PERIMETER
circumference of a basin following
the divide
f périmètre *m* du bassin
d Beckenumfang *m*

BASIN RELIEF, maximum see 1198

161 BASIN SHAPE
f forme *f* du bassin
d Form *f* des Einzugsgebietes;
Beckenform *f*

162 BATHOLITH
very large body of intrusive rock

f batholite *m*
d Batholith *m*; Fussgranit *m*;
   Pluton *m*

163 BATHOMETER
     instrument for measuring water
     depths in wells
     f bathomètre *m*
     d Brunnenpfeife *f*; Grundwasser-
        standsmessgerät *n*

164 BEACH
     shore consisting of sand or gravel
     deposits
     f plage *f*
     d Strand *m*

165 BED
     sedimentary deposit of relatively
     small thickness and great areal
     extent, separated by bedding planes
     from over- and underlying deposits
     f couche *f*; lit *m*
     d Schicht *f*

     BED, intercalated see 1053
     -, lava see 1138
     -, lower confining see 1171
     -, marker see 1188
     -, mortar see 921
     -, river see 2418
     -, stream see 2663
     -, upper confining see 2873

     BEDDING, cross see 414

166 BEDDING JOINT
     joint parallel to or on bedding plane
     f joint *m* de stratification
     d Schichtfuge *f*

167 BEDDING PLANE
     surface separating layers of
     stratified rock
     f plan *m* de stratification
     d Schichtungsebene *f*

168 BED LOAD;
     TRACTION LOAD
     detritic material carried by stream
     on or immediately above its bed
     f charriage *m*; charge *f* du lit
     d Geschiebefracht *f*

169 BEDROCK
     solid rock underlying unconsolidated
     material
     f roche *f* solide
     d Grundgestein *n*; anstehendes
        Gestein *n*; Anstehendes *n*

170 BED ROUGHNESS
     roughness of channel or river bed
     f rugosité *f* du lit
     d Bettrauhigkeit *f*

171 BELL SOCKET
     device for the retrieval of broken
     drill pipe
     f cloche *f* de repêchage
     d Fangglocke *f*

172 BENCH MARK
     fixed point used to mark elevation
     with respect to an adopted datum
     (especially for geodetic survey)
     f borne *f* repère; point *m* fixe
     d Bezugsmarke *f*; Höhenmarkierung

173 BEND
     curve in a water course
     f charnière *f*
     d Umbiegung *f*

     BEND, river see 2419

174 BENTONITIC SHALE
     shale formed at the bottom of the
     sea
     f argilite *f* benthonique
     d benthonischer Schiefer *m*

175 B-HORIZON
     illuvial horizon in which soluble
     material from the overlying
     A-horizon has been deposited
     f horizon *m* illuvial
     d Illuvialhorizont *m*;
        B-Horizont *m*; Ausfällungszone *f*

176 BICARBONATE
     HCO_3
     f bicarbonate *m*
     d Bikarbonat *n*

177 BIFURCATION
     forklike separation of a water
     course into two arms
     f bifurcation *f*
     d Flussgabelung *f*

178 BIFURCATION RATIO
     ratio of number of stream segments
     of a given order to the number of
     segments of next high order
     f indice *m* de bifurcation
     d Verzweigungsverhältnis *n*;
        Bifurkationsverhältnis *n*

179 BIOCHEMICAL OXYGEN DEMAND
     (BOD)

f demande f biochimique en
oxygène (D.B.O.)
d biochemischer Sauerstoffbedarf m (B.S.B.)

180 BIOTITE
dark iron-magnesia mica
f biotite m
d Biotit m; dunkler Glimmer m

BIT, core see 390
-, cross see 415
-, diamond drilling see 496
-, drag see 545
-, drilling see 572
-, dull see 606
-, jet see 1096
-, pilot see 2234
-, roller see 2433
-, tricone rock see 2841

181 BIT CLEARANCE
clearance between bit and bore hole
sidewall
f jeu m du trépan
d Meisselspiel n

182 BIT WEIGHT
weight exerted by string of drill
pipe and drill collar on the drilling
bit
f charge f sur l'outil
d Bohrdruck m

183 BLANK CASING
solid casing without ports or outlets
f tubage m plein
d Vollverrohrung f

184 BLASTING CAP
primary charge to set off detonation
f détonateur m
d Sprengkapsel f

BLOCK, crown see 418
-, pyroclastic see 2313

185 BLOCK AND TACKLE
hoisting device in the derrick for
lifting and lowering of drill pipe
and casing
f palan m
d Flaschenzug m

186 BLOCK DIAGRAM
f diagramme m fonctionnel
d Blockbild n; Blockdiagramm n

187 BLOCKING
f blocage f
d Verriegelung f

188 BLOCK LAVA
lava where broken fragments of
solidifying crust form blocks
f lave f à blocaux
d Blocklava f

BOD, see 179

189 BODY FORCE
f forces $f\!pl$ massiques
d Massenkräfte $f\!pl$

190 BOG
swamp
f marécage m
d Sumpf m

191 BORE
f trou m de forage
d Bohrung f

BOTTOM, river see 2420

192 BOTTOM HOLE
lowest part of a drilled hole where
drill attacks rock formation
f fond m du puits
d Bohrlochsohle f

193 BOTTOMLAND
lowland along alluvial river plain
f plaine f basse
d Flussniederung f

194 BOULDER CLAY
unassorted mixture of glacial drift
f argile f à blocaux
d Geschiebelehm m

BOUNDARY, fixed see 734

195 BOUNDARY CONDITIONS
f conditions $f\!pl$ à la limite
d Randbedingungen $f\!pl$

196 BOUNDARY LAYER
f couche f limite
d Grenzschicht f

197 BOUNDARY SPRING
spring located at boundary between
permeable formation overlying
impermeable substratum
f source f de déversement
d Schichtquelle f

198 BOURDON GAGE
pressure gage with Bourdon tube
f tube m Bourdon
d Bourdondruckdose f

199 BRACKISH WATER
water containing from 1000 to
10000 ppm of total dissolved solids
f eau *f* saumâtre
d Brackwasser *n*

200 BREAKING STRENGTH
f résistance *f* à la rupture
d Bruchfestigkeit *f*

201 BRECCIA
rock composed of angular fragments
f brèche *f*
d Breckzie *f*

202 BRIDGE CIRCUIT
circuit of a current measuring
bridge
f schéma *m* de pont
d Brückenkreis *m*

203 BRIDGING EFFECT
forming of arches in a packing of
particles
f effet *m* d'arc-boutement
d Brückenbildung *f*

204 BRINE
water containing more than 100.000
ppm total dissolved solids
f saumure *f*
d Lauge *f*

205 BRITTLE FAILURE
f cassure *f* fragile
d Sprödbruch *m*

BROOK see creek

206 BUBBLE GAGE
stage recorder based on principle of
equating a gas pressure to water level
f limnigraphe *m* à bulles
d Druckluftpegel *m*

207 BUCKET
measuring reservoir in liquid
gaging instruments

f sceau *m*
d Eimer *m*; Sammelgefäss *n*

BUCKET, slush see 2576
-, tripping see 2797

208 BUFFERED SOLUTION
solution resisting changes in the
pH value upon addition of acids or
bases
f solution-tampon *f*
d Pufferlösung *f*

209 BULK DENSITY
f poids *m* spécifique apparent
d Raumgewicht *n*; Schüttgewicht *n*

210 BULL WHEEL
drum to store cable in cable tool
drilling
f tambour *m* de forage
d Bohrtrommel *m*

211 BUOYANCY
f poussée *f* d'Archimède
d Auftrieb *m*

212 BURIED VALLEY
ancient valley buried by recent,
often glacial, deposits
f vallée *f* enterrée
d verdecktes Stromtal *n*

213 BURST
periods of heavy rainfall
f pluie *f* torrentielle
d Wolkenburch *m*

214 BUTTERFLY VALVE
f vanne-papillon *f*
d Drosselventil *n*

215 BYPASS
f by-pass *m*
d Umgehungsleitung *f*

C

CABLE, carrier see 251
-, drilling see 573
-, hoisting see 936
-, logging see 1165

216 CABLE DRILLING
method of drilling where drilling
bit is suspended on a cable
f forage *m* au câble
d Seilbohren *n*

217 CABLE EYE
f cosse *f*
d Kausche *f*

218 CABLE REEL
f tambour *m* du câble
d Seiltrommel *f*

219 CABLE SPLICING
f épissure *f* de câble
d Spleiss *m*

220 CABLE TOOL
percussion, standard kind of
drilling bit
f installation *f* de forage par
battage
d Seilschlagbohrer *m*

221 CABLE TOOL DRILLING
f forage *m* par battage au câble
d Seilschlagbohren *n*

222 CABLE WAY
cable stretched across river with
cable car from which discharge
measurements can be taken
f transporteur *m* aérien;
téléférique *m*
d Seilbahn *f*

223 CAISSON
protective chamber for the
excavation of water submerged
unconsolidated sediments
f caisson *m*
d Caisson *n*; Senkkasten *m*

224 CALCAREOUS
containing calcium carbonate
f calcareux
d kalkig; kalkhaltig

225 CALCITE
stable mineral form of $CaCo_3$

f calcite *m*
d Kalzit *n*

226 CALDERA
circular volcanic depression
f caldère *m*
d Kaldera *m*

227 CALIBRATION
experimental evaluation of the scale
readings of an instrument against
an absolute standard
f calibration *f*
d Eichung *f*

228 CALIBRATION CURVE
f courbe d'étalonnage *f*
d Eichkurve *f*

229 CALICHE
indurated layer of soil, cemented
with leached calcium carbonate
f croûte *f* calcaire; encroûtement *m*;
concrétion *f*; alios *m*
d Felspanzer *m*; Ortstein *m*;
Kalkkruste *f*

230 CALIPER
device to measure inner diameter
of a well or drilled hole
f diamétreur *m*
d Kalibermessgerät *n*

231 CALIPER LOG
vertical record of well diameter
f diagraphie de diamétreur *f*;
diamétrage *m*
d Kalibermessung *f*

232 CAMBRIAN
oldest period of the Paleozoic era
f Cambrien *m*
d Kambrium *n*

233 CANAL SEEPAGE LOSS
water lost to underground by
seepage through channel bottom or
walls; loss through cracks in lined
canals
f perte *f* par infiltration
d Seihverlust *m*

234 CANYON
deep valley with steep slopes
f cañon *m*
d Canyon *m*

CAP, blasting see 184
-, drive see 589
-, hoisting see 937

235 CAPACITY
property to contain a certain
volume or a mass
f capacité f
d Fassungsvermögen n;
Aufnahmefähigkeit f

CAPACITY, capillary see 716
-, carrying see 252
-, entrance see 655
-, exchange see 688
-, field see 716
-, field-carrying see 716
-, infiltration see 1025
-, self-cleaning see 2509
-, specific see 2614
-, storage see 2650
-, total see 2806
-, transmission see 2823
-, water retaining see 2619
-, well see 2983

236 CAPILLARITY
effect of surface forces in narrow
voids
f capillarité f
d Porensaugwirkung f;
Kapillarität f

237 CAPILLARY CAPACITY
see field capacity

238 CAPILLARY FORCE
f force f de capillarité
d Kapillarkraft f

239 CAPILLARY FRINGE
zone immediately above water
table held by capillary forces
f frange f capillaire
d Kapillarsaum m; Porensaugsaum m;
Saugsaum m

240 CAPILLARY HYSTERESIS
difference between displacement
and imbibition curve in capillary
pressure of soil tension curve
f hystérésis f capillaire
d kapillare Hysteresis f

241 CAPILLARY MIGRATION
movement of water through soil due
to capillary forces
f migration f capillaire
d Kapillarwanderung f

242 CAPILLARY RISE
phenomenon of natural rise of
water in small interstices, pores
and capillary tubes under attraction
of capillary forces
f ascension f capillaire
d Kapillaranstieg m

243 CAPILLARY WATER
water held by capillary forces above
water table in capillary fringe
f eau f capillaire; eau f de
capillarité
d Kapillarwasser n; Porensaugwasser n; Bergfeuchte f

244 CAPROCK
relatively impermeable rock overlying an oil or gas reservoir or a
gas storage site in an aquifer
f cap m
d Dach n

245 CAPSTAN
f cabestan m
d Winde f

246 CARBONATE
CO_3
f carbonate m
d Karbonat n

247 CARBONATED SPRING
f source f gazeuse naturelle (en C
d Kohlensäurequelle f;
Säuerling m

248 CARBONATE ROCKS
rocks primarily made up of
carbonate minerals
f roches f pl carbonatées
d Karbonatgestein n

249 CARBON DIOXIDE
CO_2
f dioxyde m de carbone; dioxyde m
carbonique
d Kohlendioxyd n

250 CARBONIFEROUS
geologic period of the Paleozoic
era, comprising both Pennsylvanian
and Mississippian
f Carbonifère m
d Karbon n

251 CARRIER CABLE
f câble m porteur
d Tragseil n

252 CARRYING CAPACITY
     capacity of a watercourse to
     transport solids
     f capacité *f* de transport
     d Transportfähigkeit *f*; Frachtungs-
        fähigkeit *f*; Schleppkraft *f*

253 CASING
     permanent liner of well
     f tubage *m*
     d Verrohrung *f*

     CASING, blank see 183
     -, pipe see 2237
     -, protective see 2298
     -, surface see 2713
     -, temporary see 2755

254 CASING JOINT
     welded or threaded connection for
     tubular casing
     f manchon *m* de tubage
     d Futterrohrverbinder *m*

255 CASING LINE
     cable with which casing is moved
     and put in place
     f câble *m* de tubage
     d Rohrförderseil *n*

256 CASING SHOE
     reinforced bottom part of casing
     to facilitate lowering operations
     and for protection of casing
     f sabot *m* de tubage
     d Verrohrungsschuh *m*

257 CATCHMENT
     drainage basin (British usage)
     f bassin *m* versant
     d Einzugsgebiet *n*

     CATCHMENT, water see 2928

258 CATHODIC PROTECTION
     method of corrosion prevention
     by electrochemical methods
     f protection *f* cathodique
     d kathodischer Schutz *m*

259 CATLINE
     cable connected to cathead for
     auxiliary operations
     f câble de cabestan *m*
     d Spillseil *n*

260 CAVE
     subsurface natural cavity of
     relatively great dimensions
     f caverne *f*; grotte *f*
     d Höhle *f*; Grotte *f*

261 CAVE, TO
     f s'ébouler; s'écrouler
     d einstürzen

262 CAVERNOUS ROCK
     rock containing many often
     irregular cavities
     f roche *f* caverneuse
     d kavernöses Gestein *n*

263 CAVERN WATER
     water contained in caverns
     f eaux *f pl* de cavernes
     d Höhlenwasser *n*

264 CAVING
     f éboulement *m*
     d Nachfall *m*

265 CEMENT
     technical bonding agent composed
     of finely ground sintered silica,
     lime and alumina; natural bonding
     agent
     f ciment *m*
     d Zement *m*

     CEMENT, groundwater see 898

266 CEMENT, TO
     sealing of exterior pipe or casing
     in a well to formation by a cement
     bond
     f cimenter
     d zementieren

267 CEMENTATION
     process of binding granular material
     together by deposition of cementing
     material at contact points of grains
     f cimentation *f*
     d Verkittung *f*; Zementation *f*

268 CEMENT BOND
     f adhérence *f* du ciment
     d Zementhaftung *f*

269 CEMENT GROUT
     cement slurry of pumpable consistency
     f ciment *m* d'injection
     d Einpresszement *m*

270 CEMENT SEAL
     f étanchéité *f* de ciment
     d Zementabdichtung *f*

271 CEMENT SLURRY
     liquid cement suspension
     f laitier de ciment *m*
     d Zementbrühe *f*

272 CENOZOIC
most recent geologic era
f Cénozoique *m*
d Känozoikum *n*

273 CENTRIFUGAL PUMP
f pompe *f* centrifuge
d Kreiselpumpe *f*

274 CENTROID OF STORM RAINFALL
center of gravity of area over
which rain is falling
f centre *m* de gravité d'une pluie
d Flächenzentrum *n* des Nieder-
schlages

275 CHAIN GAGE
water level measuring device
consisting of a chain
f jauge *f* à chaîne
d Kettenpegel *m*

276 CHALK
very porous, weakly consolidated
white limestone
f craie *f*
d Kreide *f*

277 CHANNEL
natural or artificial watercourse
bounded by banks
f canal *m*
d Kanal *m*

CHANNEL, alluvial see 57
-, stream see 2664

278 CHANNEL CHARACTERISTICS
hydraulic properties of stream
channel
f caractéristiques *mpl* du lit
d Flussbettbeschaffenheit *f*

CHANNEL FLOW, main see 1182

279 CHANNEL PRECIPITATION
direct precipitation on stream
channel
f précipitation *f* sur les surfaces
d'eau libre
d Niederschläge *mpl* auf Wasser-
flächen

280 CHANNEL SPRING
f source *f* de fossette
d Furchenquelle *f*

281 CHAOTIC STRUCTURE
f structure *f* chaotique
d chaotische Struktur *f*

282 CHARACTERISTIC HYDROGRAPH
hydrograph based on unit step
process
f hydrogramme *m* indiciel
d Indikatorhydrograph *m*

283 CHECK VALVE
f clapet *m* de fermeture
d Absperrventil *n*

284 CHEMICAL ANALYSIS
laboratory procedure in water
quality determination identifying
chemical constituents
f analyse *f* chimique
d chemische Analyse *f*

285 CHEMICAL DEPOSIT
sediment precipitated out of
solution by chemical action
f dépôt *m* chimique
d chemische Ausfällung *f*

286 CHEMICAL EQUIVALENT
expression of water characteristics
such as hardness or alkalinity
resulting from several ions in
solution in terms of only one
equivalent concentration
f équivalent *m* chimique
d chemisches Äquivalent *n*

287 CHEMICAL MOBILITY
tendency of an element to move in
a given hydrogeochemical
environment
f mobilité *f* chimique
d chemische Mobilität *f*

288 CHEMICAL OXYGEN DEMAND (COD)
measure of readily oxidizable
material contained in a water sample
f demande *f* chimique en oxygène
d chemischer Sauerstoffbedarf *m*

289 CHERT
amorphous silica concretion
f chaille *f*; silex *m* impur
d Feuerstein *m*; Hornstein *m*

290 CHISEL EDGE
f tranchant *m* de l'outil
d Meisselschneide *f*

291 CHLORINATION
addition of chlorine to water for
disinfection purposes
f chloration *f*
d Chlorung *f*

292 CHLORINE
Cl
f chlore *m*
d Chlor *n*

293 C-HORIZON
zone of weathered parent material
in soil profile
f horizon-C *m*; zone *f* de la roche
mère en voie d'altération; zone *f*
de départ
d C-Horizont *m*; Zone *f* des
angewitterten Ausgangsgesteins

294 CHURN DRILL
percussion drill
f foreuse *f* à percussion
d Schlagbohrer *m*

295 CIRCLE OF INFLUENCE
in radial flow circle over which
effects of pumping are felt
f cercle *m* d'influence
d Absenkungsbereich *m*

296 CISTERN
small water reservoir used to
collect surface and rain water
f citerne *f*
d Zisterne *f*

297 CLAM SHELL
excavating equipment
f drague *f* à grappin
d Greifbagger *m*

298 CLASTIC ROCK;
DETRITAL ROCK
sedimentary rock derived from
fragmentated other preexisting
rock or organic structures
f roche *f* détritique
d klastisches Gestein *n*

299 CLAY
soft plastic impervious rock
composed of clay minerals
f argile *f*
d Ton *m*

CLAY, boulder see 194

300 CLAYEY SAND
sand containing considerable
proportions of clay
f sable *m* argileux
d toniger Sand *m*

301 CLAY MINERAL
mainly hydrous aluminum or

magnesium silicates with a layer
type crystal structure
f minéraux *mpl* argileux
d Tonmineral *n*

302 CLAY PARTICLE
particle size less than 0.005 mm
(USBS)
f argile *m*
d Ton *m*

303 CLAY PLUG
fine flood deposits in a cut off
river meander
f bouchon *m* argileux
d Tonpfropfen *m*

304 CLEANOUT DRAIN
f trou *m* de vidange
d Ablassöffnung *f*

305 CLEAN SAND
sand with little or no clay content
f sable *m* propre; sable *m* pur
d reiner Sand *m*

306 CLEAVAGE
secondary planes along which rock
has a tendency to break easily
f clivage *m*
d Klüftung *f*; Spaltbarkeit *f*

307 CLIMATIC FACTOR
factor influencing hydrologic
parameters due to local climate
f facteur *m* climatique
d Klimafaktor *m*

308 CLOG, TO
action of blocking fluid flow paths
especially around a well bore
f colmater
d verstopfen; verkleben

309 CLOSED BASIN
drainage basin with no surface flow
outlet
f bassin *m* clos
d abflussloses Becken *n*

310 CLOUD
f nuage *m*
d Wolke *f*

311 CLOUDBURST
f pluie *f* torrentielle
d Wolkenbruch *m*

312 COARSE SAND
grain diameter 1 to 0.5 mm (USBS)

f   sable *m* grossier
d   Grobsand *m*

313   COARSNESS
quality of aggregates of un-consoli-
dated large diameter sand grains
f   grossièreté *f*
d   Grobkörnigkeit *f*

314   COASTAL AQUIFER
aquifer in coastal region open to
sea-water intrusions
f   couche *f*; aquifère *f* littorale
d   küstennaher Grundwasserleiter *m*

315   COASTAL PLAIN
plain adjacent to the seashore
f   plaine *f* littorale
d   Küstenebene *f*

316   COASTLINE
outline of the sea shore
f   ligne *f* de côte
d   Küstenlinie *f*

317   COATING
f   revêtement *m*
d   Überzug *m*; Auskleidung *f*

318   COCK
valve consisting of a rotating plug
f   robinet *m*
d   Hahn *m*

COD see 288

COEFFICIENT, activity see 23
-, drag see 546
-, field .... of permeability see 717
-, friction see 795
-, hygroscopic see 989
-, laboratory .... of permeability
   see 1113
-, pan see 2170
-, roughness see 2441
-, runoff see 2447
-, seepage see 2498
-, standard .... of permeability
   see 1113
-, storage see 2651
-, uniformity see 2867
-, unsaturated .... of permeability
   see 2869
-, weir see 2980
-, wilting see 3016

319   COEFFICIENT OF PERMEABILITY
f   coefficient *m* de perméabilité
d   Durchlässigkeitsziffer *f*;
   Durchlässigkeitsbeiwert *m*

COEFFICIENT OF TRANSMISSIBILIT
see transmissivity

320   COEFFICIENT OF VARIATION
standard deviation divided by mean
f   indice *m* de variation
d   relative Streuung *f*

321   COLD
f   froid
d   kalt

322   COLIFORM ORGANISM
micro organism the concentration of
which in a water sample indicates
the degree of organic pollution
f   colibacille *m*
d   Colibakterium *n*

323   COLLAPSE
f   écrasement *m*; effrondrement *m*
d   Einfallen *n*

324   COLLECTING MAIN
f   collecteur *m* principal
d   Sammelleitung *f*

325   COLLECTOR WELL
central well with horizontal sections
of screened collector pipe arranged
radially to increase yield
f   puits *m* collecteur
d   Sammelbrunnen *m*; Horizontalbrunnen *m*

COLUMN, geological see 828
-, mercury see 2026
-, mud see 2086

326   COLUMNAR JOINTING
jointing of basalt into hexagonal
vertical columns upon cooling
f   disjonction *f* en colonnes
d   Säulenklüftung *f*; säulenförmige
   Absonderung *f*

327   COMPACTION
volume reduction and lithification of
sediment due to compression
f   compaction *f*
d   Verdichtung *f*

328   COMPENSATION WATER
f   eau *f* de compensation
d   Zuschusswasser *n*

329   COMPLETE PENETRATION OF WE
property of a well that penetrates
an aquifer completely from the
upper confining bed or water table

to the lower confining bed; the well is completed over the whole thickness of the aquifer to allow radial production over its entire completed length
f pénétration f complète d'un puits
d vollkommenes Eindringen n eines Brunnens

330 COMPLETE WATER ANALYSIS
physical, chemical and bacteriological analysis of a water sample
f analyse f complète
d Vollanalyse f

331 COMPOSITION
f composition f
d Zusammensetzung f

332 COMPRESSED AIR
air compressed to a higher pressure than atmospheric
f air m comprimé
d Pressluft f; Druckluft f

333 COMPRESSIBILITY
relative change of volume with pressure of water or aquifer matrix; reciprocal of bulk modulus of elasticity of a medium
f compressibilité f
d Kompressibilität f

334 COMPRESSION WAVE
f onde f de compression
d Druckwelle f

335 COMPRESSIVE STRENGTH
f résistance f à la compression
d Druckfestigkeit f

CONCENTRATION, hydrogen-ion see 965

336 CONCENTRATION CURVE
rising limb on hydrograph curve
f courbe f de concentration
d Konzentrationskurve f

337 CONCENTRATION POINT
point at which all runoff of a given area passes
f point m de concentration
d Konzentrationspunkt m

338 CONCRETE
f béton m
d Beton m

339 CONCRETION
localized deposition of mineral matter going out of solution in sediments or tuffs, usually of nodular or irregular shape
f concrétion f
d Konkretion f

340 CONDENSATION
transition from vapor to liquid state
f condensation f
d Kondensation f

341 CONDENSATION NUCLEUS
small solid particle around which condensation occurs
f noyau m de condensation
d Kondensationskern m

CONDITIONS, boundary see 195
-, geologic see 830
-, Ghyben-Herzberg see 844
-, initial see 1034

342 CONDUCTIVE-LIQUID ANALOG
analog using electrolyte in tank as conductor
f analogie f par cuve électrolytique
d Elektrolyttankanalog n

343 CONDUCTIVE-SHEET ANALOG
analog using a sheet of electrically conducting material with high resistance as conductor
f analogie f par tissu conducteur
d Analogmodell n mit elektrisch leitender Schicht

344 CONDUCTOR
medium characterized by transporting quantities like heat, mass, electricity
f conducteur m
d Leiter m

345 CONDUIT
natural or artificial duct for water transportation
f conduite f
d Leitung f

CONE, talus see 2746

346 CONE OF INFLUENCE
depression created in water table due to withdrawal from well
f cône m d'appel
d Einflusstrichter m;
   Absenkungstrichter m

347 CONE OF RECHARGE
elevation of piezometric surface
around a recharge well
f   cône *m* de recharge
d   Auffülltrichter *m*

348 CONFINED FLOW
f   écoulement *m* de la nappe captive
d   Fliessen *n* von gespanntem Grundwasser

349 CONFINED WATER
water separated from atmosphere
by impermeable rock stratum
f   eau *f* captive; nappe *f* captive
d   gespanntes Grundwasser *n*

350 CONFINING STRATUM
impermeable rock formation
preventing horizontal or vertical
outflow out of aquifer
f   couche *f* imperméable
d   undruchlässige Schicht *f*;
Grenzschicht *f*

351 CONFLUENCE
junction point of streams
f   confluent *m*
d   Zusammenfluss *m*

352 CONFORMAL MAPPING
transposition and solution of plane
flow problems in complex plane
f   transformation *f* conforme
d   konforme Abbildung *f*

353 CONGEALED LAVA CRUST
solid crust formed on top of lava
flow due to congealing action
f   carapace *f* figée
d   Erstarrungskruste *f*

354 CONGEALING PROCESS
process of cooling and solidification
f   congélation *f*
d   Gefrierprozess *m*; Erkaltung *f*;
Erstarrungsprozess *m*

355 CONGLOMERATE
rock consisting of large well
rounded waterworn particles
f   conglomérat *m*
d   Konglomerat *n*

CONGLOMERATE, basal see 146

356 CONJUCTIVE USE
use of both surface water and
ground water
f   utilisation *f* jointe
d   Verbundwirtschaft *f*

357 CONNATE WATER
entrapped residual water in
sedimentary rocks from time of
deposition
f   eaux *f pl* connées
d   ursprüngliches Porenwasser *n*

358 CONSEQUENT RIVER
river flowing down original slope
of geologic beds or general slope
of topography
f   rivière *f* conséquente
d   Folgefluss *m*; konsequenter Fluss *n*

359 CONSOLIDATED ROCK
rock that has become hard and
coherent through compression and
lithifaction
f   roche *f* lapidifiée
d   verfestigtes Gestein *n*

360 CONSOLIDATION
binding of grains by cementing
material to solid matrix
f   consolidation *f*; lapidification *f*
d   Verfestigung *f*

361 CONSTITUENT
f   composant *m*
d   Bestandteil *m*

CONSTITUENTS, trace see 2812

362 CONSTRICTION
f   section *f* étranglée;
étranglement *m*
d   Einschnürung *f*

363 CONSUMPTIVE USE
quantity of water used annually by
crops or natural vegetation due to
transpiration, tissue building, and
evaporation from adjacent soil
f   consommation *f* totale
d   Gesamtwasserverbrauch *m*

364 CONTACT LOAD
solid material in sliding or rolling
contact with stream bed
f   charge *f* de la couche du lit
d   Geschiebebelastung *f*

365 CONTACT LOG
resistivity log where measuring
electrodes are pressed against wall
of hole
f   diagraphie *f* de contact;
diagraphie *f* de paroi; diagraphie
de microrésistivité
d   Mikrolog *n*; Kontaktlog *n*

366   CONTACT PLANE
      f   surface *f* de contact; surface *f*
          de séparation
      d   Grenzfläche *f*; Berührungsfläche *f*

367   CONTACT POTENTIAL
      electrochemical potential
      generated at the junction between two
      solutions of different concentration
      and a cation selective membrane
      such as a shale layer in S.P. logs
      f   potentiel *m* de contact
      d   Berührungspotential *n*

368   CONTACT SPRING
      spring at intersection of land
      surface with permeable water-bearing
      formation overlying less permeable
      formation
      f   source *f* de contact
      d   Schichtquelle *f*

369   CONTAMINATION
      introduction of objectionable or
      obnoxious material into water or
      waste water
      f   contamination *f*
      d   Verschmutzung *f*

      CONTAMINATION, radioactive
      see 2322

      CONTENT, air see 38
      -, moisture see 2063
      -, organic matter see 2137
      -, volumetric moisture see 2909
      -, water see 2930

370   CONTINENTAL SHELF
      continental margin extending under
      sea
      f   plateau *m* continental
      d   Kontinentalschelf *n*

371   CONTINENTAL SLOPE
      sloping part of continental margin
      f   talus *m* continental
      d   Kontinentalabsatz *m*

372   CONTINUOUS STREAM
      stream continuous in space from
      source to discharge point
      f   rivière *f* continue
      d   durchgehender Fluss *m*

373   CONTINUITY EQUATION
      f   équation *f* de continuité
      d   Kontinuitätsgleichung *f*;
          Kontinuitätsgesetz *n*

374   CONTOUR LINE
      f   courbe *f* de niveau
      d   Höhenlinie *f*; Höhenschicht-
          linie *f*

375   CONTRIBUTING REGION
      region contributing to well
      discharge in inclined watertable
      flow
      f   zone *f* d'appel
      d   Entnahmegebiet *n*; Entnahme-
          fläche *f*

376   CONTROL
      combined effect of channel charac-
      teristics (area, shape, slope, rough-
      ness) on rating curve
      f   facteurs *mpl* d'influence
      d   Einflussfaktoren *mpl*

      CONTROL, geologic see 831

377   CONTROL GATE
      f   vanne *f* de contrôle
      d   Kontrollschieber *m*

378   CONTROL VALVE
      f   vanne *f* de réglage; soupape *f*
          de commande
      d   Regelventil *n*; Steuerventil *n*

379   CONVECTIVE PRECIPITATION
      shower precipitation due to moist
      air being lifted over heated areas
      (thermal gradient)
      f   précipitation *f* de convection
      d   konvektiver Niederschlag *m*

380   CONVERGENCE
      net horizontal inflow of moisture
      per unit area
      f   convergence *f*
      d   Konvergenz *f*

381   CONVERSION FACTOR
      factor used to transform measured
      quantities in analog study to
      equivalent ground water terms
      f   facteur *m* de conversion
      d   Umrechnungsfaktor *m*;
          Umrechnungszahl *f*

382   CONVEYANCE
      physical characteristics of cross
      section of channel describing ability
      to transmit water
      f   capacité *f* de transport
      d   Transportfähigkeit *f*;
          Durchlassfähigkeit *f*

383   COOLING JOINT
      joint due to shrinkage of cooling
      rock mass
      f joint *m* de refroidissement
      d Erstarrungskluft *f*

384   COOLING WATER
      water used only for cooling purposes
      f eau *f* de refroidissement
      d Kühlwasser *n*

385   COOL SPRING
      spring water temperature below
      mean annual surface temperature
      f source *f* froide
      d Arkatopege *f*

386   COQUINA
      porous limestone composed of
      broken shell
      f lumachelle *f*
      d Schillkalk *m*; Muschelkalk *m*

387   CORE
      cylindrical plug of rock obtained by
      special core drilling operations for
      detailed geological studies
      f carotte *f*
      d Bohrkern *m*

388   CORE ANALYSIS
      petrophysical analysis of a drilled
      rock core sample
      f analyse *f* de carotte
      d Bohrkernuntersuchung *f*

389   CORE BARREL
      tubular part of core drilling device
      that contains the cut rock sample
      during drilling operations
      f tube *m* carottier
      d Kernrohr *n*

390   CORE BIT
      tubular and internally hollow
      drilling bit cutting cylindrical rock
      samples
      f tête *f* de carottier
      d Kernbohrkrone *f*

391   CORE CATCHER
      annular spring retaining core in
      core barrel
      f arrache-carotte *m*
      d Kernfänger *m*

392   CORE DRILLING
      drilling method producing a cylin-
      drical rock sample of the penetrated
      formation

      f carottage *m*
      d Kernbohren *n*

393   CORRASION
      physical erosion due to particles
      moved by wind and water
      f corrasion *f*
      d Korrasion *f*

394   CORROSION INHIBITOR
      chemical additive to water and
      drilling fluids neutralizing their
      corrosive properties
      f inhibiteur *m* de corrosion
      d Korrosionsverhütungsmittel *n*

395   CORROSIVE
      property of water attacking its
      conduits
      f corrosif
      d korrosiv

396   COUNTER CURRENT
      f contre-courant *m*
      d Gegenstrom *m*; Gegenströmung *f*

      COVER, mechanical see 2015
      -, snow see 2579
      -, vegetation see 2887

397   CRACK
      tight joint
      f cassure *f*
      d Kluft *f*; Riss *m*

      CRACK, dessication see 483
      -, mud see 2087

398   CRANK
      f manivelle *f*
      d Kurbel *f*

399   CRATER LAKE
      water body accumulated in an
      impervious volcanic crater
      f lac *m* de cratère
      d Kratersee *m*

400   CREEK;
      BROOK
      f watercourse of lesser volume than
      a river
      f ruisseau *m*
      d Bach *m*

401   CREEP
      slow plastic deformation of a solid
      f fluage *m*
      d plastische Verformung *f*;
         Kriechen *n*

402 CREEP FLOW
flow with creeping motion where
inertial terms have been dropped
f écoulement *m* très lent
d sehr langsame Fliessbewegung *f*

403 CREST
f sommet *m*
d Gipfelpunkt *m*

CREST, flood see 745

404 CREST LINE
line connecting crests (e.g. as a
divide)
f ligne *f* de crête
d Gipfellinie *f*

405 CREST SEGMENT
top part of hydrograph
f pointe *f*
d Spitzensegment *n*

406 CREST-STAGE INDICATOR
mechanical gage preserving the
indication of highest water level
f indicateur *m* de pointe;
échelle *f* à maximums
d Spitzenwertanzeiger *m*

407 CRETACEOUS
most recent geologic period of the
Mesozoic era
f Crétacé *m*
d Kreide *n*

408 CREVASSE
fissure in a glacier or other ice
body
f crevasse *f*
d Gletscherspalte *f*

409 CREVICE
opening in a rock formation or a
glacier
f fenie *f*; crevasse *f*
d Spalte *f*

410 CRITICAL DEPTH
depth of flow in open channel when
specific energy is minimum
f profondeur *f* critique
d kritische Wassertiefe *f*

411 CRITICAL DEPTH FLUME
Venturi or Parshall flume for
discharge measurements
f jaugeur *m* Parshall
d Venturikanal *m*

412 CRITICAL FLOW
open channel flow with Froude
Number equal to unity
f écoulement *m* critique
d kritsche Fliessgeschwindigkeit *f*

413 CROOKED HOLE
bore hole deflected from the vertical
f sonde *f* tordue
d Schlüsselloch *n*

414 CROSS BEDDING
oblique deposition of thin beds with
respect ot main planes of stratification
f stratification *f* entrecroisée
d Kreuzschichtung *f*

415 CROSS BIT
drilling bit with the chisel edges
arranged crosswise
f outil *m* à section en croix
d Kreuzmeissel *m*

416 CROSS FAULT
fault oblique or at right angles to
strike direction of beds
f faille *f* perpendiculaire
d Querverwerfung *f*

417 CROSS SECTION
vertical section of a geologic profile
f coupe *f* transversale
d Querschnitt *m*

418 CROWN BLOCK
block at the top of a drilling rig
containing pulleys for the draw
works
f moufle *m* fixe
d Kronenblock *m*

419 CRUSHED GRAVEL
f gravillon *m* concassé
d Grobsplitt *m*

420 CRYOLOGY
study of water dealing with solid
forms of water
f cryologie *f*
d Cryologie *f*

421 CRYSTALLINE ROCK
rock constituted by minerals in
crystalline state, very often highly
impermeable
f roche *f* cristalline
d kristallines Gestein *n*

422 CUESTA
unsymmetrical ridge due to gently

dipping stratum; hogback
f côte *f*
d Schichtstufe *f*

423   CULVERT
f ponceau *m*
d Durchlass *m*

424   CUMULATIVE PRODUCTION
sum total of volumetric discharge
of a well since production began
f production *f* cumulée
d Gesamtproduktion *f*

425   CURB
upper part of well casing near
surface
f revêtement *m*
d Einfassung *f*

CURB, well see 2986

426   CURIE (C)
measure of radioactivity by disintegration; 37×10^{12} disintegrations
per second
f curie *m*
d Curie *f*

CURRENT, counter see 396
-, density see 462
-, earth see 614
-, stray see 2661

427   CURRENT ELECTRODE
in a well logging circuit the
electrode furnishing the current
f électrode *f* de courant
d Stromelektrode *f*

428   CURRENT METER
device to measure current velocity
directly at a given point
f moulinet *m*
d Stromgeschwindigkeitsmesser *m*;
Fügelmessgerät *n*

CURVE, adjustment see 27
-, backwater see 133
-, calibration see 228
-, concentration see 336
-, desorption see 482
-, drawdown see 563
-, duration see 609
-, flow duration see 755
-, flow-mass see 758
-, groundwater recession see 908
-, lateral see 1132
-, mass see 1191
-, normal see 2113
-, pressure buildup see 2290
-, rating see 2342
-, recession see 2354
-, resistivity-spacing see 2400
-, summation see 2702
-, time-drawdown see 2792
-, type see 2855

429   CURVE FITTING
fitting of experimental data points
f lissage *m*
d Ausgleichung *f*

430   CUTICULAR TRANSPIRATION
evaporation from moist membranes
of plants
f transpiration *f* cuticulaire
d kutikuläre Transpiration *f*

431   CUTTING BLADE
cutting edge of a rotary drilling bit
f lame *f* coupante
d Schneide *f*

432   CUTTINGS
rock chips loosened from the bottom
hole by drilling action
f déblais *m* de forage
d Bohrklein *n*

433   CYCLE
regular periodic occurrence of an
event
f cycle *m*
d Zyklus *m*

CYCLE, hydrologic see 975
-, water see 2932

434   CYCLONIC PRECIPITATION
moderate precipitation in low
pressure area
f précipitation *f* cyclonique
d zykonaler Niederschlag *m*

D

435 DAM
structure across a watercourse
used to impound water
f barrage *m*
d Staudamm *m*; Talsperre *f*

DAM, groundwater see 899
-, overflow see 2158

436 DAMPING
process of gradually reducing
amplitude of a periodic event
such as acoustic oscillations in
velocity logging
f amortissement *m*
d Dämpfung *f*

437 DAMPING EFFECT
f effet *m* d'amortissement
d Dämpfungseffekt *m*

438 DARCY'S LAW
emprical law relating specific
discharge during fluid flow through
porous media to a permeability
coefficient K and a hydraulic
gradient
f Loi *f* de Darcy
d Darcysches Gesetz *n*

439 DARCY (UNIT) (d)
practical unit, measure of intrinsic
permeability has dimension of
L^2 in cgs system: 10^{-8} cm^2
f Darcy *m* (d)
d Darcy *n* (d)

440 DARCY VELOCITY;
SEEPAGE VELOCITY; SPECIFIC
DISCHARGE
ficticious flow velocity through
total cross sections area of porous
medium including solids
f vitesse *f* Darcy; vitesse *f*
   apparente; vitesse *f* de filtration
d Darcy Geschwindigkeit *f*;
   Filtergeschwindigkeit *f*;
   Durchgangsgeschwindigkeit *f*

441 DATA
f données *f pl*
d Angaben *f pl*; Daten *f pl*

DATUM, zero see 3029

442 DATUM PLANE
reference level to which topographic
or water levels in well are related
f plan *m* de comparaison; niveau *m*
   de référence
d Bezugsebene *f*; Bezugsniveau *n*

443 DEAD WATER
standing, stagnant water
f eau *f* morte
d Stehendwasser *n*

444 DEBRIS
coarse rock fragments resulting
from erosion and disintegration of
bedrock
f débris *m*
d Schutt *m*

445 DECAY PRODUCT
f produit *m* de désintégration
   radioactive
d Zerfallsprodukt *n*

446 DECLOGGING
cleaning of clogged well surfaces
or screens
f nettoyage *m* de la paroi colmatée
   d'un puits; décolmatage *m*
d Reinigung *f* verklebter Zufluss-
   flächen

447 DECOMPOSE, TO
f décomposer
d zersetzen

448 DEEP WELL DRILLING
f forage *m* profond
d Tiefbohrung *f*

449 DEEP WELL TURBINE PUMP
f pompe *f* à turbine immergée
d unterwasser Turbinenpumpe *f*

450 DEFORMATION
changing of form, volume and
relative position of rock masses
f déformation *f*
d Verformung *f*; Formveränderung *f*

451 DEGRADATION
geological action of wearing down
a surface
f dégradation *f*
d Abtragung *f*

452 DEGREE OF AERATION
ratio of volume of air in sample
to sample volume
f degré *m* d'aération
d Belüftungsgrad *m*

453 DEGREE OF CEMENTATION
degree to which a rock has been
solidified due to cementation
f degré *m* de lapidifaction
d Zementationsgrad *m*; Verfestigungsgrad *m*

454 DEGREE OF SATURATION
ratio of volume of water to volume
of pores
f degré *m* de saturation
d Sättigungsgrad *m*

455 DELAY
lapse time between signal emission
and signal reception in seismic
logging
f retard *m*
d Verzögerung *f*

456 DELTA
triangular deposit of sediments at
the inflow of a river into the
ocean or a lake
f delta *m*
d Delta *n*; Flussmündungsgebiet *n*

457 DELTAIC DEPOSITS
f dépôts *mpl* deltaiques
d Delta-Ablagerungen *fpl*

458 DEMAND
rate of draft from an aquifer or
reservoir to meet a certain demand
f demande *f* en eau
d Nachfrage *f*; Verbrauch *m*

DEMAND, oxygen see 2164
-, water see 2933

459 DEMINERALIZATION
removal of mineral matter from
water
f déminéralisation *f*
d Entmineralisierung *f*

460 DENDRITIC
tree-like pattern
f dentritique; arborescent
d verästelt; dendritisch

461 DENSITY
f densité *f*
d Dichte *f*

DENSITY, bulk see 209
-, drainage see 550
-, mass see 1192
-, snow see 2580
-, specific see 2615
-, weight see 2978

462 DENSITY CURRENT
current due to weight density
differences in the fluid under
consideration
f courant *m* de densité
d Dichteströmung *f*; konvektive
Strömung *f*

463 DENUDATION
wearing away of overlying loose
rock to top of bedrock
f dénudation *f*
d Abtragung *f*; Denudation *f*;
Massenabtrag *m*; Landerniedrigun

464 DEPARTURE
in SP logging deflection from the
base (shale) line
f anomalie *f* de la courbe PS
d Abweichung *f* von der Basislinie
der SP Kurve; Eindringung *f*

465 DEPLETION
withdrawal of water at a greater
rate than replenishment
f épuisement *m*
d Vorratsverminderung *f*;
Erschöpfung *f*

DEPOSIT, alluvial fan see 59
-, chemical see 285
-, eolian see 658
-, glacial see 845
-, moraine see 2077
-, organic see 2136
-, point-bar see 2255
-, sedimentary see 2494

466 DEPOSITION FACTOR
factor describing settling of
suspended solid within pore space
f facteur *m* de déposition
d Absetzfaktor *m*

DEPOSITS, deltaic see 457

467 DEPRESSION
small hollow in a surface
f dépression *f*
d Vertiefung *f*

468 DEPRESSION SPRING
spring originating at intersection of
land surface with water table
f source *f* de dépression
d Muldenquelle *f*

DEPTH, critical see 410
-, invasion see 1077
-, normal see 2114
-, transpiration see 2826

DEPTH FLUME, critical see 411

469 DEPTH GAGE
a) any device to measure depths
   as to water level in well, etc.
b) spec.: gage for the measurement
   of the river stage
f a) jauge *f* de profondeur
  b) jauge *f* fluviale
d a) Tiefenanzeiger *m*
  b) Pegel *m*

470 DEPTH OF EVAPORATION
f hauteur *f* d'évaporation
d Verdunstungshöhe *f*

471 DEPTH OF PENETRATION
depth to which electrical field
penetrates into subsurface as a
function of electrode spacing
f profondeur *f* de pénétration
d Eindringungstiefe *f*

472 DEPTH OF PRECIPITATION
f hauteur *f* de précipitation
d Niederschlagshöhe *f*

473 DEPTH OF RAINFALL
f hauteur *f* pluviométrique
d Regenhöhe *f*

474 DEPTH OF SNOW
f profondeur *f* de la neige
d Schneetiefe *f*

475 DERRICK
frame structure containing hoisting
devices in a drilling installation
f derrick *m*
d Bohrturm *m*

476 DESALINATION
process of salt removal
f dessalage *m*
d Entsalzung *f*

477 DESANDER
device for the separation of sand
from well water
f dessableur *m*
d Sandabscheider *m*

478 DESERT
region where net moisture inflow is
too small to support any vegetation
f désert *m*
d Wüste *f*

479 DESICCATION
removal of moisture by evaporation,
drying
f dessiccation *f*; séchage *m*
d Austrocknung *f*; Trocknen *n*

480 DESIGN FLOOD
most severe flood to be entered
in design calculations for engineering
works
f crue *f* utilisée pour un calcul
d Hochwasserberechnungsgrund-
lage *f*

481 DESIGN STORM
most severe storm used as base for
hydrologic and engineering designs
f averse *f* utilisée dans les calculs
d Niederschlagberechnungsgrund-
lage *f*

482 DESORPTION CURVE
curve of moisture content versus
soil moisture tension
f courbe *f* de désorption
d Desorptionskurve *f*

483 DESSICATION CRACK
crack due to shrinkage of a drying
volume (e.g. mud)
f joint *m* de dessiccation
d Trocknungsriss *m*

DETENTION, surface see 2714

484 DETENTIONS OF FLOW
f rétention *f* de l'écoulement
d Rückhaltung *f*

485 DETONATOR
small high powered primary explosive
charge used to set off main charge
f détonateur *m*
d Sprengkapsel *f*

DETRITAL ROCK, see clastic rock

486 DETRITUS
loose material originating from
disintegrated and weathered rock
f détritus *m*
d Schutt *m*; Detritus *m*

487 DEVIATION
deflection of a recording from a base
line such as shale line in SP logging
f déviation *f*
d Abweichung *f*

DEVIATION, mean see 2003

488 DEVONIAN
geologic period of the Paleozoic
era
f Dévonien *m*
d Devon *n*

489 DEWATER, TO
f drainer; dénoyer
d entwässern

490 DEWATERING
f drainage *m* d'eau; dénoyage *m*
d Entwässern *n*

491 DEW FORMATION
f formation *f* de rosée
d Taubildung *f*

492 DEW-POINT
point at which dew formation starts
for given temperature and humidity
conditions
f point *m* de rosée
d Taupunkt *m*

493 D-HORIZON
zone of bedrock in soil profile
f horizon *m* de la roche-mère
d Zone *f* des unverwitterten
Ausgangsmaterials

494 DIAGENESIS
post depositional physical and
chemical changes in sediment
f diagénèse *f*
d Diagenese *f*; Gesteinsbildung *f*

DIAMETER, effective see 621
-, external see 696
-, inside see 1042
-, well see 2988

DIAMOND industrial see 1020

495 DIAMOND DRILLING
drilling method where diamond
studded bits are used
f forage *m* au diamant
d Diamantbohren *n*

496 DIAMOND DRILLING BIT
drilling bit studded with industrial
diamonds or containing diamond
fragments in an abrasive matrix
f trépan *m* au diamant
d Diamantbohrkrone *f*

497 DIASTROPHISM
epirogenetic and orogenetic
movements of the earth's crust

f diastrophisme *m*
d Diastrophismus *m*

498 DIATOMITE
powdered silica of diatomes
f diatomite *m*; terre *f* d'infusoires
d Diatomeenerde *f*; Infusorienerde

499 DIELECTRIC CONSTANT
f constante *f* diélectrique
d Dielektrizitätskonstante *f*;
dielektrische Konstante *f*

500 DIELECTRIC LOSS
f perte *f* diélectrique
d dielektrische Verschiebung *f*

501 DIFFERENTIAL PRESSURE
f pression *f* différentielle
d Druckunterschied *m*;
Differentialdruck *m*

502 DIFFUSION
f diffusion *f*
d Diffusion *f*

DIFFUSION, molecular see 2067

503 DIFFUSION CONSTANT
f coefficient *m* de diffusion
d Diffusionskonstante *f*

DIFFUSION WELL, see recharge we

504 DIG, TO
action of mechanical excavation
of earth or rock other than drilling
f creuser
d ausschachten; graben

505 DIKE
wall or embankment protecting
lowlands from being flooded
f digue *f*
d Deich *m*

506 DIKE
sheet-like igneous rock intrusion
cutting across sediments
f filon *m*
d Gang *m*

507 DIMPLE SPRING
f source *f* ponctuelle
d Punktquelle *f*

508 DIOPSIDE
calcium silicate formed by contact
metamorphism
f diopside *m*
d Diopsid *m*

509 DIORITE
plutonic rock of crystalline
structure with predominantly light
and few basic components
f   diorite *m*
d   Diorit *m*

510 DIP
angle of inclination of a bed with
the horizontal at right angle to the
direction of strike
f   pendage *m*
d   Einfallen *n*

DIP, original see 2140

511 DIPMETER SURVEY
logging method where the dip of the
penetrated strata is measured
f   pendagemétrie *f*
d   Schichtneigungsmessung *f*

512 DIRECT CURRENT
f   courant *m* direct
d   Gleichstrom *m*

513 DIRECTIONAL DERIVATIVE
f   dérivée *f* directionnelle
d   richtungsgebundene Ableitung *f*

514 DIRECT RUNOFF;
DIRECT SURFACE RUNOFF;
STORM RUNOFF
runoff entering stream promptly
after rainfall
f   ruissellement *m* de surface direct
d   direkter Oberflächenabfluss *m*

515 DISCHARGE
volumetric flow of water through
a given cross section
f   écoulement *m*; déchargement *m*
d   Abfluss *m*; Ausfluss *m*; Durchfluss *m*

DISCHARGE, artificial see 116
-, evaporation see 678
-, groundwater see 900
-, hydraulic see 952
-, maximum see 1199
-, natural see 2098
-, pump see 2304
-, specific see 440

516 DISCHARGE, TO
action of fluid outflow or
throughflow
f   débiter
d   spenden; ausfliessen

517 DISCHARGE HYDROGRAPH
graph showing discharge of water
as a function of time
f   hydrogramme *m* d'écoulement
d   Abflussganglinie *f*;
Abflusshydrograph *m*

518 DISCHARGE PIPE
pipe through which a pump
discharges
f   tuyau *m* de refoulement;
tuyau *m* de débit
d   Druckrohr *n*

519 DISCHARGE PRESSURE
pressure at which a certain
discharge takes place
f   pression *f* de refoulement
d   Förderdruck *m*

520 DISCONFORMITY
geological unconformity between
parallel beds, often with some series
missing
f   discontinuité *f*
d   Diskordanz *f*

521 DISCONTINUITY
point where a mathematical function
becomes nondefined
f   discontinuité *f*; singularité *f*;
d   Diskontinuität *f*

522 DISCRETE VALUE
f   valeur *f* discontinue
d   diskrete Grösse *f*; diskontinuierlicher Wert *m*

523 DISPERSION
f   dispersion *f*
d   Verteilung *f*; Zerstreuung *f*;
Dispersion *f*

DISPERSION, hydrodynamic see 963

524 DISPERSION ZONE
zone of intermixing in miscible
flow or in sea water encroachment
f   zone *f* de dispersion
d   Dispersionszone *f*

525 DISPLACEMENT
process of replacing one fluid in
a porous medium by another
f   déplacement *m*
d   Verdrängung *f*

DISPLACEMENT, miscible,
see 2054

526 DISPLACEMENT PUMP
   f pompe *f* foulante
   d Verdrängungspumpe *f*

527 DISPOSAL WELL
   injection well through which waste
   water is disposed into the underground
   f puits *m* d'injection; puits *m*
     absorbant
   d Schluckbohrung *f*;
     Versenkbrunnen *m*

528 DISSOLVE, TO
   f dissoudre
   d auflösen

   DISTRIBUTION, area elevation
   see 106
   -, frequency see 790
   -, grain size see 865
   -, random see 2334
   -, saturation see 2471

529 DISTRIBUTION GRAPH
   graph showing the frequency
   distributions of the variates
   f graphique *m* de distribution
   d Verteilungskurve *f*

530 DISTURBANCE
   in geology: any change of the
   original position of rocks by folding
   or faulting
   f accident *m*
   d Störung *f*

531 DISTURBED SAMPLE
   sample disturbed with respect to
   its original mode of packing and
   sedimentation
   f échantillon *m* perturbé
   d gestörte Probe *f*

532 DITCH
   shallow but long depression in the
   ground surface
   f fossé *m*
   d Graben *m*

   DITCH, drainage see 552

533 DITCH METHOD
   water spreading method by ditches
   f méthode *f* d'infiltration par
     fossés
   d Rieselgrabenverfahren *n*

534 DIURNAL
   covering a period of 24 hours

   f diurne
   d täglich

535 DIVERT, TO
   f déverser
   d ableiten

536 DIVIDE
   line connecting highest topographic
   elevations that separate one
   drainage basin from another
   f ligne *f* de séparation (des eaux);
     ligne *f* de partage
   d Wasserscheide *f*; Scheide *f*

   DIVIDE, drainage see 552
   -, groundwater see 901, 902
   -, topographic see 2800

537 DIVINING ROD
   forklike branch or wire used in
   water witching
   f baguette *f* divinatoire
   d Wünschelrute *f*

538 DOLINE
   solution sinkhole in a karst region
   f doline *f*
   d Karsttrichter *m*; Doline *f*

539 DOLOMITE
   rock composed mainly of dolomite
   mineral $Ca\,Mg\,(CO_2)_2$
   f dolomie *m*
   d Dolomit *m*

540 DOUBLE ACTING PUMP
   f pompe *f* à double effet
   d doppelt wirkende Pumpe *f*

541 DOWNSTREAM
   f en aval
   d flussabwärts

542 DOWNWARPING
   down bending of stratum to form a
   depression or syncline
   f ploiement *m* vers le bas
   d Eindellung *f*; Einmuldung *f*

543 DOWSING;
   WATER WITCHING
   method of prospecting for water
   with a divining rod
   f hydromancie *f*
   d Wünschelrutenmutung *f*;
     Wassermutung *f* durch
     Wünschelrutengänger

544 DRAG
   resistance force of flowing fluid on

solid boundary
f résistance f à l'écoulement
   traînée f
d Strömungswiderstand m

545 DRAG BIT
rotary drilling bit
f outil m à lames
d Blattmeissel m

546 DRAG COEFFICIENT
f coefficient m de traînée
d Widerstandsbeiwert m

547 DRAIN
opening for a complete emptying
of a reservoir or container
f vidange m
d Ablass m

DRAIN, cleanout see 304

DRAINAGE, acid mine see 17
-, gravity see 882
-, internal see 1065
-, mine see 2045
-, roof see 2434

548 DRAINAGE AREA
horizontal projection of an area
drained by a particular river system
f aire f de drainage
d Abflussgebiet n; Einzugsgebiet n,
   Entwässerungsgebiet n

549 DRAINAGE BASIN
area contributing to runoff which
sustains streamflow
f bassin m versant
d Niederschlagsgebiet n

550 DRAINAGE DENSITY
ratio of total channel segments
lengths cumulated for all orders
to basin area
f densité f du réseau; densité f
   de drainage
d Flussdichte f

551 DRAINAGE DITCH
small channel through which
surface waters can drain off
f fossé m de drainage
d Entwässerungsgraben m

552 DRAINAGE DIVIDE
rim of a drainage basin
f ligne f de partage; ligne f de
   crête
d Wasserscheide f

553 DRAINAGE GALLERY
f galerie f de drainage
d Entwässerungsstollen m

554 DRAINAGE NETWORK
system of streams and rivers
draining a given basin
f réseau m de drainage;
   réseau m hydrographique
d Gewässernetz n;
   Abflussnetz n

555 DRAINAGE PATTERN
geometric arrangement of stream
segments in a drainage system
f configuration f de drainage
d Entwässerungsanordnung f

556 DRAINAGE RADIUS
radius of zone actually supplying
water to a pumping well
f rayon m d'appel
d Einzugsradius m

557 DRAINAGE RATIO
ratio of runoff to precipitation
f coefficient m de ruissellement;
   coefficient m d'écoulement
d Abflussfaktor m

558 DRAINAGE SYSTEM
network of streams and tributaries
f réseau m hydrographique;
   réseau m de drainage
d Entwässerungsnetz n

559 DRAIN TILE
porous pipe used for collection of
excess ground water
f tuyau m de drainage
d Dränagerohr n

560 DRAIN VALVE
f robinet m de vidange
d Ablasshahn m

561 DRAW
natural depression or small valley
f dépression f de la surface
d Delle f

562 DRAWDOWN
difference between the elevation of
initial piezometric surface and its
position after pumping
f rabattement m; baisse f du
   niveau dynamique
d Absenkung f; Absenkungsbetrag m

DRAWDOWN, residual see 2393
-, specific see 2616

563 DRAWDOWN CURVE
plot of drawdown with radial
distance from well
f   courbe *f* rabattement-distance;
    courbe *f* de dépression
d   Absenkungskurve *f*

564 DRAW WELL
f   puits *m* à poulie
d   Ziehbrunnen *m*

565 DRAW WORKS
hoisting installation for the
positioning and operation of drill
pipe in a drilling rig
f   treuil *m* de forage
d   Hebewerk *n*

DRIFT, glacial see 846

566 DRIFT SAND
sand transported by wind action
f   sable *m* éolien
d   Treibsand *m*

567 DRILL
f   trépan *m*
d   Bohrer *m*

DRILL, churn see 294

568 DRILL, TO
action of bringing down a hole by
cutting and removal of earth or rock
material
f   forer
d   bohren

569 DRILL COLLAR
heavy section of drill pipe above
bit to give the necessary weight
on the bit
f   masse *f* tige
d   Schwerstange *f*

570 DRILLER'S LOG
log obtained through inspection of
cuttings by driller
f   diagraphie *f* du foreur
d   Bohrprotokoll *n*

571 DRILLING
penetration of rock formations
with a drill
f   forage *m*
d   Bohren *n*

DRILLING, air see 39
-, cable see 216
-, cable tool see 221

-, core see 392
-, deep well see 448
-, diamond see 495
-, exploration see 692
-, full hole see 799
-, percussion see 2194
-, shot see 2539

572 DRILLING BIT
lower part of drill often replaceable
in actual contact with the bottom
hole where the rock face is disintegrated by chipping, abrasion, or
scraping
f   outil *m* à forage; trépan *m*
d   Bohrmeissel *m*; Bohrkrone *f*

DRILLING BIT, diamond see 496

573 DRILLING CABLE
cable on which the drill string is
suspended
f   câble *m* de manoeuvre
d   Bohrseil *n*

574 DRILLING CREW
team of workers operating a drilling
rig
f   équipe *f* de foreurs
d   Bohrmannschaft *f*

575 DRILLING FLUID
general term for fluid circulating
through drill pipe and annulus in
order to carry drill cuttings to the
surface; see also drilling mud
f   fluide *m* de forage
d   Bohrflüssigkeit *f*; Bohrspülung *f*

576 DRILLING FOREMAN
f   chef *m* foreur
d   Bohrmeister *m*

577 DRILLING HOOK
hook to which swivelhead and drill-
string is attached
f   crochet *m* de forage
d   Bohrhaken *m*

578 DRILLING LINE
drilling cable
f   câble *m* de forage
d   Bohrseil *n*

579 DRILLING MUD
drilling fluid with heavy solid
suspension of mud base and drill
cuttings, often thixotropic
f   boue *f* de forage
d   Bohrschlamm *m*; Bohrschmand *m*

580 DRILLING RATE
    rate at which drilling progresses
    f   vitesse *f* de forage
    d   Bohrgeschwindigkeit *m*

581 DRILLING RIG
    a) frame structure over the drilling
       platform or, in a wider sense,
    b) the complete drilling installation
    f   a) mât de forage;
        b) installations *fpl* de forage
    d   a) Bohrturm *m*; Bohrgerüst *n*;
        b) Bohranlage *f*

582 DRILLING-TIME LOG
    log of drilling rate versus depth
    f   diagraphie *f* de l'avancement
    d   Bohrzeitprotokoll *n*

583 DRILL PIPE STRING
    length of all connected drill pipes
    f   train *m* de tiges
    d   Bohrstrang *m*

584 DRILL STEM
    string of connected drill pipe
    f   tiges *fpl* de forage
    d   Bohrgestänge *n*

585 DRILL STEM TEST (DST)
    open hole productivity test of a
    sealed off formation under pressure
    by way of the normally used drill stem
    f   essai *m* des couches par les tiges
        de forage; drill-stem-test *m*
    d   Gestängetest *m*; Drillstemtest *m*

586 DRINKING WATER
    f   eau *f* potable
    d   Trinkwasser *n*

587 DRIPSTONE
    rock formed by evaporation of
    dripping water film containing calcite
    f   colonne *f* de pierre formée
        par des concrétions calcaires
    d   Tropfstein *m*

588 DRIVE, TO
    action of making hole by desplace-
    ment of earth material
    f   enfoncer
    d   eintreiben

589 DRIVE CAP
    protective cap on upper end of
    pipe string receiving impacts
    from driving mechanism
    f   casque *m* de battage
    d   Treibkappe *f*

590 DRIVE CLAMP
    clamp transmitting impact to pipe

in driving a well
    f   collier *m* de battage
    d   Treibschelle *f*

591 DRIVEN WELL
    well driven into loose sedimentary
    material by impacts of a driving
    mechanism
    f   puits *m* enfoncé
    d   gerammter Brunnen *m*;
        Schlagbrunnen *m*

592 DRIVE POINT;
    SAND POINT
    screened cylindrical pipe section
    with steel cone at bottom of pipe in
    well driven through unconsolidated
    formations
    f   cône *m* de sondage
    d   Treibspitze *f*; Rammspitze *f*;
        Bohrspitze *f*; Schlagbrunnenspitze *f*

593 DRIVER
    weight with which impact on pipe
    is created
    f   sonnette *f*
    d   Ramme *f*

594 DRIVING BAR
    f   colonne *f* de battage
    d   Treibstange *f*

595 DROP HAMMER
    f   mouton *m*
    d   Rammbär *m*

596 DROUGHT
    period of moisture deficiency and
    absence of water for plant growth
    f   sécheresse *f*
    d   Trockenheit *f*; Dürre *f*

597 DROWNED
    condition of underground openings
    such as caverns of mines that have
    been flooded
    f   inondé
    d   ersoffen

598 DRUM
    cylinder on which rope or cable
    is reeled in drilling operations;
    cylinder containing graph paper in
    recording operations
    f   tambour *m*
    d   Trommel *f*; Walze *f*

    DRUM, recording see 2365

599 DRUMLIN
    hill of glacial drift

f   drumlin *m*
d   Drumlin *m*; Rundhöcker *m*

600   DRY CELL
f   pile *f* sèche
d   Trockenbatterie *f*

601   DRY HOLE
hole not obtaining any production;
non-productive well
f   puits *m* sec
d   trockene *f* Bohrung;
Fehlbohrung *f*

602   DRY ICE
CO_2 in solid form at $-78.5^{\circ}C$
f   glace *f* carbonique; neige *f*
carbonique
d   Trockeneis *n*

603   DRYING OVEN
f   étuve *f*
d   Trockenofen *m*; Trockenschrank *m*

604   DRY RESIDUE
f   résidu *m* sec
d   Trockenrückstand *m*

605   DUG WELL
excavated well
f   puits *m* creusé
d   gegrabener Brunnen *m*;
Schachtbrunnen *m*; Kesselbrunnen *m*

606   DULL BIT
f   outil *m* usé
d   stumpfer Meissel *m*

607   DUNE SAND
wind blown sand forming stable or
wandering dunes

f   sable *m* de dune
d   Dünensand *m*

608   DUPUIT'S ASSUMPTION
simplifying assumption for the
solution of a free surface well flow
problem
f   hypothèses *f pl* de Dupuit
d   Dupuit'sche Annahme *f*

609   DURATION CURVE
cumulative frequency curve of a
continuous time series (of
hydrologic parameters)
f   courbe *f* de durée;
courbe *f* des débits classés
d   Dauerlinie *f*;
Dauerkurve *f*

610   DUTY OF WATER
quantity of irrigation water needed
for crop maturing
f   demande *f* en eau d'irrigation
d   Bewässerungsbedarf *m*

611   DYNAMIC SIMILARITY
scaling procedure of model and
prototype where the relationship
of dynamic parameters is retained
f   similitude *f* dynamique
d   dynamische Ähnlichkeit *f*

612   DYNAMITE CHARGE
f   charge *f* de dynamite
d   Dynamitladung *f*

613   DYNAMOMETER
device measuring the momentum
force of stream velocity
f   dynamomètre *m*
d   Dynamomometer *n*; Kraftmesser
Fliessdruckmesser *m*

E

614 EARTH CURRENT
natural telluric current present
in the earth's crust
f courant *m* tellurique
d Erdstrom *m*

615 EARTHFLOW
flow of water saturated earth
material in form of a mud stream
f glissement *m* de terrain
d Gleitfrana *f*

616 EARTHQUAKE
movement of the earth's crust due
to elastic waves originating from a
disturbance (epicenter)
f séisme *m*; tremblement *m* de terre
d Erdbeben *n*

617 EARTH TIDE
displacing effect of lunar attraction
on earth's crust
f marée *f* terrestre
d Erdgezeitenbewegung *f*

618 ECCENTRIC WELL
well not in center or circle of
influence
f puits *m* excentrique
d exzentrischer Brunnen *m*

619 EDDY
non laminar circulation of fluid at
boundaries of flow separation
f tourbillon *m*
d Wirbel *m*

EFFECT, bridging see 203
-, damping see 437
-, electrokinetic see 638
-, end see 647
-, skin see 2566

620 EFFECTIVE ABSTRACTIONS
difference between total precipitation
and effective precipitation
f pertes *f pl* par absorption
d effektive Rückhaltung *f*

621 EFFECTIVE DIAMETER
10 percentile size, i.e. 10 per cent
diameter smaller than this diameter
f diamètre *m* effectif
d wirksamer Korndurchmesser *m*

622 EFFECTIVE PERMEABILITY
f perméabilité *f* effective
d effektive Durchlässigkeit *f*

623 EFFECTIVE POROSITY;
PRACTICAL POROSITY
porosity concept only taking into
account the porespace that will
yield water under gravity; see
also specific yield
f porosité *f* libre; capacité *f*
effective d'absorption
d wirksame Porosität *f*

624 EFFECTIVE POROSITY
porosity concept only taking into
account interconnected pores
f porosité *f* utile; porosité *f*
ouverte
d effektive Porosität *f*

625 EFFECTIVE PRECIPITATION
part of precipitation contributing
entirely into direct runoff
f précipitation *f* efficace
d effektiver Niederschlag *m*

626 EFFECTIVE RAINFALL
effective precipitation when only
rainfall is involved
f pluie *f* efficace
d effektiver Regen *m*

EFFICIENCY, barometric see 141
-, temperature see 2753
-, tidal see 2784

627 EFFLUENT
outflow
f effluent *m*
d Ausfluss *m*

628 EFFLUENT STREAM;
GAINING STREAM
stream abstracting water from
ground water body, hence depleting
groundwater reserves
f rivière *f* alimentée par la nappe
d wasseraufnehmender Fluss *m*

629 EFFUSIVE ROCK
igneous rock produced by magmatic
material flowing out of or over the
earth's surface

f roche f extrusive
d Ergussgestein n

630 EFFUSION
extrusion of liquid igneous rock
on earth's surface
f effusion f; épanchement m
d Erguss m; Effusion f

631 ELASTIC PROPERTIES
properties describing deformation
of a solid
f propriétés f pl élastiques
d elastische Eigenschaften f pl

632 ELECTRICAL RESISTIVITY
f résistivité f électrique
d spezifischer elektrischer Widerstand m

633 ELECTRIC LOG
all well records obtained by
electrical (esp. resistivity) methods
f carottage m électrique
d elektrisches Kernen n

634 ELECTRO-CHEMICAL GAGING
flow measurement based on electric
detection of electrolyte tracer flow
f jaugeage m chimique
d Salzgeschwindigkeitsverfahren n

635 ELECTROCHEMICAL POTENTIAL
electrical potential due to differences
in ion concentrations of different
solutions in a bore hole environment
f potentiel f électrochimique
d elektrochemisches Potential n

ELECTRODE, current see 427
-, guard see 911
-, moving see 2082

636 ELECTRODE SPACING
distance between electrodes in
electric logging devices
f espacement m des électrodes
d Elektrodenabstand m

637 ELECTROFILTRATION
passage of filtrate through a
membrane under a voltage difference
f électrofiltration f
d Elektrofiltration f

638 ELECTROKINETIC EFFECT
motion of solids in suspension under
the influence of an electric field
f effet m électrocinétique
d elektrokinetischer Effekt m

639 ELECTROLYTE
f électrolyte m
d Elektrolyt m

640 ELEVATION
f élévation f
d Höhe f

ELEVATION DISTRIBUTION, area
see 106

641 ELEVATION HEAD
f énergie f de position
d Druckhöhe f

642 ELUTRIATION
washing process by decantation
with water
f élutriation f
d Aufschlämmen n

643 EMBANKMENT
natural or artificial lateral boundary
of a river
f berge f
d Ufer n; Uferböschung f

644 EMBOUCHURE
mouth of a river
f embouchure f
d Mündung f

645 EMULSION BREAKER
f désémulsifiant m
d Emulsionsspalter m

646 ENCROACHMENT
landward advancement of saline
waters into coastal aquifers;
displacement of clean water by
pollutants
f envahissement m
d Eindringen n; Vordringen n

647 END EFFECT
disturbance introduced by inflow
and outflow section in flow experiment
f effet m de bouts
d Endeffekt m

648 ENDOGENIC
pertaining to geological process
originating within the earth
f endogène
d endogen; innenbürtig

ENERGY, free surface see 786

649 ENERGY BALANCE
f bilan m énergétique
d Energiebilanz f

650 ENERGY GRADE LINE
f ligne f de charge
d Energielinie f

651 ENERGY HEAD
hydraulic head plus velocity head
f charge f totale
d Gesamthöhe f der Energielinie

652 ENERGY LINE
f ligne f de charge
d Energielinie f

653 ENERGY TRANSFER
f transfert m d'énergie
d Energieumsatz m

654 ENTHALPY
heat content
f enthalpie f
d Wärmeinhalt m; Entalpie f

655 ENTRANCE CAPACITY
property of soil to let water
infiltrate; maximum value of this
property
f capacité f de pénétration
d Eindringungskapazität f

656 ENTROPHY
degree of thermodynamic disorder
f entrophie f
d Entropie f

657 EOCENE
geologic epoch in the Tertiary
period
f Eocène m
d Eozän n

658 EOLIAN DEPOSIT
sediment material deposited by
wind action
f dépôt m éolien
d Windablagerung f

659 EPHEMERAL STREAM
stream flowing only in direct
response to precipitation
f rivière f éphémère
d kurzfristig fliessender Fluss m

660 EPILIMNION
upper layer of stratified water
f épilimnion m
d Epilimnion n

661 EPOCH
subdivision of a period in the
geologic time scale
f époque f
d Epoche f

EPOCH, glacial see 847

EQUATION, continuity
-, hydrologic see 976

662 EQUATION OF HYDROLOGIC
EQUILIBRIUM
mass balance for a ground water
basin
f bilan m régional
d Gebietsbilanz f

663 EQUATION OF STATE
f équation f d'état
d Zustandsgleichung f

664 EQUIPOTENTIAL LINE
line of equal potential
f équipotentielle f
d Linie f gleiches Potentials

EQUIVALENT, chemical see 286
-, moisture see 2065
-, water see 2934

665 EQUIVALENT PER MILLION (EPM)
number of equivalent weights in a
million parts per weight of solution
f équivalent m par million
d Äquivalenzgewicht n pro Million

666 ERA
largest subdivision of the geologic
time scale
f ère f
d Zeitalter n

667 ERODIBLE
susceptible to erosion
f érodible
d erodierbar

668 EROSION
sequence of processes of disintegration
and transportation of rock material
f érosion f
d Erosion f; Abtragung f

EROSION, bank see 137
-, sheet see 2533

669 EROSIONAL PROCESS
f processus m d'érosion
d Erosionsvorgang m;
Abtragungsvorgang m

670 EROSION SURFACE
land surface resulting from the
action of erosion
f surface f d'érosion
d Erosionsfläche f;
Abtragungsfläche f

671 EROSIVENESS
capacity to erode
f pouvoir *m* érosif
d Erosionsfähigkeit *f*

672 ESCARPMENT
steep slope, often the result of
faulting
f escarpement *m*
d Steilabfall *m*; Stufe *f*

673 ESKER
stratified fluvio-glacial deposits
in form of ridges
f esker *m*
d Oser *m*; Wallberg *m*

674 ESTUARY
lower course of river discharging
into sea and subject to tidal currents
f estuaire *m*
d Mündung *f*

675 EUTROPHICATION
f eutrophication *f*
d Eutrophierung *f*

676 EVAPORATE
sedimentary rock formed by
evaporation and precipitation of
saline waters
f évaporit *m*
d Evaporit *m*; Saltzgestein *n*

677 EVAPORATION
change of water from liquid or solid
state into gaseous state through
heat exchange
f évaporation *f*
d Verdunstung *f*; Evaporation *f*

EVAPORATION, reservoir see 2391

678 EVAPORATION DISCHARGE
direct discharge of ground water
to atmosphere through evaporation
f débit *m* d'évaporation
d Bodenverdunstung *f*;
Wasserabgabe *f* durch Verdunstung

679 EVAPORATION LOSS
loss of precipitated water that is
discharged to atmosphere by
evaporation
f perte *f* par évaporation
d Verdunstungsverlust *m*

680 EVAPORATION OPPORTUNITY
amount of water made available for
discharge into atmosphere

f disponibilité *f* en eau (pour
l'évaporation)
d verfügbares Wasser *n* (für die
Verdunstung)

681 EVAPORATION PAN
open tank used to measure evaporatic
f bac *m* évaporatoire
d Verdunstungskessel *m*

682 EVAPORATION REDUCTION
rate control of escape of water
vapor from an open surface
f réduction *f* de l'évaporation
d Verdunstungsverminderung *f*

683 EVAPORATION SUPPRESSION
complete prevention of evaporation
by mechanical or physico-chemical
means (e.g. monomolecular layer)
f suppression *f* de l'évaporation
d Verdunstungsunterdrückung *f*

684 EVAPORATIVITY
evaporative power
f pouvoir *m* évaporant
d Verdunstungsvermögen *n*

685 EVAPORITE ROCKS
f roche *f* hydatogène
d Eindampfungsgestein *n*;
Salzgestein *n*

686 EVAPOTRANSPIRATION
return of water in vapor form to
atmosphere through combined action
of evaporation, plant transpiration
and sublimation
f évapotranspiration *f*
d Evapotranspiration *f*;
Gesamtverdunstung *f*

EVAPOTRANSPIRATION,
potential see 2279

687 EXCAVATE, TO
f creuser
d graben; ausgraben

EXCHANGE, gas see 815
-, heat see 925

688 EXCHANGE CAPACITY
f pouvoir *m* d'échange ionique
d Austauschvermögen *n*;
Austauschfähigkeit *f*

689 EXOGENIC
pertaining to processes on or near
the surface of the earth

f   exogène
d   exogen; aussenbürtig

690   EXPANSION JOINT
f   joint *m* d'expansion
d   Ausdehnungsverbindung *f*

691   EXPERIMENTAL BASIN
basin chosen for the thorough
study of hydrological phenomenon
f   bassin *m* échantillon
d   Beobachtungsgebiet *n*;
Versuchsbecken *n*

EXPLORATION, geophysical
see 839

692   EXPLORATION DRILLING
drilling for the purpose of subsurface
geological reconnaissance
f   forage *m* de reconnaissance
d   Schürfbohrung *f*; Aufschlussbohrung *f*

693   EXPLOSION
f   explosion *f*
d   Sprengung *f*; Explosion *f*

694   EXPLOSIVE
f   explosif *m*
d   Sprengstoff *m*

695   EXPOSURE SITE
f   endroit *m* exposé
d   Messtelle *f*

696   EXTERNAL DIAMETER
f   diamètre *m* extérieur
d   Aussendurchmesser *m*

697   EXTERNAL LOADS
external loads causing water level
fluctuation in well
f   charge *f* extérieure; charge *f*
accidentelle
d   externe Belastung *f*; Fremdbelastung *f*

698   EXTRUSIVE ROCK
see effusive rock
f   roche *f* extrusive
d   Extrusivgestein *n*; Ergussgestein *n*

F

699 **FACIES**
lithologic appearance of a rock
f faciès *m*
d Fazies *f*

700 **FACIES CHANGE**
f changement *m* de faciès
d Fazieswechsel *m*

FACTOR, climatic see 307
-, conversion see 381
-, deposition see 466
-, form see 780
-, formation see 776
-, formation-resistivity see 778
-, leakage see 1145
-, lithologic see 1156
-, scaling see 2479
-, structural see 2678
-, weighing see 2977
-, wind see 3017

701 **FAILING WELL**
well yielding less water with time
f puits *m* tarissant
d versiegender Brunnen *m*

702 **FALL**
gross slope of a river
f chute *f*; pente *f*
d Reliefenergie *f*; Gefäll *n*

703 **FAMILY OF CURVES**
f famille *f* de courbes
d Kurvenschaar *f*

FAN, alluvial see 58
-, talus see 2747

704 **FAN SHOOTING**
method of arranging shot holes in
a seismic survey
f tir *m* en éventail
d Fächerschiessen *n*

705 **FATHOMETER**
water depth measuring device
f sondeur *m* de la profondeur d'eau
d Wassertiefenmessgerät *n*

706 **FAULT**
fracture of a rock mass along which
dislocation has taken place
f faille *f*
d Verwerfung *f*; Sprung *m*

FAULT, cross see 416
-, longitudinal see 1168
-, normal see 2115
-, reverse see 2406

707 **FAULT LINE**
intersection of the fault with the
surface of the earth or any other
plane of reference
f ligne *f* de faille
d Verwerfungslinie *f*

708 **FAULT PLANE**
plane on which dislocation and
relative movement has taken place
f plan *m* de faille
d Verwerfungsebene *f*

709 **FAULT SCARP**
elevation formed by movement of
blocks along a fault plane
f escarpement *m* de faille
d Bruchstufe *f*; Verwerfungsstufe *f*

710 **FAULT ZONE**
zone with numerous small parallel
faults
f zone *f* failleuse
d Verwerfungszone *f*; Störungszone *f*

711 **FEEDING DEVICE**
f doseur *m*
d Dosiergerät *n*

712 **FELDSPAR**
very common group of rock forming
minerals
f feldspath *m*
d Feldspat *m*

713 **FERRIC OXIDE**
Fe_2O_3, rust, hematite
f oxyde *m* ferrique
d Eisenoxyd *n*; Eisenrost *m*

714 **FERRITO ZONE**
zone of iron oxide accumulation in
soil under humid climate
f horizon *m* ferrugineux; alios *m*
ferrugineux
d eisenhaltige Ausfällungszone *f*

715 **FERRUGINOUS**
f ferrugineux
d eisenhaltig

FIELD, vector see 2886
-, well see 2998
-, wind see 3018

716   FIELD CAPACITY;
      FIELD-CARRYING CAPACITY;
      CAPILLARY CAPACITY
      soil moisture retained by capillarity,
      not removable by gravity drainage;
      specific retention
      f   capacité *f* au champ, capacité *f*
          capillaire
      d   Feldkapazität *f*

717   FIELD COEFFICIENT OF
      PERMEABILITY
      defined for field temperature
      conditions in gpd/ft^2 under a unit
      gradient
      f   coefficient *m* de perméabilité
          Darcy sur le terrain
      d   Feldwert *m* der Durchlässig-
          keitsziffer

718   FIELD SURVEY
      measurements taken in the field
      f   étude *f* sur terrain
      d   Felduntersuchung *f*

719   FIELD TEST
      test run in the field under normal
      field conditions
      f   essai *m* sur le terrain
      d   Feldversuch *m*

720   FIELD VELOCITY OF GROUND
      WATER
      actual interstitial velocity
      f   vitesse *f* de terrain
      d   tatsächliche Grundwasserfliess-
          geschwindigkeit *f*
          Abstandsgeschwindigkeit *f*

721   FIELD WORK
      f   travaux *mpl* de terrain
      d   Feldarbiet *m*

      FILL, gravel see 872
      -, valley see 2878

722   FILL TERRACE
      elevated valley surface formed by
      aggregation
      f   terrasse *f* de remblaiement;
          terrasse *f* d'accumulation
      d   Aufschüttungsterrasse *f*;
          Aufschotterungsterrasse *f*

723   FILTER
      screen through which water enters
      a well
      f   filtre *m*
      d   Filter *m*

724   FILTER CAKE
      cake of solid residue left on filter
      f   cake *m* de boue; gâteau *m* de
          boue; dépôt *m* de filtration
      d   Filterkuchen *m*

725   FILTER PLANT
      f   installation *f* de filtration
      d   Filteranlage *f*

      FILTRATION SPRING
      see seepage spring

726   FINE GRAINED SAND
      f   sable *m* fin
      d   Feinsand *m*

727   FINE GRAVEL
      rock aggregates of 2 - 1 mm
      diameter (USBS)
      f   sable *m* très gros
      d   feiner Kies *m*

728   FINE SAND
      grain diameter 0.25 to 0.1 mm
      (USBS)
      f   sable *m* fin
      d   Feinsand *m*

729   FINITE DIFFERENCES METHOD
      method of solution for partial
      differential equations
      f   méthode *f* par différences finies
      d   Methode *f* der endlichen
          Differenzen

730   FIRN
      compacted granular snow
      f   névé *m*
      d   Firn *m*

731   FISHING TOOL
      device for the retrieval of broken
      or stuck drilling tools
      f   outil *m* de repêchage
      d   Fangwerkzeug *n*

732   FISHTAIL
      drilling bit with fish tail like double
      winged cutting edges
      f   outil *m* bilame
      d   Fischschwanzmeissel *m*

733   FISSURE
      open joint or crack in rocks
      f   fissure *f*; crevasse *f*
      d   Spalte *f*

734   FIXED BOUNDARY
      f   limite *f* fixe
      d   festgelegte Grenze *f*

735 FLANK
limb of a fold
f flanc *m*
d Flanke *f*; Schenkel *m*

736 FLASH FLOOD
relatively short but very intense
flood
f torrent *m*
d Sturzflut *f*

737 FLEXIBLE HOSE
f flexible *m*; tuyeau *m* flexible
d Schlauch *m*; biegsamer Schlauch *m*

738 FLEXURE
bend in stratum with one flank or
limb only
f flexure *f*
d Flexur *f*

739 FLOAT
f flotteur *m*
d Schwimmer *m*

740 FLOAT GAGE
device indicating or recording
water level with a float
f limnigraphe *m* à flotteur;
niveau *m* à flotteur
d Schwimmerschreibpegel *m*;
Flüssigkeitsstandanzeiger *m* mit
Schwimmer

741 FLOATING PAN
evaporation pan floating in water
body with drum floats
f bac *m* flottant
d Flossverdunstungskessel *m*

742 FLOCCULATION
f floculation *f*
d Ausflockung *f*; Ausfällung *f*

743 FLOOD
high river flow overtopping banks
f inondation *f*; crue *f*
d Überschwemmung *f*; Hochwasser *n*; Ausuferung *f*

FLOOD, design see 480
-, flash see 736

744 FLOOD-CONTROL
all measures to prevent or
diminish the effects of flooding
f protection *f* contre les crues
d Hochwasserschutz *m*

745 FLOOD CREST
peak of flood wave

f pointe *f* de crue
d Hochwasserscheitel *m*

746 FLOODING METHOD
recharge method by flooding
recharge area
f méthode *f* d'infiltration par
inondation
d Überschwemmungsmethode *f*

747 FLOODMARKS
marks left on fixed objects by
flood waters
f délaissés *mpl* de crue
d Hochwasserspuren *fpl*

748 FLOOD PLAIN
area of overbank flow
f zone *f* inondable; plaine *f*
d'inondation
d Überschwemmungsgebiet *n*;
Ausuferungsgebiet *n*

749 FLOOD PROFILE
continuous line representing the
water surface for a given rate of
flow
f profil *m* de crue
d Hochwasserlängsschnitt *m*

750 FLOOD ROUTING
f propagation *f* de crues
d Hochwasserweiterleitung *f*

751 FLOOD WATER
f eau *fpl* en crue
d steigendes Wasser *n*

752 FLOOD WAVE
f onde *f* de crue
d Flutwelle *f*

753 FLOTATION
f flottation *f*
d Flotieren *n*

FLOW, base see 149
-, confined see 348
-, creep see 402
-, critical see 412
-, gage see 803
-, groundwater see 910
-, high see 932
-, interaquifer see 1050
-, irrotational see 1083
-, laminar see 1121
-, low see 1173
-, main channel see 1182
-, open channel see 2131

FLOW, overland see 2159
-, potential see 2280
-, pyroclastic see 2314
-, radial see 2321
-, rapid see 2337
-, recession see 2355
-, return see 2404
-, saturated see 2469
-, sheet see 2534
-, steady see 2644
-, stream see 2666
-, subsurface see 2689, 2690
-, subsurface storm see 2690
-, tranquil see 2816
-, unconfined see 2858
-, uniform see 2866
-, unsaturated see 2870
-, unsteady see 2871
-, virgin see 2895

754 FLOW, TO
    f couler
    d fliessen

755 FLOW DURATION CURVE
    curve of cumulative streamflow
    versus corresponding per cent of
    time
    f courbe f de durée des débits
    d Dauerlinie f der Abflussmenge

756 FLOWING ARTESIAN WELL
    well with piezometric surface
    above ground surface
    f source f artésienne en libre
       débit
    d frei fliessender artesischer
       Brunnen m

757 FLOWING PRESSURE
    f pression f en débit
    d Fliessdruck m

758 FLOW-MASS CURVE
    mass curve with runoff discharge
    as hydrologic quantity; integral
    curve of hydrograph
    f courbe f du débit cumulé
    d Summenganglinie f

759 FLOWMETER
    instrument to measure volumetric
    flowrate
    f débimètre m
    d Durchflussmessgerät n

    FLOWMETER, mass see 1193
    -, volumetric see 2908

760 FLOW NET
    net of orthogonal streamlines

and equipotential lines applied in
the graphical solution of Laplace's
equation
    f réseau m orthogonal des lignes
       de courant et des courbes
       isopièzes
    d Strömungsnetz n;
       Strom-und Potentialliniennetz n

761 FLOW RATE
    volumetric rate of flow
    f débit m
    d Fliessrate f; Spende f

762 FLOW REGIMEN
    systematic behavior of a flow
    system as controlled by gravity,
    viscous or intomolecular forces
    (i.e. turbulent regimen)
    f régime m
    d Regime n

763 FLOW RESISTANCE
    f résistance f à l'écoulement
    d Fliesswiderstand m

764 FLOWTEST
    f essai m d'écoulement
    d Fliesstest m

765 FLOW WITH WATER TABLE
    unconfined flow
    f écoulement m en nappe phréatique
    d Grundwasserfluss m mit freier
       Oberfläche

766 FLUID
    f fluide m
    d Flüssigkeit f

    FLUID, drilling see 576
    -, homogeneous see 942

767 FLUID-VELOCITY LOG
    vertical record of fluid velocities
    in a well bore
    f diagraphie f de la vitesse
       d'écoulement
    d Fliessgeschwindigkeitslog n

768 FLUME
    channel supported on or above ground
    f rigole f
    d Gerinne n; Rinne f

    FLUME, critical depth see 411
    -, measuring see 2010

769 FLUORESCEIN
    f florescéine f
    d Fluoreszein n

770 FLUORITE
fluorspar, CaF_2
f fluorine *f*
d Flusspat *m*

771 FLUSHED ZONE
in electric logging practice the
zone around the well bore completely
invaded by the mud filtrate
f zone *f* envahie
d geflutete Zone *f*

772 FLUX
volume flow per unit area in unit
time
f flux *m*
d spezifischer Fluss *m*

773 FOLD
bend in stratum with two flanks,
often in anticlinal and synclinal
sequence
f pli *m*
d Falte *f*

774 FOOT VALVE
f clapet *m* de fond
d Bodenventil *n*

FORCE, body see 189
-, capillary see 238
-, gravity see 883
-, osmotic see 2144
-, viscous see 2898

775 FORCE POTENTIAL
f potentiel *m* de force
d Kraftpotential *n*

FORMATION, dew see 491
-, lacustrine see 1117
-, multiaquifer see 2093
-, rock see 2429

776 FORMATION FACTOR
ratio of bulk resistivity of
saturated sample to resistivity of
saturating solution
f facteur *m* de formation
d Formationsfaktor *m*

777 FORMATION OF RAIN
f formation *f* de pluie
d Regenbildung *f*

778 FORMATION-RESISTIVITY FACTOR
see formation factor
f facteur *m* de formation
d Formationswiderstandsfaktor *m*

779 FORMATION TEMPERATURE
temperature prevailing in a given
subsurface formation
f température *f* de formation
d Formationstemperatur *f*

780 FORM FACTOR
factor indicating shape and form of
mineral aggregates influencing their
hydrodynamic properties
f facteur *m* de forme
d Formfaktor *m*

781 FOUNTAIN
free flowing well or spring
f fontaine *f*
d Springbrunnen *m*; Quelle *f*

782 FRACTURE
breakage of rock strata
f fracture *f*
d Bruch *m*

783 FRACTURE SPRING
spring with outflow openings
consisting of fractures
f source *f* de fissures
d Kluftquelle *f*

784 FRACTURING
formation of breaks in a rock due
to folding or faulting
f fracturation *f*
d Bruchbildung *f*

FRACTURING, hydraulic see 953
-, well see 2990

785 FRAME
superstructure containing working
parts in drilling rig assembly
f monture *f*
d Gestell *n*; Rahmen *m*

786 FREE SURFACE ENERGY
f énergie *f* libre de surface
d freie Oberflächenenergie *f*

787 FREEZING POINT
point at which a liquid solidifies
f point *m* de congélation
d Gefrierpunkt *m*

788 FREQUENCY
number of occurrences of a variabl
f fréquence *f*
d Frequenz *f*; Häufigkeit *f*

FREQUENCY, stream see 2667

789 FREQUENCY ANALYSIS
     f analyse f fréquentielle
     d Frequenzanalyse f;
        Häufigkeitsanalyse f

790 FREQUENCY DISTRIBUTION
     distribution of the number of
     occurrences of a variate
     f distribution f de fréquence
     d Häufigkeitsverteilung f

791 FRESH WATER
     water containing from 0 to 1000 ppm
     total dissolved solids
     f eau f douce
     d Frischwasser n; Süsswasser n

792 FRESH-WATER BARRIER
     barrier of fresh water injected to
     stop inflow of sea water into coastal
     aquifer
     f barrage m souterrain en eau
        douce
     d Süsswasserbarriere f

793 FRESH WATER LENS
     lenticular form of fresh water body
     under oceanic islands
     f lentille f d'eau douce
     d Frischwasserlinse f

794 FRIABLE
     f friable; fragile
     d brüchig; mulmig

795 FRICTION COEFFICIENT
     f coefficient m de frottement
     d Reibungsbeiwert m

796 FRICTION HEAD
     head loss due to energy
     dissipation by friction
     f perte f de charge
     d Reibungsverlust m

797 FRONT RANGE
     the outer part of a mountain
     range rising above the plain
     f avant-montagne f
     d Vorgebirge n

798 FROST IN THE SOIL
     f gel m dans le sol
     d Bodenfrost m

     FROST ZONE, annual see 84

799 FULL HOLE DRILLING
     drilling method where total cross
     section of hole is removed (as
     opposed to core drilling)
     f forage m plein diamètre
     d Vollbohrverfahren n

800 FUMAROLE
     volcanic exhalation of gases,
     mainly water vapor
     f fumerolle f
     d Fumarole f

801 FUNICULAR REGIME
     distribution of continuous liquid phase
     along pore walls with gaseous phase at
     pore center
     f régime m d'eau funiculaire
     d funikuläres Wasser n;
        zusammenhängendes Oberflächen-
        haftwasser n

G

802 GABBRO
dark alkaline plutonic rock with very
low feldspar content
f   gabbro *m*
d   Gabbro *m*

GAGE, Bourdon see 198
-, bubble see 206
-, chain see 275
-, float see 740
-, hook see 943
-, mercury see 2027
-, natural see 2099
-, nonrecording see 2112
-, precipitation see 2288
-, rain see 2331
-, recording see 2366
-, snow see 2582
-, staff see 2630
-, storage see 2652
-, tape see 2748
-, wire see 3019

803 GAGE FLOW
f   débit *m* jaugé
d   Eichfluss *m*

804 GAGE PRESSURE
normally pressure above atmospheric, absolute pressure minus
reference pressure
f   surpression *f* atmosphérique
d   Atmosphärenüberdruck *m*

805 GAGE TANK
tank used for volume measurements
f   bac *m* de jaugeage; réservoir-
     jaugeur *m*
d   Messtank *m*

806 GAGE WELL
stilling well in which stage
measurements are performed
f   puits *m* de limnigraphe
     puits *m* de mesure
d   Schwimmerschacht *m*;
     Messchacht *m*

807 GAGE ZERO
f   zéro *m* de l'échelle
d   Skalennullpunkt *m*; Pegelnull-
     punkt *m*

GAGING, electro-chemical
see 634
-, water see 2935

808 GAGING STATION
point at which stage measurements
are performed
f   station *f* de jaugeage
d   Messtation *f*; Messwarte *f*

GAINING STREAM
see effluent stream

809 GALVANOMETER
sensitive current meter
f   galvanomètre *m*
d   Galvanometer *n*

810 GAMMA LOG
vertical record of gamma-ray
measurements in a well
f   diagraphie *f* de rayons gamma
d   Gammalog *n*

811 GARNET
accessory mineral in igneous and
metamorphic rocks
f   grenat *m*
d   Granat *m*

812 GAS
f   gaz *m*
d   Gas *n*

813 GAS BEARING
containing gas
f   gazéifère
d   gasführend

814 GAS CUSHION
irretrievable gas pumped into an
aquifer to form reservoir space for
the storage of natural gas
f   matelas *m* de gaz
d   Gaspolster *n*

815 GAS EXCHANGE
f   échange *m* de gaz
d   Gasaustausch *m*

816 GAS EXPANSION METHOD
measurement of porosity based on
Boyle-Mariotte's gas laws
f   méthode *f* par expansion de gaz;
     méthode *f* par compression
     (Mariotte)
d   Gasausdehnungsmehtode *f*
     (Boyle-Mariotte)

817 GAS EXTRACTION
f dégazage *m*
d Entgasung *f*

818 GASKET
f étanchéité *f*; joint *m*;
garniture *f*
d Dichtung *f*

819 GAS PIPE LINE
f gazoduc *m*
d Gasleitung *f*; Gasfernleitung *f*

820 GAS SATURATION
f saturation en gaz *f*
d Gassättigung *f*

821 GAS TRAP
f séparateur de gaz *m*
d Gasabscheider *m*

GATE, main see 1183

822 GATE VALVE
f vanne *f* principale
d Schieber *m*; Hauptschieber *m*

823 GEAR PUMP
f pompe *f* à engrenage
d Zahnradpumpe *f*; Getriebepumpe *f*

824 GEOCHEMISTRY
science of the qualitative and
quantitative identification of the
elements and their distribution in
the earth
f géochimie *f*
d Geochemie *f*

825 GEODESY
science of measuring the geometrical
properties of the earth
f géodésie *f*
d Geodäsie *f*; Vermessungskunde *f*

826 GEOHYDROLOGIC UNIT
combination of aquifers and
confining beds in a distinct
hydrologic system
f groupe *m* géohydrologique
d geohydrologische Einheit *f*

827 GEOHYDROLOGY
branch of hydrology relating to
quantitative treatment of groundwater occurrence and flow
f géohydrologie *f*; hydrologie *f*
des nappes souterraines
d Geohydrologie *f*; Hydrologie *f*
des Grundwassers

828 GEOLOGICAL COLUMN
vertical cross section through a
sequence of formations
f coupe *f* lithologique
d Schichtprofil *n*

829 GEOLOGICAL SECTION
vertical section through a sequence
of rock masses or strata
f coupe *f* géologique
d geologischer Schnitt *m*

830 GEOLOGIC CONDITIONS
f conditions *f pl* géologiques
d geologische Verhältnisse *n pl*

831 GEOLOGIC CONTROL
influence of geologic factors on
hydrogeologic features
f facteur *m* d'influence hydrogéologique
d geologische Beeinflussung *f*;
hydrologischer Parameter *m*

832 GEOLOGIC CORRELATION
correlation of geologic formations
as shown in logs over a given area
f corrélation *f* géologique
d geologische Korrelation *f*

833 GEOLOGIC LOG
vertical cross section of the
lithologic column indicating geologic
and petrographic data
f diagraphie *f* géologique;
coupe *f* lithologique
d geologisches Log *n*

834 GEOMETRIC MEAN
f moyenne *f* géométrique
d geometrisches Mittel *n*

835 GEOMETRIC SIMILARITY
model-prototype length ratio
f similitude *f* géométrique
d geometrische Ähnlichkeit *f*

836 GEOMORPHIC PROCESS
process responsible for the
formation and alteration of the
earth's surface
f procédé *m* géomorphique
d landschaftsformender Vorgang *m*

837 GEOMORPHOLOGY
science of the origin and evolution
of land forms
f géomorphologie *f*
d Geomorphologie *f*

838 GEOPHONE
instrument to pick up seismic
signals in the audio frequency
range
f sismomètre *m*
d Geophon *n*

839 GEOPHYSICAL EXPLORATION
exploration of subsurface features
by indirect or geophysical methods
f exploration *f* géophysique
d geophysikalische Exploration *f*

840 GEOPHYSICS
science of the physical properties
of the earth
f géophysique *f*
d Geophysik *f*

841 GEOTHERMAL
f géothermique
d geothermisch

842 GEOTHERMAL GRADIENT
increase of temperature with depth
(1°C per 100 ft.)
f gradient *m* géothermique
d geothermischer Gradient *m*

843 GEYSER
intermittent thermal spring
f source *f* geysérienne; geyser *m*
d Geysir *m*; Springquelle *f*

844 GHYBEN-HERZBERG CONDITIONS
equilibrium condition at interface
of immiscible fresh-water bodies
and salt-water bodies in coastal
aquifers
f conditions *f pl* de Ghyben-Herzberg
d Ghyben-Herzberg'sche
Bedingungen *f pl*

845 GLACIAL DEPOSIT
sedimentary deposits due to
transport in glaciers
f dépôt *m* glaciaire
d Glazialablagerung *f*

846 GLACIAL DRIFT
sediment material contained, transported and deposited by glaciers
f éboulis *m* glaciaire
d Gletscherschutt *m*

847 GLACIAL EPOCH
time in earth's history during which
extensive glaciation occurred
f période *f* glaciaire
d Eiszeit *f*

848 GLACIAL GROOVE
groove cut into bedrock by rock
fragments at the bottom of a moving
glacier
f cannelure *f* glaciaire
d Gletscherfurche *f*

849 GLACIAL TILL
drift material directly deposited
by ice
f argile *f* à blocaux
d Geschiebemergel *m*

850 GLACIATION
covering of land surface by glacier
ice
f glaciation *f*
d Vergletscherung *f*

851 GLACIER
extensive body of ice covering the
land surface
f glacier *m*
d Gletscher *m*

GLACIER, active see 21

852 GLACIER MILK
white colored melt water issued
from glacier
f lait *m* de glacier
d Gletschermilch *f*

853 GLACIER TONGUE
f lobe *m* du glacier
d Gletscherzunge *f*

854 GLACIOLOGY
science concerned with the
formation and action of ice
accumulations on the earth
f glaciologie *f*
d Glaziologie *f*

855 GNEISS
highly metamorphic rock of about
same mineral composition as granit
f gneiss *m*
d Gneiss *m*

856 GOOSE NECK
f col *m* de cygne
d Spülkopfkrümmer *m*

857 GORGE
narrow passage or canyon in a
mountain system
f gorge *f*
d Schlucht *f*

858 GRABEN
depression formed by a fault block
moving downward on the two
bounding faults
f   bloc *m* affaissé
d   Graben *m*; Tiefscholle *f*

859 GRADATION
leveling of a surface to a common
level
f   aplanissement *m*; nivellement *m*
d   Einebnung *f*

GRADATION, lateral see 1133

860 GRADE
inclination, slope
f   degré *m*
d   Steigung *f*; Neigung *f*

861 GRADIENT
maximum value of the directional
derivative
f   gradient *m*
d   Gradient *m*

GRADIENT, geothermal see 842
-, hydraulic see 954

862 GRAIN PACKING
spatial arrangement of grains forming
porous medium
f   arrangement *m* des grains;
    tassement *m* des grains
d   Kornpackung *f*

GRAINS, well sorted see 3000

863 GRAIN SHAPE
geometrical aspect of grain
f   forme *f* d'une particule
d   Korngestalt *f*

864 GRAIN SIZE
f   taille *f* des grains
d   Korngrösse *f*

865 GRAIN SIZE DISTRIBUTION
f   distribution *f* granulométrique
d   Korngrössenverteilung *f*

866 GRANODIORITE
acid plutonic rock
f   granodiorite *m*
d   Granodiorit *m*

867 GRANULAR
of structure clearly showing grain
shape
f   granuleux
d   körnig

868 GRANULE
small rounded grain or rock fragment
f   granule *f*
d   Körnchen *n*; Korn *n*

869 GRAPNEL
f   grappin *m*
d   Glückshaken *m*; Fanghaken *m*

870 GRAVEL
waterworn rounded rock grains
and fragments
f   gravier *m*
d   Kies *m*

GRAVEL, crushed see 419
-, fine see 727
-, outwash see 2150

871 GRAVEL ENVELOPE
gravel fill introduced around filter
screen in a well
f   enveloppe *f* de gravier
d   Kiesmantel *m*

872 GRAVEL FILL
f   remblai *m* de gravier
d   Schotterfüllung *f*

873 GRAVEL PACKING
gravel envelope surrounding
perforated casing in a well
f   filtre *m* de gravier
d   Kiesschüttung *f*

874 GRAVEL PIT
f   gravière *f*
d   Kiesgrube *f*

875 GRAVEL WALL
gravel packing around screened
well to increase effective diameter
f   filtre *m* de gravier
d   Kiesfilter *m*

876 GRAVIMETER
instrument to measure gravity,
especially gravity anomalies
f   gravimètre *m*
d   Gravimeter *n*; Schweremesser *m*

877 GRAVIMETRIC MOISTURE CONTENT
ratio of water weight to weight of
solid particles
f   teneur *f* en humidité par
    gravimétrie
d   gravimetrischer Feuchtegehalt *m*

878 GRAVITATIONAL WATER
water that can be drained by gravity

f eau f de gravité; eau f
   gravifique
d Schwerewasser n

GRAVITY, specific see 2618

879 GRAVITY ACCELERATION
   f accélération f de la pesanteur
   d Erdbeschleunigung f

880 GRAVITY ANOMALY
   discrepancy between theoretically
   expected and actually measured
   gravity
   f anomalie f de la gravité
   d Schwereanomalie f

881 GRAVITY COMPONENT
   component acting in the direction
   of gravitation
   f composante f de gravitation
   d Schwerekomponente f

882 GRAVITY DRAINAGE
   flow of water towards a well under
   its own weight
   f drainage m par gravité
   d Schwerkraftentwässerung f

883 GRAVITY FORCE
   f force f de gravité
   d Schwerkraft f

884 GRAVITY METHOD
   geophysical method of measuring
   density differences of geological
   structures
   f méthode f gravimétrique
   d Schweremessmethode f

885 GRAVITY SPRING
   spring flowing under gravity
   f source f de déversement
   d Auslaufquelle f

886 GRAYWACKE
   metamorphosed sandstone with
   high feldspar content
   f grauwacke m
   d Grauwacke f

887 GREENSAND
   sand containing glauconite
   f sable m vert
   d Grünsand m

GROUND ICE, see anchor ice

888 GROUNDING
   f mise f à la terre
   d Erdung f

889 GROUND LEVEL
   f niveau m du sol
   d Geländeoberfläche f

890 GROUND SLOPE
   inclination of the ground surface
   with the horizontal
   f inclinaison f du terrain
   d Geländeneigung f

891 GROUND TERMINAL
   terminal connecting an electrical
   system to the ground
   f mise f à la terre; borne f de
     mise à la terre
   d Erdungsanschluss m

892 GROUND WATER;
   PHREATIC WATER
   that part of the underground or subsurface water that is contained in th
   zone of saturation. Its lower limits
   are the zone of rock flowage or the
   lower confining bed, its upper limit
   are the upper confining bed or the
   water table
   f eaux f pl souterraines; eau f
     phréatique
   d Grundwasser n

GROUND WATER, native see 2097
-, perched see 2190

893 GROUNDWATER ARTERY
   tubular body of permeable water-
   filled material surrounded by confir
   beds
   f veine f d'eau
   d Grundwasserader f

894 GROUNDWATER BARRIER
   see groundwater dam
   f barrière f naturelle dans un
     aquifère; barrage m souterrain
   d Grundwasserbarriere f

895 GROUNDWATER BASIN
   area throughout which groundwate
   drains towards the same point; ca
   be larger than drainage basin if
   permeable layers extend outside o
   topographic divide
   f bassin m hydrogéologique
   d Grundwasserbecken n;
     Grundwassereinzugsgebiet n

896 GROUNDWATER CAPTURE
   f captage m des eaux souterrain
   d Grundwassererschliessung f

897 GROUNDWATER CASCADE
flow of groundwater over a subsurface barrier
f cascade *f* souterraine
d Grundwasserüberfall *m*

898 GROUNDWATER CEMENT
cementing material precipitating at
the water table
f ciment *m* illuvial
d Grundwasserzement *m*;
Ausfällungszement *m*

899 GROUNDWATER DAM
geological stratum serving as a
subsurface dam
f barrage *m* souterrain naturel,
seuil *m* hydraulique;
barrière *f* naturelle dans un
aquifère
d Grundwassersperre *f*;
Untergrundsperre *f*

900 GROUNDWATER DISCHARGE
f débit *m* en eau souterraine
d Grundwasserspende *f*

901 GROUNDWATER DIVIDE
in well hydraulics streamline with
no flow, boundary of aquifer region
contributing to well discharge
f périmètre *m* d'appel
d Grundwasserscheide *f*

902 GROUNDWATER DIVIDE
dividing line between two ground
water basins
f ligne *f* de partage entre deux
bassins hydrogéologiques
d Grundwasserscheide *f*

GROUNDWATER FLOW
see groundwater runoff

903 GROUNDWATER INVENTORY
complete quantitative accounting
for all volumes of groundwater
f bilan *m* des nappes souterraines
d Grundwasserbestandsaufnahme *f*

904 GROUNDWATER LEVEL
f niveau *m* de la nappe phréatique;
niveau *m* piézométrique (d'une
nappe libre)
d Grundwasserspiegel *m*

905 GROUNDWATER MOUND
f protubérance *f* de la nappe
d Grundwassererhebung *f*

906 GROUNDWATER PROVINCE
f province *f* des eaux souterraines
d Grundwasserprovinz *f*

907 GROUNDWATER RECESSION
f abaissement *m* de la nappe
phréatique; décrue *f*
souterraine
d Grundwasserabsenkung *f*

908 GROUNDWATER RECESSION CURVE
f courbe *f* d'abaissement;
courbe *f* de tarissement
d Grundwasserabsenkungskurve *f*

909 GROUNDWATER RESERVOIR
reservoir in the void space beneath
the water table
f réservoir *m* en eaux souterraines
d Grundwasserreservoir *n*;
Grundwasserspeicher *m*

910 GROUNDWATER RUNOFF;
GROUNDWATER FLOW
runoff due to deep percolation
from groundwater body
f écoulement *m* souterrain
d Grundwasserabfluss *m*

911 GUARD ELECTRODE
f électrode *f* écran
d Schirmelektrode *f*

912 GUIDE SHOE
f sabot *m* de guidage
d Führungsschuh *m*

913 GULLY
deep erosional channel
f chenal *m*
d Rinne *f*; Erosionsrinne *f*

914 GUN PERFORATOR
f perforatuer *m* à balles
d Kugelschussapparat *m*

915 GUY WIRE
fixed wire for the stabilization of
a drilling rig
f câble *m* d'ancrage
d Halteseil *n*

H

916 HALF-LIFE
f demi-vie *f*
d Halbwertszeit *f*

917 HALITE
rock salt
f sel gemme *m*
d Steinsalz *n*

918 HALOMORPHIC SOIL
saline and alkali soils
f sol *m* halomorphe
d salzhaltiger Boden *m*

HAMMER, air see 41
-, drop see 595
-, water see 2936

919 HARDENING
process of induration
f endurcissement *m*
d Verhärtung *f*

HARDNESS, permanent see 2202
-, temporary see 2756
-, total see 2807

920 HARDNESS OF WATER
sum of calcium and magnesium ions
expressed as equivalent amount of
calcium carbonate ($CaCO_2$); property
to form insoluable salts of fatty
acid (soap)
f dureté *f*
d Härte *f*; Wasserhärte *f*

921 HARDPAN;
MORTAR BED
secondary calcium carbonate
cementations in lower part of soil
profile
f horizon *m* durci
d Konkretionskruste *f*;
Felspanzerbildung *f*

922 HEAD
f charge *f*
d Höhe *f*; Druckhöhe *f*

HEAD, elevation see 641
-, energy see 651
-, friction see 796
-, hydraulic see 955
-, injection see 1037
-, piezometric see 2230

-, pressure see 2293
-, suction see 2694
-, velocity see 2890

923 HEAD LOSS
f perte *f* de charge
d Druckverlust *m*

924 HEAD WATER
upper reach of stream
f cours *m* supérieur
d Oberlauf *m*; Quellgebiet *n*

925 HEAT EXCHANGE
f échange *m* de chaleur
d Wärmeaustausch *m*

926 HEAT OF CONDENSATION
heat released in transforming a
substance from its vapor to its
liquid state
f chaleur *f* de condensation
d Kondensationswärme *f*

927 HEAT OF VAPORIZATION
heat necessary to change water
from liquid to gaseous state
f chaleur *f* de vaporisation
d Verdampfungwärme *f*

HEAT OF VAPORIZATION, latent
see 1130

928 HEAT TRANSFER
f transfert *m* de chaleur
d Wärmeumsatz *m*

HEAT, sensible see 2511

929 HELE-SHAW APPARATUS
parallel plate model to simulate
two-dimensional potential flow
f appareil *m* de Hele-Shaw
d Hele-Shawmodell *n*

930 HETEROGENEOUS
unequal spatial distribution of
aquifer properties
f hétérogène
d heterogen; ungleichförmig

931 HIGH BANK
f rive *f* haute
d Steilufer *n*

932   HIGH FLOW
      f   débit *m* de crue
      d   Hochwasserabfluss *m*

933   HIGH-WATER
      f   crue *f*; hautes-eaux *f pl*
      d   Hochwasser *n*

934   HODOGRAPH PLANE
      velocity plane, used in solution of
      free surface flow problems
      f   plan *m* d'hodographe
      d   Isotachenebene *f*

935   HOIST
      f   treuil *m* de levage
      d   Hebewerk *n*; Hebewinde *f*

936   HOISTING CABLE
      f   câble *m* de levage
      d   Förderseil *n*

937   HOISTING CAP
      removable cap with a ring to permit
      hoisting of drill pipe
      f   tête *f* de levage
      d   Hebekappe *f*

938   HOISTING CRANE
      f   grue *f* de levage
      d   Hebekran *m*

939   HOLDING TANK
      f   bac *m* intercepteur
      d   Auffangbehälter *m*

940   HOLE
      f   trou *m*; trou *m* de forage;
          sonde *f*
      d   Loch *n*; Bohrung *f*; Sonde *f*

      HOLE, bottom see 192
      -, crooked see 413
      -, dry see 601
      -, sink see 2563
      -, test see 2763
      -, uncased see 2857

941   HOMOGENEOUS
      even spatial distribution of aquifer
      properties
      f   homogène
      d   homogen; gleichförmig

942   HOMOGENEOUS FLUID
      fluid occurring in single phase
      f   fluide *m* homogène
      d   homogene Flüssigkeit *f*

      HOOK, drilling see 578

943   HOOK GAGE
      gage for the precise position
      measurement of liquid levels
      f   pointe *f* de mesure
      d   Stechpegel *m*

944   HOPPER
      f   trémie *f*
      d   Aufgabebunker *m*

      HORIZON, A- see 37
      -, B- see 175
      -, C- see 293
      -, D- see 493

945   HORNBLENDE
      see amphibole
      f   hornblende *m*
      d   Hornblende *f*

946   HORST
      block having been uplifted along its
      boundary faults
      f   bloc *m* surélevé
      d   Horst *m*; Hochscholle *f*

947   HORTON NUMBER
      expresses relative intensity of
      erosion process in drainage basin
      f   nombre *m* de Horton
      d   Horton-Zahl *f*

948   HOUSING
      f   carter *m*
      d   Gehäuse *n*

949   HUMIDITY
      f   humidité *f*
      d   Feuchte *f*

      HUMIDITY, absolute see 5
      -, relative .... of atmosphere
      see 2383

950   HYDRATION
      penetration of water into the crystal
      structure of a compound
      f   hydration *f*
      d   Hydratation *f*

951   HYDRAULIC CONDUCTIVITY
      ease with which water is conducted
      through an aquifer
      f   conductivité *f* hydraulique;
          coefficient *m* de Darcy
      d   hydraulische Leitfähigkeit *f*

952   HYDRAULIC DISCHARGE
      discharge of ground water through
      springs or wells

f débit *m* hydraulique
d hydraulischer Ausfluss *m*

953 HYDRAULIC FRACTURING
formation of artificial fractures
in rock system around a well by
high pressure fluid injections
f fracturation *f* hydraulique
d hydraulische Rissbildung *f*

954 HYDRAULIC GRADIENT
f gradient *m* hydraulique
d hydraulischer Gradient *m*

955 HYDRAULIC HEAD
energy per unit weight of fluid
f énergie *f* hydraulique;
hauteur *f* hydraulique
d Fliessdruck *m*

956 HYDRAULIC JUMP
standing surge of water passing
from below critical depth in open
channel flow; abrupt depth variation
in rapidly varying channel flow
f ressaut *m* hydraulique
d hydraulischer Sprung *m*

957 HYDRAULIC PROFILE
vertical section of the piezometric
surface
f section *f* hydraulique; profil *m*
de dépression
d hydraulisches Profil *n*

958 HYDRAULIC RADIUS
ratio of filled cross sectional area
to wetted perimeter
f rayon *m* hydraulique
d hydraulischer Radius *m*

959 HYDRAULIC ROTARY
rotary drilling method with
hydraulic drive
f rotary *m* à commande hydraulique
d Rotarybohren *n* mit hydraulischem
Antrieb

960 HYDRAULICS
f hydraulique *f*
d Hydraulik *f*

961 HYDROCHLORIC ACID
f acide *m* hydrochlorique
d Salzsäure *f*

962 HYDRODYNAMIC CONDUCTIBILITY
f conductibilité *f* hydrodynamique;
hydroconductibilité *f*
d hydrodynamische Leitfähigkeit *f*

963 HYDRODYNAMIC DISPERSION
dynamic dispersion of fluid
particles in flow through a porous
medium due to velocity changes in the
pore channels
f dispersion *f* hydrodynamique
d hydrodynamische Dispersion *f*

964 HYDROGEN BONDING
f liaison *f* hydrogène
d Wasserstoffbrückenbindung *f*

965 HYDROGEN-ION CONCENTRATION
pH
f concentration *f* en ions d'hydrogèr
d Wasserstoffionenkonzentration *f*

966 HYDROGEN SULFIDE
H_2S
f hydrogène *m* sulfuré
d Schwefelwasserstoff *m*

967 HYDROGEOCHEMISTRY
geochemistry as related to the
occurrence of water
f hydrogéochimie *f*
d Hydrogeochemie *f*

968 HYDROGEOLOGY
study of subsurface waters in their
geological context
f hydrogéologie *f*
d Hydrogeologie *f*

969 HYDROGRAPH
time record of stream discharge
at a given cross section of stream
or of stream surface elevation at
a given point
f hydrogramme *m*
d Ganglinie *f* des Wasserstandes;
Abflussganglinie *f*; Hydrograph *m*

HYDROGRAPH, characteristic
see 282
-, discharge see 517
-, simple see 2559
-, stage see 2633
-, synthetic unit see 2742
-, well see 2992

970 HYDROGRAPH SEPARATION
separation of hydrograph into its
different components to analyze
flow contributions
f décomposition *f* de l'hydrogramme; analyse *f* de
l'hydrogramme
d Aufspaltung *f* der Abflussganglinie

971 HYDROGRAPHY
geographical description of water
bodies on earth's surface
f hydrographie *f*
d beschreibende Gewässerkunde *f*;
   Hydrographie *f*

972 HYDROLACCOLITH
mounds raised by formation of
ice lenses in permafrost soil
f laccolith *m* de glace
d Eislakkolith *m*

973 HYDROLOGIC BARRIER
lithologic formation preventing
horizontal movement of ground
water
f barrière *f* hydrologique
d Grundwasserbarriere *f*

974 HYDROLOGIC BUDGET
quantitative accounting of all
water volumes and their change
with time for a given basin or
province
f bilan *m* hydrologique
d Wasserhaushalt *m*

975 HYDROLOGIC CYCLE
f cycle *m* hydrologique
d hydrologischer Kreislauf *m*

976 HYDROLOGIC EQUATION
f équation *m* hydrologique
d hydrologische Grundgleichung *f*

977 HYDROLOGY
study of atmospheric, surface,
and subsurface waters and their
connection with the water cycle
f hydrologie *f*
d Gewässerkunde *f*;
   Hydrologie *f*

978 HYDROLYSIS
f hydrolyse *f*
d Hydrolyse *f*

979 HYDROMETEOROLOGY
meteorology dealing with water in
the atmosphere
f hydrométéorologie *f*
d Hydrometeorologie *f*

980 HYDROMETRIC STATION
station at which usually a number
of hydrometric measurements
are performed
f station *f* hydrométrique
d hydrometrische Messtelle *f*

981 HYDROMETRY
science of water measurements
f hydrométrie *f*
d Hydrometrie *f*

982 HYDROPHILIC
having great affinity for water
f hydrophile
d wasseranziehend

983 HYDROPHOBIC
repelling water
f hydrophobe
d wasserabstossend

984 HYDROPHYTE
plant requiring large amount of
moisture for growth
f hydrophyte *f*
d Wasserpflanze *f*; Hydrophyte *f*

985 HYDROSPHERE
part of earth containing liquid or
solid water
f hydrosphère *f*
d Hydrosphäre *f*

986 HYDROSTATIC PRESSURE
f pression *f* hydrostatique
d hydrostatischer Druck *m*

987 HYETOGRAPH
graph of rainfall intensity against
time
f hyétogramme *m*
d Ganglinie *f* der Niederschlagsintensität

988 HYGROMETER
apparatus for the direct measurement
of the relative humidity in the
atmosphere
f hygromètre *m*
d Hygrometer *n*

989 HYGROSCOPIC COEFFICIENT
amount of absorbed water on
surface of soil particles in an
atmosphere of 50% relative
humidity at 25°C
f coefficient *m* hygroscopique
d Hygroskopizität *f*

990 HYGROSCOPICITY
f pouvoir *m* hygroscopique
d Hygroskopizität *f*;
   Wasseranziehungskraft *f*

991 HYGROSCOPIC NUCLEUS
small solid particle around which

water condensates (cloud
formation)
f   noyeau *m* hygroscopique
d   hygroskopischer Kern *m*

992   **HYGROSCOPIC WATER**
condensed water at solid surface
f   eau *f* hygroscopique
d   hygroskopisches Wasser *n*

993   **HYPOLIMNION**
deep layer in stratified water
f   hypolimnion *m*
d   Hypolimnion *n*

994   **HYSTERESIS**
f   hystérésis *f*
d   Hysteresis *f*; Remanenzerscheinung *f*

HYSTERESIS, capillary see 240

I

995 ICE
crystallized water, below freezing
point
f glace *f*
d Eis *n*

ICE, anchor see 72
-, dry see 602
-, ground see 72
-, interstitial see 1068

996 ICE CAP
f calotte *f* glaciaire
d Eiskappe *f*

997 IGNEOUS ACTIVITY
all processes connected with the
intrusion and formation of igneous
rocks
f activité *f* magmatique;
volcanisme *m*
d Vulkanismus *m* (im weiteren
Sinne)

998 IGNEOUS ROCK
rocks formed by solidification of
intrusive or extrusive molten
magma
f roche *f* ignée
d Magmagestein *n*

999 ILLITE
a clay mineral
f illite *m*
d Illit *m*

1000 IMAGE WELL
imaginary well in the complex plane
f puits *m* fictif
d imaginärer Brunnen *m*

1001 IMBIBITION
fluid displacement in porous media
due to capillary forces alone
f imbibition *f*
d kapillarer Verdrängungsvorgang *m*;
Imbibition *f*

1002 IMMISCIBLE
quality of liquids showing clear
interface at contact with each other;
not miscible
f immiscible
d nicht mischbar

1003 IMPEDANCE
apparent resistance of a conductive
system when alternating current is
applied
f impédance *f*
d induktiver Widerstand *m*;
Impedanz *f*

1004 IMPELLER
f roue *f* à aubes
d Schaufelrad *n*; Laufrad *n*

1005 IMPERMEABLE
impervious to flow of fluids such
as an aquiclude
f imperméable
d undurchlässig

1006 IMPERVIOUS
not permitting passage of water
f non perméable
d undurchlässig

1007 IMPERVIOUS LENS
impermeable, lens-shaped body of
sediment in an otherwise permeable
aquifer
f lentille *f* imperméable
d undurchlässige Linse *f*

1008 IMPORTED WATER
water coming from outside of a
groundwater basin under consideration
f eaux *fpl* d'importation
d eingeführtes Wasser *n*;
Fremdwasser *n*

1009 IMPOUND
collect water by damming
f refouler; emmagasiner
d stauen; eindämmen

1010 INCLINOMETER
instrument to measure the inclination
of a surface
f inclinomètre *m*
d Neigungsmesser *m*

1011 INCOHERENT MATERIAL
unconsolidated material
f matériel *m* non-consolidé
d loses Material *n*; nicht
zusammenhängendes Material *n*

1012 INCOMPRESSIBLE
f incompressible
d inkompressibel

1013 INCRUSTATION
deposition of mineral matter by
water
f incrustation *f*
d Krustenbildung *f*

1014 INDUCED ACTIVITY
activity or response of a system
that has been subject to an artifical
excitation
f activité *f* induite
d induzierte Aktivität *f*

1015 INDUCED INFILTRATION
increased infiltration from a
surface water body due to planned
lowering of the original water table
f infiltration *f* provoquée
d künstliche Einsickerung *f*

1016 INDUCED RECHARGE
method of withdrawing ground water
in strategic points to induce natural
recharge
f alimentation *f* initiée
d induzierte Grundwasseranreicherung *f*

1017 INDUCTION
f induction *f*
d Induktion *f*

1018 INDUCTION LOG
resistivity log using induced
currents
f diagraphie *f* par induction
d Induktionslog *n*

1019 INDURATED ROCK
rock hardened and solidified by a
diagenetic process
f roche *f* endurcie
d verfestigtes Gestein *n*

1020 INDUSTRIAL DIAMOND
f diamant *m* industriel
d Industriediamant *m*

1021 INDUSTRIAL WATER
f eaux *f pl* d'usage
d Brauchwasser *n*; Nutzwasser *n*

1022 INFILTRABILITY
ease of infiltration
f capacité *f* d'infiltration
d Eindringkapazität *f*

1023 INFILTRATION
flow of water through soil surface
into underground
f infiltration *f*
d Einsickerung *f*

INFILTRATION, induced see 1015

1024 INFILTRATION BASIN
basin in which water is spread for
recharge
f bassin *m* d'épandage
d Versickerungsbecken *n*

1025 INFILTRATION CAPACITY
maximum rate at which soil can
absorb precipitation for given
conditions
f capacité *f* d'absorption
d Einsickerfähigkeit *f*

1026 INFILTRATION GALLERY
horizontal conduit to intercept
groundwater
f galerie *f* d'infiltration
d Infiltrationsstrecke *f*

1027 INFILTRATION INDEX
average rate of infiltration throughout a given rain storm
f indice *m* infiltration
d Infiltrationsindex *m*

1028 INFILTRATION WATER
water above watertable with
predominantly vertical downward
component of motion
f eaux *f pl* d'infiltration
d Sickerwasser *n*

1029 INFILTROMETER
apparatus measuring the amount of
infiltration
f infiltromètre *m*
d Infiltrometer *n*

1030 INFILTROMETER TEST
f essai *m* d'infiltromètre
d Infiltrometeruntersuchung *f*

1031 INFLOW
f afflux *m*; affluence *f*
d Zufluss *m*

INFLOW, lateral see 1134

1032 INFLUENT STREAM,
LOSING STREAM
stream recharging groundwater
reservoir

f rivière *f* alimentant la
    nappe
d wasserabgebender Fluss *m*

1033 INITIAL ABSTRACTION
maxiumum amount of rainfall
absorbed without producing runoff;
initial losses
f pertes *f pl* initiales
d Anfangsverluste *f pl*

1034 INITIAL CONDITIONS
f conditions *f pl* initiales
d Anfangsbedingungen *f pl*

1035 INITIAL PRESSURE
f pression *f* initiale
d Anfangsdruck *m*

1036 INJECT, TO
introduction of pressurized fluids
into a porous subsurface formation
f injecter
d einpressen

1037 INJECTION HEAD
swivel head connector through
which drilling fluid is injected into
the drill pipe
f tête *f* d'injection
d Spülkopf *m*

INJECTION METHOD, mercury
see 2028

1038 INJECTIVITY
capacity of a well or formation to
accomodate pumped in liquid
f injectivité *f*
d Schluckfähigkeit *f*; Aufnahme-
    fähigkeit *f*

1039 INLAND LAKE
f lac *m* intérieur
d Binnensee *m*

1040 INLET CHAMBER
f chambre *f* d'aspiration
d Saugraum *m*

1041 INLET OPENING
f orifice *m* d'adduction
d Einflussöffnung *f*

1042 INSIDE DIAMETER
f diamètre *m* intérieur
d Innendruchmesser *m*;
    lichte Weite *f*

1043 INSOLATION
irradiation by the sun

f insolation *f*
d Insolation *f*; Sonnenbestrahlung *f*

1044 INSTABILITY PHENOMENON
f phénomène *m* d'instabilité
d Instabilitätserscheinung *f*

1045 INSULATED STREAM
stream neither receiving nor
abstracting water from ground water
body because of an impermeable bed
f rivière *f* isolée
d isolierter Fluss *m*

1046 INSULATING SLEEVE
f gaine *f* isolante
d Schutzhülle *f*; Isolierhülle *f*

1047 INSULATION JOINT
f joint *m* isolant
d Isolierverbindung *f*

1048 INTAKE AREA
area where inflow to aquifer takes
place
f surface *f* d'alimentation
d Einzugsgebiet *n*

1049 INTEGRATING CIRCUIT
circuit averaging scintillometer
pulses over known time interval
f circuit *m* intégrant
d Integratorschaltung *f*

INTENSITY, rain see 2333
-, rainfall see 2329
-, relief see 2386
-, shear see 2528

1050 INTERAQUIFER FLOW
flow between aquifers through
fracture openings or through
wellbore
f exutoire *m* souterrain
d Zwischenfluss *m*

1051 INTERBEDDED
pertaining to beds or sedimentary
material intercalated in a parallel
fashion into a main stratum
f intercalé
d mit Schichteinschaltungen *f pl*
    versehen; mit Zwischenmitteln
    n pl versehen

1052 INTERBEDDING
bed between layers of different
material
f couche *f* intercalée
d Zwischenmittel *n*

1053 **INTERCALATED BED**
f couche *f* intercalaire
d Zwischenmittel *n*

1054 **INTERCEPT**
f intercepte *m*; point *m* d'interception
d Schnittpunkt *m*

1055 **INTERCEPTION**
abstraction of direct rainfall on
vegetation cover
f interception *f*
d Interzeption *f*; Abfangen *n*;
    Tropfenabfang *m*

1056 **INTERCEPTION LOSS**
part of rainfall retained by aerial
portion of vegetative cover
f perte *f* d'interception
d Interzeptionsverlust *m*;
    Tropfenabfang *m*

1057 **INTERDIGITATION**
lateral interlocking of sedimentary
series
f interdigitation *f*
d Verzahnung *f*; fingerförmiges
    Eingreifen *n*

1058 **INTERFACE**
contact plane of two immiscible
liquids
f interface *m*
d Grenzfläche *f*

1059 **INTERFACIAL TENSION**
f tension *f* interfaciale
d Grenzflächenspannung *f*

1060 **INTERFLOW**
subsurface runoff
f écoulement *m* hypodermique
d unechter Grundwasserabfluss *m*

1061 **INTERGRANULAR STRESS**
stress between grains in solid
matrix
f tension *f* intergranulaire
d Zwischenkornspannung *f*

1062 **INTERMITTENT SPRING**
spring flowing at intervals
f source *f* intermittente
d intermittierende Quelle *f*

1063 **INTERMITTENT STREAM**
stream flowing intermittently
f fleuve *m* intermittent
d intermittierender Fluss *m*;
    periodisch fliessender Strom *m*

1064 **INTERMONTANE BASIN**
basin lying between two mountain
ranges
f bassin *m* d'entremont
d Zwischengebirgszone *f*

1065 **INTERNAL DRAINAGE**
drainage in a closed basin not
reaching the sea
f drainage *m* endoréique
d Abflusslosigkeit *f*

1066 **INTERRUPTED STREAM**
stream interrupted over space;
    discontinous stream
f rivière *f* interrompue
d versinkender Fluss *m*

1067 **INTERSTICE**
small interstitial space between
solid rock matrix particles
f espace *m* interstitiel
d Zwischenraum *m*; Porenraum *m*

INTERSTICE, original see 2141
-, secondary see 2492

1068 **INTERSTITIAL ICE**
ice occurring below the surface in
the pores of the soil
f glace *f* interstitielle
d Poreneis *n*

1069 **INTERSTITIAL WATER**
water held in small wedge like
interstices at grain contact
f eau *f* angulaire; eau *f* cunéiforme
d Porenwinkelwasser *n*;
    Zwickelwasser *n*

1070 **INTRAPERMAFROST WATER**
ground water within the permafrost
horizon
f eau *f* dans la zone du pergelisol
d Grundwasser *n* im Permafrostber

1071 **INTRINSIC PERMEABILITY**
characteristic resistance to flow
of porous medium alone, independent
of fluid properties
f perméabilité *f* intrinsèque
d absolute Permeabilität *f*

1072 **INTRUSION**
body of ingenous rock cutting through
or replacing older rock
f intrusion *f*
d Intrusion *f*; Eindringung *f*

INTRUSION, sea water see 2491

1073 INTRUSIVE ROCK
igneous rock remaining below the
earth's surface
f roche *f* intrusive
d Intrusivgestein *n*

1074 INUNDATION
covering of an area by flood waters
f inondation *f*
d Überschwemmung *f*

1075 INVADED ZONE
in electric logging zone into which
an appreciable amount of mud
filtrate has penetrated
f zone *f* envahie
d geflutete Zone *f*

1076 INVASION
in logging penetration of a fluid
into the porous medium
f invasion *f*
d Eindringen *n*

INVASION, water see 2937

1077 INVASION DEPTH
depth to which drilling mud
filtrate penetrates into formation
f profondeur *f* envahie
d Eindringungstiefe *f*

1078 INVERSION
negative lapse rate (increase in
temperature with altitude)
f inversion *f*
d Inversion *f*; Temperaturumkehr *f*

INVERTED WELL
see recharge well

1079 ION MOBILITY
ease with which ions move in an
electrolytical solution
f mobilité *f* des ions
d Mobilität *f* der Ionen

1080 IRREDUCIBLE SATURATION
lowest water saturation obtainable
by mechanical reduction methods
f saturation *f* irréductible
d irreduzierbare Sättigung *f*

1081 IRRIGATION
artificial watering of fields for
crop production
f irrigation *f*
d Bewässerung *f*

1082 IRRIGATION REQUIREMENT
water needed for crop production
exclusive of precipitation
f demande *f* en eau d'irrigation
d Bewässerungsbedarf *m*

1083 IRROTATIONAL FLOW
potential flow, flow with no
rotational component
f écoulement *m* irrotationnel
d wirbelfreier Fluss *m*

1084 ISOBATH
line of equal depth
f isobathe *f*
d Isobathe *f*; Tiefenlinie *f*

1085 ISOCHRONE
line connecting waterlevel in
observation wells for one given
instant
f isochrone *f*
d Isochrone *f*; Zeitgleiche *f*

1086 ISOHYET
line of equal rainfall
f ligne *f* isohyète; courbe *f* isohyète
d Regengleiche *f*; Isohyete *f*

1087 ISOPIESTIC LINE
contour on piezometric surface
connecting points of equal static
level
f isopièze *f*; hydroisohypse *f*
d Grundwassergleiche *f*

1088 ISOPLETH
line of equal distance from point
of outflow of a basin
f ligne *f* isoplèthe
d Abstandsgleiche *f*

1089 ISOPOTAL LINE
line of equal infiltration capacity
f ligne *f* isopotale
d Linie *f* gleicher Eindringkapazität

1090 ISOTHERM
line of equal temperatures
f isotherme *f*
d Isotherme *f*

1091 ISOTOPE
f isotope *m*
d Isotop *n*

1092 ISOTROPIC
quality of aquifer where properties
remain the same in all directions
f isotropique
d isotropisch

J

1093 JACK
f cric *m*
d Hebevorrichtung *f*; Winde *f*

1094 JARS
in cable drilling: interlocked
gliding links above drill collar
permitting stuck bit to be jerked
free
f coulisse *f* de forage
d Rutschschere *f*

1095 JET
f jet *m*
d Strahl *m*; Düse *f*

1096 JET BIT
drilling tool where some of the
abrasive effect is due to jets
f outil à jet *m*
d Düsenmeissel *m*

1097 JET PUMP
f pompe *f* à jet
d Düsenstrahlpumpe *f*

1098 JETTED WELL
well formed by cutting action of a
water stream or jet
f puits *m* creusé par jets d'eau
d Spülbohrung *f*

1099 JOINT
junction or connection of mechanical
elements (as drill pipe and tubing)
f joint *m*
d Verbindung *f*

1100 JOINT
fracture in rock along the plane
of which no movement or dislocation
has taken place
f joint *m*; diaclase *f*
d Kluft *f*; Diaklase *f*

JOINT, bedding see 166
-, casing see 254
-, cooling see 383
-, expansion see 690
-, insulation see 1047
-, reducing see 2373
-, threaded see 2778
-, tool see 2799
-, welded see 2981

1101 JOINT PLANE
f plan *m* de diaclase
d Kluftfläche *f*

1102 JUNCTION POTENTIAL
electrochemical potential
developed at the junction of two
solutions of different concentration
f potentiel *m* de jonction
d Berührungspotential *n*

1103 JURASSIC
geologic period of the Mesozoic era
f Jurassique *m*
d Jura *n*

1104 JUVENILE WATER
water that has not been part of
hydrosphere before, derived from
interior of earth
f eaux *f pl* juvéniles
d juveniles Wasser *n*

K

1105 KAME
stratified glacial sand and gravel
deposit forming small hill
f kame *m*
d Kame *f*

1106 KAOLIN
common clay mineral
f kaolin *m*
d Kaolin *n*

1107 KARST
limestone terrane marked by very
large solution openings
f karst *m*
d Karst *m*

1108 KARST REGION
f région *f* karstique
d Karstgebiet *n*

1109 KELLEY
square section of drill pipe
transmitting rotary movement from
rotary table to the drill stem
f tige *f* carrée
d Mitnehmerstange *f*

1110 KICK
short deflection of a pointer or trace
f top *m*
d Ausschlag *m*

1111 KINEMATIC SIMILARITY
f similitude *f* cinématique
d kinematische Ähnlichkeit *f*

1112 KLINKENBERG EFFECT
slip of gas molecules at pore wall
giving apparently higher permeability
than obtained by liquid measurements
f effet *m* Klinkenberg
d Klinkenbergeffekt *m*

L

1113 LABORATORY COEFFICIENT
OF PERMEABILITY;
STANDARD COEFFICIENT OF
PERMEABILITY
defined for controlled temperature
conditions ($60°$F) gpd per f^2 under
unit gradient (see Meinzer unit)
f coefficient m de perméabilité du
laboratoire
d Labor - Durchlässigkeitsbeiwert m

1114 LABORATORY DATA
f données fpl de laboratoire;
données fpl expérimentales
d Versuchswerte mpl;
Laboratoriumsdaten fpl

1115 LACCOLITH
dome shaped intrusive rock body
f laccolith m
d Lakkolith m

1116 LACUSTRINE
pertaining to lakes
f lacustre
d lakustre

1117 LACUSTRINE FORMATION
sedimentary formation in a lake
f formation f lacustre
d lakustre Bildung f; lakustre
Formation f

1118 LAGOON
body of relatively shallow water
near sea shore, with or without
direct connection to the sea
f lagune f
d Lagune f; Haff n

1119 LAG TIME
time lapse between the onset of
a given event and the produced
results; in drilling: time for
cuttings to be carried out from the
bottom hole to the surface
f retard m; temps m de réponse
d Verzögerung f

1120 LAKE
body of fresh inland water
f lac m
d See m; Binnensee m

LAKE, crater see 399
-, inland see 1039
-, reservoir see 2392
-, salt see 2457
-, volcanic see 2904

1121 LAMINAR FLOW
f écoulement m laminaire
d laminare Strömung f;
Schichtströmung f

1122 LAMINATION
layering or very thin bedding of
sedimentary rocks
f lamination f
d Schichtung f; Lamination f

1123 LAND-FORM
topographic feature of the earth's
surface
f forme f morphologique
d Landform f

1124 LAND PAN
evaporation pan to measure
evaporation from a land surface;
pan mounted on land surface
f bac m d'évaporation au dessus
du terrain
d Landverdunstungskessel m

1125 LANDSLIDE
sliding down of earth and rock on
a slope
f glissement m de terrain
d Landrutsch m; Hangrutsch m

1126 LAND SUBSIDENCE
subsidence of surface (due to
pumping of underlying aquifer or
other mining activities)
f affaissement m de la surface;
subsidence f de la surface
d Oberflächenabsenkung f

1127 LAND SURFACE
part of lithosphere usually not
covered by water
f surface f terrestre
d Landoberfläche f

1128 LAND-USE
particular utilization of a surface
especially with respect to its
influence on the hydrologic cycle

f   utilisation f des terres
d   Landverwendung f; Landnutzung f

1129   LAPSE RATE
vertical temperature gradient in
the atmosphere
f   gradient m vertical de la
température
d   vertikaler Temperaturgradient m

1130   LATENT HEAT OF VAPORIZATION
f   chaleur f de vaporisation latente
d   latente Verdampfungswärme f

1131   LATERAL CORING
method of taking samples from the
sidewall of the well
f   prélèvement m latéral
d   Probenahme f aus der Bohrlochswand

1132   LATERAL CURVE
resistivity log taken with long
effective spacing of electrodes
f   diagramme m latéral
d   Laterologaufnahme f

1133   LATERAL GRADATION
f   nivellement m latéral
d   seitliche Einebnung f

1134   LATERAL INFLOW
f   afflux m latéral
d   seitlicher Zufluss m

1135   LATERAL MORAINE
galcial deposit at flank of a glacier,
often constituted by debris from
valley walls
f   moraine f latérale
d   Seitenmoräne f

1136   LATERITE
tropical ferruginous clay soil
f   latérite f
d   Laterit m

1137   LATERITIC SOIL
red colored soil with high iron
oxide content
f   sol m latéritique
d   Lateriterde f

LAVA, block see 188
-, pillow see 2233

1138   LAVA BED
lava flow of considerable areal
extend and relatively small
thickness

f   couche f de lave
d   Lavaschicht f

LAVA CRUST, congealed see 353

1139   LAVA FLOW PLATEAU
f   plate-forme f d'effusion
d   Ergusstafel f

1140   LAVA TUBE
empty tubular supply channel from
which liquid lava has drained
f   tunnel m de lave
d   Lavatube f; Lavaröhre f

1141   LAYER
sheetlike deposit of sediment;
bed or stratum of rock
f   couche f
d   Schicht f; Lage f

LAYER, boundary see 196

1142   LEACHING
washing out by dissolution
f   lessivage m
d   Auslaugung f; Laugung f

1143   LEAK
opening in an aquiclude that
permits penetration of water from
other formations into main aquifer
f   fuite f
d   Leck n; Undichtigkeit f

1144   LEAK DETECTOR
f   détecteur m de fuites
d   Suchgerät n

1145   LEAKAGE FACTOR
factor describing leakage flow into
or out of leaky aquifer
f   facteur m de fuite
d   Undichtigkeitsfaktor m

1146   LEAKANCE
leakage coefficient, ratio of
hydraulic conductivity of semiconfining
stratum to its thickness
f   coefficient m de fuite
d   Undichtigkeitszahl f

1147   LEAKY AQUIFER
aquifer overlain or underlain by
semipermeable strata from or into
which water will flow
f   couche f aquifère à fuites
d   leckender Grundwasserleiter m

1148   LEVEE
artificial bank to prevent overbank

flow of a river
f levée *f*; digue *f*
d Damm *m*; Deich *m*

LEVEE, natural see 2100

1149 LEVEL
surface of water in a well or standing
reservoir
f niveau *m*
d Höhe *f*; Spiegel *m*

LEVEL, base see 150
-, ground see 889
-, groundwater see 904
-, mean sea see 2004
-, salinity see 2453
-, sea see 2487
-, water see 2939

1150 LIFT
vertical pumping distance between
water level in the well to surface
f hauteur *f* d'aspiration
d Saughöhe *f*

LIFT, air see 42
-, suction see 2695

1151 LIGHT SPOT
reflected light spot from a galvanometer mirror
f spot *m* lumineux
d Lichtpunkt *m*

1152 LIMESTONE
sedimentary deposit of carbonate
rock
f calcaire *m*
d Kalkstein *m*

LIMESTONE, algal see 50
-, argillaceous see 109

1153 LIMITING VALUE
f valeur *f* limite
d Grenzwert *m*

1154 LIMNOLOGY
study of lakes
f limnologie *f*
d Limnologie *f*

LINE, air see 43
-, bailing see 2462
-, base see 152
-, casing see 255
-, contour see 374
-, crest see 404
-, drilling see 579

-, energy see 652
-, energy grade see 650
-, equipotential see 664
-, fault see 707
-, isopiestic see 1087
-, isopotal see 1089
-, recharge see 2358
-, regression see 2380
-, sand see 2462
-, shale see 2523
-, snow see 2583
-, suction see 2697
-, wet see 3007
-, wire see 3020

1155 LIQUID
incompressible or very little
compressible fluid
f liquide *m*
d Flüssigkeit *f*

LIQUID, mother see 2079

1156 LITHOLOGIC FACTOR
factor influencing composition,
texture, and sequence of rock types
f facteur *m* lithologique
d lithologischer Faktor *m*

1157 LITHOLOGY
physical properties and aspect of a
rock
f lithologie *f*
d Lithologie *f*

1158 LITHOSOL
rocky soil
f sol *m* rocheux
d Steinboden *m*; Felsboden *m*

1159 LITHOSPHERE
part of earth's crust containing
solid rocks
f lithosphère *f*
d Lithosphäre *f*

1160 LITTORAL ZONE
coastal strip
f littoral *m*
d Litoral *n*; Küstenbereich *m*

LOAD, base see 153
-, basin see 168
-, contact see 364
-, natural see 2101
-, permanent see 2203
-, permissible see 2210
-, saltation see 2455
-, suspended see 2730
-, traction see 168

-, wash see 2917
-, waste see 2920

LOADS, external see 697

1161 LOAM
calcareous clay
f limon *m*
d Lehm *m*

1162 LODGEMENT TILL
till deposited from slowly melting
ice at base of glaciers
f argile *m* à blocaux; éboulis *m*
glaciaire
d Grundmoränengeschiebe *n*

1163 LOESS
eolian deposit of very fine sand
f loess *m*
d Löss *m*

1164 LOG
record of drilling operations and
formations drilled
f log *n*; diagraphie *f*
d Bohrprotokoll *n*; Log *n*

LOG, acoustic see 18
-, caliper see 231
-, contact see 365
-, driller's see 570
-, drilling-time see 583
-, electric see 633
-, fluid-velocity see 767
-, gamma see 810
-, geologic see 833
-, induction see 1018
-, neutron see 2108
-, radioactivity see 2324
-, restitivity see 2399
-, temperature see 2754

1165 LOGGING CABLE
f câble *m* de diagraphie
d Messkabel *n*

1166 LOGGING TRUCK
truck in which all logging, recording,
and control instruments are housed
f camion *m* d'enregistrement;
camion *m* de diagraphie
d Messwagen *m*

1167 LOG INTERPRETATION
f interprétation *f* des diagraphies
d Logauswertung *f*

1168 LONGITUDINAL FAULT
fault having the same direction of
strike as surrounding strata

f faille *f* longitudinale
d Längsverwerfung *f*

1169 LONGITUDINAL WAVE
f onde *f* longitudinale
d Longitudinalwelle *f*

1170 LOOSEST PACKING
three dimensional arrangement of
particles with highest possible void
volume per unit cell
f arrangement *m* le plus lâche;
empilement *m* le plus lâche
d poröseste Packung *f*

LOSING STREAM, see influent stream

LOSS, canal see 233
-, dielectric see 500
-, evaporation see 679
-, head see 923
-, interception see 1056
-, mud see 2090
-, well see 2995

1171 LOWER CONFINING BED
impermeable bed underlying an
aquifer
f mur *m* imperméable (d'un aquifer);
imperméable *m*; substratum *m*
imperméable
d Grundwassersohle *f*; Sohlschicht *f*

1172 LOWER COURSE
part of water course near discharge
point
f cours *m* inférieur
d Unterlauf *m*

1173 LOW FLOW
lowest sustained flow during base
runoff conditions of a river
f débit *m* d'étiage
d Niedrigwasserabfluss *m*

1174 LOW WATER
f basses-eaux *f pl*
d Niedrigwasser *n*

1175 LYSIMETER
experimental installation to evaluate
infiltration and evapotranspiration
under field or natural conditions
f lysimètre *m*
d Lysimeter *n*

M

1176 MACROPORE
pore with dimensions such that
capillary forces become less
important during flow
f macropore *m*
d Grosspore *f*; Makropore *f*

1177 MAGMA
molten rock substance formed within
the earth from which igneous rocks
originate
f magma *m*
d Magma *n*

1178 MAGMATIC WATER
water in or derived from magma
f eaux *fpl* magmatiques
d magmatisches Wasser *n*;
endogenes Wasser *n*

1179 MAGNETIC SURVEY
geophysical method of mapping
magnetic fields
f étude *f* magnétique
d Magnetometerkartierung *f*

1180 MAGNETIC SUSCEPTIBILITY
f susceptibilité *f* magnétique
d magnetische Suszeptibilität *f*

1181 MAGNETITE
accessory mineral of igneous rocks,
iron ore
f magnétite *m*
d Magnetit *m*

MAIN, collecting see 324

1182 MAIN CHANNEL FLOW
f écoulement *m* du cours principal
d Wasserführung *f* im Haupt-
flusslauf

1183 MAIN GATE
f vanne *f* maîtresse
d Hauptschieber *m*

1184 MANOMETER
pressure measuring device,
pressure gauge
f manomètre *m*
d Manometer *n*

1185 MAP
f carte *f*
d Karte *f*

MAPPING, conformal see 352
-, surface see 2718

1186 MARBLE
dense metamorphic calc-silicate or
magnesia rock
f marbre *m*
d Marmor *m*

1187 MARINE WATER
ocean water having invaded coastal
aquifers; sea water
f eau *f* de mer
d Meerwasser *n*

MARK, bench see 172
-, rippel see 2412

1188 MARKER BED
bed with characteristic features that
can be followed over large areas
for identification purposes
f couche *f* caractéristique
d Leithorizont *m*

1189 MARL
calcarous clay
f marle *f*
d Mergel *m*

1190 MASS CONSERVATION
f conservation *f* massique
d Massenerhaltung *f*

1191 MASS CURVE
graph of cumulative values of a
hydrological quantity against time
f courbe *f* de masse; courbe *f* des
valeurs cumulées
d Summenkurve *f*; Mengenlinie *f*;
Summenganglinie *f*

1192 MASS DENSITY
mass per unit volume of a substance
f densité *f* massique
d Dichte *f*

1193 MASS FLOWMETER
measuring device for mass flow
rates
f débimètre *m* massique
d Massenflussmessgerät *n*

1194 MASSIVE STRUCTURE
homogeneous structure without any
oriented features

f   structure *f* massive
d   massige Textur *f*

1195   MASS TRANSFER
f   transfert *m* massique
d   Stoffübertragung *f*

1196   MAST
f   mât *m* de forage
d   Mast *m*; Bohrmast *m*

1197   MATCH POINT
common point in Theis' superposition method
f   point *m* arbitraire
d   Bezugspunkt *m*

1198   MAXIMUM BASIN RELIEF
elevation difference between basin
mouth and highest point within
basin perimeter
f   relief *m* maximum
d   grösster Reliefunterschied *m*

1199   MAXIMUM DISCHARGE
maximum discharge of a river
during a flood
f   débit *m* de pointe
d   Spitzenabfluss *m*

2000   MAXIMUM EVENT
f   événement *m* maximum
d   Maximalereignis *n*

MEAN, annual see 85
-, arithmetic see 111
-, geometric see 834

2001   MEANDER
looplike bend in river due to lateral
erosion activities
f   méandre *m*
d   Mäander *m*

2002   MEANDER BELT
zone within which meandering of
stream occurs
f   zone *f* des méandres
d   Mäandergürtel *m*

2003   MEAN DEVIATION
linear mean of absolute deviations
f   écart *m* moyen
d   lineare Streuung *f*

2004   MEAN SEA LEVEL
f   niveau *m* moyen des mers
d   mittlere Meereshöhe *f*

2005   MEAN VALUE
statistical average, measure of

central tendency
f   valeur *f* moyenne
d   Mittelwert *m*

2006   MEASURE
f   mesure *f*
d   Messung *f*

MEASUREMENT, wading see 2911

2007   MEASURING CIRCUIT
f   circuit *m* de mesure
d   Messkreis *m*

2008   MEASURING COIL
f   bobine *f* de mesure
d   Messpule *f*

2009   MEASURING DUCT
f   canal *m* de jaugeage
d   Messgerinne *n*

2010   MEASURING FLUME
artificial channel used for discharge
measurements
f   jaugeur *m*
d   Messrinne *f*

2011   MEASURING REEL
f   treuil *m* de jaugeage
d   Messwinde *f*

2012   MEASURING STICK
f   échelle *f*
d   Pegel *m*; Messlatte *f*

2013   MEASURING TUBE
f   tube *m* à mesure; éprouvette *f*
d   Messzylinder *m*

2014   MEASURING WEIR
device to measure flow rates
indirectly through the weir head
f   déversoir *m* à mesure
d   Messwehr *n*

2015   MECHANICAL COVER
mechanical covering of a free water
surface to prevent evaporation
(e.g. styrofoam particles)
f   couverture *f* mécanique
d   mechanische Abdeckung *f*

2016   MEDIAN
value dividing frequency of variates
in two equal portions
f   médiane *f*
d   Zentralwert *m*; Medianwert *m*

2017   MEDICINAL SPRING
spring with healing properties

f   source *f* thérapeutique
d   Heilquelle *f*

2018   MEDIUM SAND
grain diameter 0.5 to 0.25 mm
(USBS)
f   sable *m* moyen
d   mittelkörniger Sand *m*

2019   MEINZER UNIT
measure of hydraulic conductivity
gpd per ft^2 under hydraulic
gradient of unity (USGS - adoption)
f   Unité *f* Meinzer (USA)
d   Meinzereinheit *f* (USA)

MELT, snow see 2584

2020   MELTING
passage from solid to liquid state
due to temperature increase
f   fusion *f*
d   Schmelzen *n*

2021   MELTING POINT
temperature at which a solid
substance is transformed into
its liquid state
f   point *m* de fusion
d   Schmelzpunkt *m*

2022   MELTWATER
water derived from melting of snow
pack or of glacier
f   eau *f* de fonte
d   Schmelzwässer *npl*

2023   MEMBRANE MODEL
simulation of piezometric surface
by rubber membrane
f   modèle *m* à membrane élastique
d   Membranmodell *n*

2024   MEMBRANE POTENTIAL
electrochemical potential arising
at a membrane that separates two
solutions of different concentrations
f   potentiel *m* de membrane
d   Membranpotential *n*

2025   MENISCUS
free surface or interface formed
by liquid in a capillary tube
f   ménisque *m*
d   Meniskus *m*

2026   MERCURY COLUMN
cylindrical bore in a manometer
filled with mercury
f   colonne *f* de mercure
d   Quecksilbersäule *f*

2027   MERCURY GAGE
f   manomètre *m* à mercure
d   Quecksilbermanometer *n*

2028   MERCURY INJECTION METHOD
measurement of porosity by
mercury injection into sample
f   méthode *f* par injection de
    mercure
d   Quecksilberinjektionsverfahren *n*

2029   MESH
opening in sieve screen, number of
openings per inch
f   maille *f*
d   Masche *f*

2030   MESH SIZE
f   ouverture *f* des mailles
d   Maschenweite *f*

2031   MESOPHYTE
plant growing under intermediate
moisture conditions
f   mésophyte *m*
d   Mesophyte *f*

2032   MESOZOIC
geologic era preceding Cenozoic era
f   Ère *f* Mésozoique
d   Mesozoikum *n*

METAL, alkali see 53
-, monel see 2070

2033   METAMORPHIC WATER
water once associated with rocks
during their metamorphism
f   eaux *fpl* régénérées (par le
    métamorphisme)
d   metamorphes Wasser *n*

2034   METEORIC WATER
water recently involved in atmospheric circulation
f   eaux *fpl* météoriques
d   meteorisches Wasser *n*

2035   METEOROLOGY
science dealing with all physical
phenomena occuring in the atmosphe
f   météorologie *f*
d   Wetterkunde *f*; Meteorologie *f*

METER, current see 428
-, rotating see 2438
-, soil-moisture see 2592
-, water see 2942

2036   METERING PUMP
pump with a very constant and preci

volumetric delivery
f   pompe *f* doseuse
d   Dosierpumpe *f*

METHOD, backwashing see 130
-, basin see 158
-, ditch see 533
-, finite differences see 729
-, flooding see 746
-, gas expansion see 816
-, gravity see 884
-, mercury injection see 2028
-, numerical see 2117
-, recovery see 2369
-, tracer flow see 2815

2037   METHOD OF APPLICATION
f   méthode *f* d'application
d   Anwendungsmethode *f*

2038   METHOD OF IMAGES
theoretical treatment of hydraulic
effects of physical boundaries by
introduction of image sources or
sinks in a complex plane
f   principe *m* des images
d   Verfahren *n* imaginärer Ab-
bildungen in der komplexen
Ebene

2039   METHOD OF ITERATION
f   méthode *f* par itération
d   Iterationsmethode *f*

2040   MICA SCHIST
f   micaschiste *m*
d   Glimmerschiefer *m*

2041   MICROFISSURE
f   fissure *f* capillaire
d   Haarriss *m*

2042   MICROPORE
f   micropore *m*
d   Mikropore *f*; Kleinstpore *f*

2043   MICRO STRAINER
f   microtamis *m*
d   Feinsieb *n*; Mikrosieb *n*

2044   MIGRATION
movement of water or other fluid
in the geologic substratum, mostly
by natural causes
f   migration *f*
d   Wanderung *f*

MIGRATION, capillary see 241

MINE, surface see 2719

2045   MINE DRAINAGE
waters coming from or passing
through surface or subsurface mine
workings
f   eaux *f pl* de mine
d   Grubenwässer *f pl*; Grubenabflusswässer *n pl*

MINE DRAINAGE, acid see 17

MINERAL, accessory see 10
-, clay see 301

2046   MINERAL OIL
f   huile *f* minérale
d   Mineralöl *n*

2047   MINERALS
mineral components of a rock,
often in macrocrystalline form
f   minéraux *m pl*
d   Mineralien *n pl*

2048   MINERAL SPRING
spring water having high mineral
content
f   source *f* minérale
d   Mineralquelle *f*

2049   MINE WATER
water accumulating in a mine
f   eau *f* de mine
d   Grubenwasser *n*

2050   MINIMUM EVENT
f   événement *m* minimum
d   Minimalereignis *n*

2051   MINING OF GROUND WATER
permanent depletion of ground
water reserves
f   production *f* d'eau en excès
des réserves d'exploitation
d   Grundwasserabbau *m*

2052   MIOCENE
geologic epoch in the Tertiary
period
f   Miocène *m*
d   Miozän *n*

2053   MISCIBLE
f   miscible
d   mischbar

2054   MISCIBLE DISPLACEMENT
displacement of a fluid saturating
a porous medium by another fluid
completely miscible with the first
f   déplacement *m* miscible

d Verdrängung *f* mit einem
Lösungsmittel

2055 MISSISSIPPIAN
geologic period of the Paleozoic era
f Carbonifère *m* inférieur
d Unterkarbon *n*

2056 MIXING LENGTH
length over which mixing occurs,
especially of momentum in
turbulent flow
f longueur *f* de mélange
d Mischlänge *f*

2057 MIXING RATIO
f coefficient *m* de mélange
d Mischverhältnis *n*

2058 MODE
most frequently occurring variate in
a frequency distribution
f mode *m*
d dichtester Wert *m*; häufigster
Wert *m*

2059 MODEL
simplified system bearing some
physical similiarity to prototype
f modèle *m*
d Modell *n*

MODEL, membrane see 2023
-, sand see 2463

2060 MODEL TECHNIQUE
method of solving complex physical
problems by using simplified
models
f technique *f* des modèles
d Modellverfahren *n*

2061 MODEL TEST
f essai sur modèle *m*
d Modellversuch *m*

MOISTURE, antecedent-soil
see 89

2062 MOISTURE ACCUMULATION
f accumulation *f* d'humidité
d Feuchteansammlung *f*

2063 MOISTURE CONTENT
gravimetric water vapor content
of air
f teneur *f* en humidité
d Feuchtigkeitsgehalt *m*

MOISTURE CONTENT, gravimetric
see 877

MOISTURE CONTENT, volumetric s
2909

2064 MOISTURE DEFICIENCY
water required to restore moisture
to field capacity in dessicated soil
f déficit *m* en humidité
d Bodenfeuchtedefizit *n*

2065 MOISTURE EQUIVALENT
soil moisture retained against a
gravitational force of 1000 g.
f équivalent *m* d'humidité
d Feuchteäquivalent *n*

MOISTURE POTENTIAL, see
capillary potential

2066 MOLECULAR ATTRACTION
f attraction *f* moléculaire
d molekulare Anziehungskraft *f*

2067 MOLECULAR DIFFUSION
f diffusion *f* moléculaire
d Molekulardiffusion *f*

2068 MOLLISOL
soil layer subject to annual
thawing and freezing, often mobile
when thawed
f mollisol *m*
d Fliesschicht *f*

2069 MOMENTUM
f moment *m* cinétique
d Impuls *m*

2070 MONEL METAL
f monel *m*
d Monel-Metall *n*

2071 MONOCLINE
tilted stratum
f monoclinal *m*
d Schichtflexur *f*; monoklinale
Flexur *f*

2072 MONOELECTRODE SONDE
f sonde *f* monoélectrode
d Einzelelektrodensonde *f*

2073 MONOMOLECULAR FILM
layer of monomolecular thickness
of a polar substance spread over a
free water surface to prevent
evaporation
f couche *f* monomoléculaire
d monomolekulare Schicht *f*

2074 MONTMORILLONITE
clay mineral containing MgO in its
structure

f   montmorillonite *m*
d   Montmorillonit *m*

2075 MOOR
wet peat bog
f   tourbière *f*
d   Moor *n*

2076 MORAINE
sand and rock material carried and
deposited by glacier
f   moraine *f*
d   Moräne *f*

MORAINE, lateral see 1135
-, recessional see 2352
-, terminal see 2759

2077 MORAINE DEPOSIT
f   dépôt *m* morainique
d   Moränenablagerung *f*;
Moränenschutt *m*

2078 MORPHOMETRIC ANALYSIS
geodetic and geometric description
of basin and stream network
f   analyse *f* hypsométrique
d   morphometrische Analyse *f*

MORTAR BED, see hardpan

2079 MOTHER LIQUID
residual salt solution
f   eau-mère *f*
d   Mutterlauge *f*

MOUNTAIN, table see 2743

2080 MOUNTAIN CHAIN
series of mountains forming long
stretched chain like line
f   chaîne *f* de montagnes
d   Gebirgskette *f*

MOUTH, basin see 159

2081 MOUTH OF A WELL
orifice at upper end of well
f   tête *f* de puits; entrée *f* du puits
d   Borhlochsmund *m*; Brunnenöffnung *f*

2082 MOVING ELECTRODE
electrode travelling vertically in a
well that is logged
f   électrode *f* mobile
d   bewegliche Elektrode *f*

2083 MUD
water saturated fine clayey earth
material

f   boue *f*
d   Schlamm *m*

MUD, drilling see 576

2084 MUD ADDITIVE
various chemical additives to
change the chemical and physical
properties of a drilling mud
f   additif *m* de boue de forage
d   Spülungszusatz *m*

2085 MUD CIRCULATION
complete circuit through which the
drilling mud passes during operations
f   circulation *f* de boue
d   Spülungskreislauf *m*

2086 MUD COLUMN
column of drilling mud in a well
f   colonne *f* de boue
d   Spülungssäule *f*

2087 MUD CRACK
cracks appearing in drying mud
surfaces due to shrinkage
f   fente *f* de dessiccation
d   Trockenriss *m*

2088 MUD FILTRATE
part of drilling fluid that has
passed the filter cake formed at
the side wall of the well
f   filtrat *m* de boue
d   Spülungsfiltrat *n*

2089 MUDFLOW
flow of water saturated rock debris
f   coulée *f* de boue
d   Schlammstrom *m*; Mure *f*

2090 MUD LOSS
loss of drilling fluid into a thief
zone or permeable layer of the
formations penetrated
f   perte *f* de boue
d   Spülungsverlust *m*

2091 MUD PORT
opening in drilling tool through
which drilling mud extrudes
f   sortie *f* de boue
d   Spülungsauslass *m*

2092 MUD PUMP
f   pompe *f* à boue
d   Spülungspumpe *f*

2093 MULTIAQUIFER FORMATION
formation with several aquifers

overlying each other
f système *m* de couches
  aquifères superposées
d Grundwasserstockwerk *n*

2094 MULTIAQUIFER WELL
well completed and tapping several
aquifers
f puits *m* développé dans plusieurs
  nappes superposées
d Brunnen *m* in einem Grundwasserstockwerk

2095 MULTIPLE REFLECTIONS
seismic waves that have been
reflected at several bedding planes
f réflexions *f pl* multiples
d multiple Reflexionen *f pl*

2096 MYLONITE
crushed and laminated rock
f mylonite *m*
d Mylonit *m*; Mahlgestein *n*

N

2097 NATIVE GROUND WATER
original ground water
f   eau *f* phréatique indigène
d   ursprüngliches Grundwasser *n*

2098 NATURAL DISCHARGE
discharge of water into surface
water bodies or springflow
f   exutoire *m* naturel (de la nappe
phréatique)
d   natürlicher Grundwasseraustritt *m*

2099 NATURAL GAS
f   gaz naturel *m*
d   Erdgas *n*

2100 NATURAL LEVEE
river bank raised by river's own
depositions
f   levée *f* de rive
d   Uferdamm *m*

2101 NATURAL LOAD
sediment carried by stable stream
f   charge *f* stabilisée
d   natürliche Frachtung *f*

2102 NATURAL STREAM
f   rivière *f* naturelle
d   natürlicher Fluss *m*;
ubeeinflusster Strom *m*

2103 NATURAL WATER
water with mineral content as
occurring under natural conditions
f   eau *f* naturelle
d   natürliches Wasser *n*

2104 NECK
volcanic pipe filled with lava
f   diatrème *m*
d   Diatrema *n*; Stielgang *m*

NET, flow see 760

2105 NET RADIATION
sum of incident and reflected sun
and sky shortwave radiation plus
incident and reflected atmospheric
long-wave radiation
f   différence *f* du rayonnement;
rayonnement *m* net
d   Nettoeinstrahlung *f*

2106 NETWORK
f   réseau *m*
d   Netz *n*

NETWORK, drainage see 554
-, rain gage see 2332
-, resistance-capacity see 2395
-, synoptic see 2741

2107 NEUTRALITY POINT
separation point between acid and
basic solution with a pH of 7.0
f   point *m* neutre
d   Neutralitätspunkt *m*

2108 NEUTRON LOG
vertical recording of induced
neutron reactions, especially
sensitive to hydrogen content of
porous rocks
f   diagraphie *f* neutron
d   Neutronenlog *n*

2109 NEUTRON SOURCE
source producing fast neutrons
f   source *f* de neutrons
d   Neutronenquelle *f*

2110 NITROGEN
N_2
f   azote *m*
d   Stickstoff *m*

2111 NODE POINT
intersection point on grid
f   noeud *m*
d   Netzpunkt *m*; Knotenpunkt *m*

2112 NONRECORDING GAGE
standard rain gage (8 in standard in
USA)
f   pluviomètre *m* standard
d   Niederschlagsmesser *m*;
Standardgerät *n*

2113 NORMAL CURVE
recording of a resistivity
measurement where spacing between
current and measuring electrode is
small compared to spacing of
measuring electrodes
f   diagraphie *f* à espacement normal;
normale *f*
d   Normale *f*

2114 NORMAL DEPTH
depth at which uniform flow occurs
in open channel
f   profondeur *f* normale
d   normale Wassertiefe *f*

2115 NORMAL FAULT
     fault showing relative downward
     movement on the fault plane
     f   faille f directe
     d normale Verwerfung f;
        Abschiebung f

     NUCLEUS, condensation see 341
     -, hygroscopic see 991

2116 NUMBER OF REVOLUTIONS
     f   nombre m de tours
     d Drehzahl f

2117 NUMERICAL METHOD
     f   méthode f numérique
     d numerische (Lösungs-) Methode f

2118 NUMERICAL SOLUTION
     f   solution f numérique
     d numerische Lösung f

O

2119   OASIS
limited area in the desert supplied
with water
f   oasis *m*
d   Oase *f*

2120   OBSEQUENT RIVER
river flowing in direction opposite
to that of the dip of underlying strata
f   rivière *f* obséquente
d   Stirnfluss *m*; obsequenter Fluss *m*

2121   OBSERVATION WELL
well drilled for the purpose of
making observations such as water
level or pressure recordings
f   puits *m* d'observation; sonde *f*
d   Beobachtungsbohrung *f*

2122   OBSIDIAN
volcanic glass
f   obsidienne *f*
d   Obsidian *m*

2123   OCEAN
body of salt water; sea
f   océan *m*
d   Ozean *m*; Weltmeer *n*

2124   OCEANIC WATER
sea water with a total salt content
of about 34,500 ppm.
f   eau *f* de mer
d   Meerwasser *n*

OIL, mineral see 2046

2125   OIL FIELD WATER
f   eaux *f pl* des gisements
pétrolifères
d   Ölfeldwässer *n pl*

2126   OIL RESERVOIR
f   gisement *m* de pétrole
d   Erdöllagerstätte *f*

2127   OIL WELL
f   puits *m* de pétrole
d   Ölbohrung *f*

2128   OLIGOCENE
geologic epoch in the Tertiary
period
f   Oligocène
d   Oligozän *n*

2129   OLIVINE
peridot mineral occurring in ultra
basic igneous rocks
f   olivine *f*
d   Olivin *n*

2130   OOLITIC
of spherical or ovoidal shape
f   oolithique
d   oolithisch

2131   OPEN CHANNEL FLOW
f   écoulement *m* dans un canal
d   Fliessen *n* in offenem Kanal

2132   OPEN SYSTEM
system where matter and energy
may cross system boundary
f   système *m* ouvert
d   offenes System *n*

2133   OPERATING FLOOR
f   plate-forme *f* de service
d   Bedienungsbühne *f*; Werkbühne *f*

2134   OPTIMIZATION
f   optimisation *f*
d   Optimierung *f*

2135   ORDOVICIAN
geologic period of the Paleozoic era
f   Ordovicien *m*
d   Ordovizium *n*

2136   ORGANIC DEPOSIT
depostis of calcareous and siliceous
remains of animals
f   dépôt *m* organogène
d   organogene Ablagerung *f*

2137   ORGANIC MATTER CONTENT
f   teneur *f* en matière organique
d   organischer Inhalt *m*

2138   ORGANIC POLLUTION
contamination originating from
organic sources
f   pollution *f* organique
d   organische Verunreinigung *f*

2139   ORIENTATION
directional arrangement of
nonspherical grains in a sand
aggregate
f   orientation *f*
d   Orientierung *f*; richtungsmässige
Anordung *f*

2140 ORIGINAL DIP
      dip due to deposition of sediments
      f pendage *m* original
      d ursprüngliches Einfallen *n*

2141 ORIGINAL INTERSTICE
      interstice formed during rock
      formation stage
      f porosité *f* d'interstice primaire;
         interstice *m* de formation
      d ursprünglicher Porenraum *m*

2142 OROGRAPHIC PRECIPITATION
      precipitation due to mechanical
      lifting of air over a ground relief
      f précipitation *f* de relief
      d orographischer Niederschlag *m*

2143 ORTHOGONALITY
      f orthogonalité *f*
      d Orthogonalität *f*

2144 OSMOTIC FORCE
      f force *f* osmotique
      d osmotische Kraft *m*

2145 OSMOTIC PRESSURE
      f pression *f* osmotique
      d osmotischer Druck *m*

2146 OUTCROP
      open exposure of bedrock or
      otherwise buried material
      f affleurement *m*
      d Aufschluss *m*

2147 OUTFLOW
      f effluent *m*; écoulement *m*
      d Ausfluss *m*; Abfluss *m*

2148 OUTPUT VOLTAGE
      voltage available at terminals of a
      power supply
      f tension *f* aux bornes
      d Klemmenspannung *f*

2149 OUTWASH
      glacial drift deposited by meltwater
      streams
      f dépôt *m* d'eau de fonte
      d Schmelzwasserablagerung *f*

2150 OUTWASH GRAVEL
      glacial drift material deposited by
      streams from glacier
      f gravier *m* fluvioglaciaire
      d ausgewaschener Kies *m*

2151 OUTWASH PLAIN
      plain in front of glacier composed
      of outwash material

      f plaine *f* de lavage
      d Sandrebene *f*

2152 OVEN-DRY
      degree of dryness of porous sample
      after drying in oven at specified
      temperature
      f sec à l'étuve
      d ofentrocken

2153 OVERBANK AREA
      area covered by flood waters
      overtopping natural of artificial
      river banks
      f surface *f* du lit majeur
      d Ausseruferungsgebiet *n*

2154 OVERBURDEN
      total thickness of all strata over-
      lying an aquifer or other formation
      f couverture *f*; toit *m*
      d Deckschichten *fpl*

2155 OVERBURDEN PRESSURE
      pressure exerted by weight of the
      overburden column
      f pression *f* géostatique
      d Überlagerungsdruck *m*

2156 OVERFLOW
      f déversoir *m* de trop-plein
      d Überlauf *m*

2157 OVERFLOW, TO
      spill over containing walls
      f déborder
      d überlaufen

2158 OVERFLOW DAM
      f barrage *m* déversoir
      d Überflusswehr *n*

2159 OVERLAND FLOW
      surface runoff flowing over land
      surface towards channel
      f ruissellement *m* de surface;
         ruissellement *m* sur le terrain
      d Oberflächenabfluss *m*

2160 OVERLOAD
      load above the normal rating; exces
      load still tolerable to system
      f surcharge *f*
      d Überlast *f*

2161 OVERPRESSURE
      excess pressure
      f pression *f* excédentaire
      d Überdruck *m*

2162 OVERTHRUST
      upthrust fault with very low angle
      of dip and relatively large net
      displacement
      f chevauchement *m*
      d Überschiebung *f*

2163 OXYGEN
      O$_2$

f oxygène *m*
d Sauerstoff *m*

2164 OXYGEN DEMAND
      ability of substances to utilize
      dissolved oxygen in water
      f demande *f* en oxygène
      d Sauerstoffbedarf *m*

P

2165 PACKER
sealing device in well to separate
flow from different horizons
f packer *m*; garniture *f*;
   étanchéité *m*
d Packer *m*; Dichtung *f*

2166 PACKING
three dimensional arrangement of
particles
f arrangement *m*; empilement *m*;
   tassement *m*
d Packung *f*; Lagerung *f*;
   Anordnung *f*

PACKING, grain see 862
-, gravel see 873
-, loosest see 1170
-, hightest see 2787

2167 PACKING GLAND
f presse-étoupe *m*
d Stopfbüchse *f*

2168 PALEOCENE
oldest geologic epoch in the
Tertiary period
f Paléocène *m*
d Paläozän *n*

2169 PALEOZOIC
geologic era preceding Mesozoic
era
f Ère *f* Paléozoïque
d Paläozoikum *n*

PAN, evaporation see 681
-, floating see 741
-, land see 1124
-, sunken see 2705

2170 PAN COEFFICIENT
coefficient to correlate high rate of
evaporation in pan to evaporation rate
from larger water bodies
f coefficient *m* de réduction d'un bac;
   coefficient *m* du bac
d Kesselumrechnungskoeffizient *m*

2171 PARENT MATERIAL
material from which soil or sediment was formed
f roche *f* mère
d Ausgangsmaterial *n*

2172 PARTIALLY PENETRATED WELL
well not penetrating aquifer
completely to impervious bedrock
f puits *m* imparfait; puits *m*
   incomplet
d unvollkommener Brunnen *m*

2173 PARTIAL PRESSURE OF VAPOR
f pression *f* partielle
d Partialdruck *m*

2174 PARTICLE
smallest individual constituent of
an aggregate
f particule *f*
d Teilchen *n*; Partikel *n*

PARTICLE, clay see 302
-, soil see 2595

2175 PARTING
separation of sedimentary rock
along the bedding planes
f délitement *m*
d Schichtfuge *f*

2176 PARTS PER MILLION (PPM)
weight per weight of solution;
expression of concentration
f parties *fpl* par million
d Teil *n* pro Million

2177 PATHOGENIC BACTERIA
disease inducing bacteria
f bactéries *fpl* pathogènes
d krankheitserregende Bakterien *f*

PATTERN, drainage see 555
-, pumping see 2306
-, storm intensity see 2655
-, trellis drainage see 2834

2178 PEAK
f pointe *f*; valeur *f* maximale
d Spitze *f*; Spitzenwert *m*;
   Höchstwert *m*

2179 PEAK RUNOFF
f écoulement *m* de pointe
d Spitzenabfluss *m*

2180 PEAT
decomposed mainly vegetable
matter
f tourbe *f*
d Torf *m*

2181 PEBBLE
smooth rounded stone
f caillou *m*; galet *m*
d Kieselstein *m*; Kiesel *m*

2182 PEDIMENT
inclined erosion surface covered
with thin fluvial deposits
f pédiment *m*
d Fussfläche *f*; Pediment *n*

2183 PELLICULAR WATER
water adhering to soil particles
by molecular forces
f eau *f* pelliculaire; eau *f* de
tension superficielle
d Häutchenwasser *n*

2184 PENDULAR REGIME
saturation regime where porous
medium has lowest possible
saturation in form of pendular rings
at grain contacts
f régime *m* des eaux cunéiformes
d Porenwinkelwasserregime *n*;
Pendulärregime *n*

2185 PENEPLAIN
degradation surface without relief
f pénéplaine *f*
d Fastebene *f*; Rumpfebene *f*

2186 PENETRABLE
f pénétrable
d durchdringbar; durchlässig

PENETRATION, complete .... of
well see 329

2187 PENETRATION RATE
f vitesse *f* d'avancement
d Vorschubgeschwindigkeit *f*;
Bohrfortschritt *m*

2188 PENNSYLVANIAN
geologic period of the Paleozoic era
f Carbonifère *m* supérieur
d Oberkarbon *n*

2189 PEN TRACE
ink, magnetic, or photographic line
traced on drum of a recording gage
or meter
f trace *f* du stylet
d Schreibspur *f*

2190 PERCHED GROUNDWATER
isolated continuous body of water
suspended above water table
f nappe *f* perchée
d schwebendes Grundwasser *n*

2191 PERCHED WATER TABLE
free surface of a continuous body
of water suspended above main
water table
f surface *f* d'une nappe perchée
d schwebender Grundwasserspiegel *m*

2192 PERCOLATE
to flow through saturated void space
f percoler
d durchsickern; durchströmen

2193 PERCOLATION
movement of water through saturated
interior pore space
f percolation *f*
d Sickerströmung *f*; Filterströmung *f*

2194 PERCUSSION DRILLING
f forage *m* par battage
d Schlagbohrverfahren *n*

2195 PERENNIAL SPRING
spring discharging throughout the
year
f source *f* pérenne
d Dauerquelle *f*; perennierende
Quelle *f*

2196 PERENNIAL STREAMS
stream flowing above surface all
the time
f rivière *f* pérenne
d perennierender Fluss *m*

2197 PERENNIAL YIELD
sustained yield
f débit *m* d'écoulement pérenne
d Dauerspende *f*

2198 PERFORATION
holes or openings in well casing to
permit water inflow into well
f perforation *f*
d Perforation *f*; Durchlöcherung *f*

PERIMETER, basin see 160
-, wetted see 3010

2199 PERIOD
subdivision of an era in the geologic
time scale
f période *f*
d Periode *f*

PERIOD, wetting see 3011

2200 PERMAFROST
ground perennially below the freezing
temperature
f pergelisol *m*
d Dauerfrost *m*; Permafrost *m*; Gefrornis

2201 PERMAFROST TABLE
upper limit of permafrost
f limite *f* supérieure du pergelisol
d obere Permafrostgrenze *f*

2202 PERMANENT HARDNESS
noncarbonate hardness
f dureté *f* permanente; dureté *f*
non-carbonatée
d bleibende Härte *f*; permanente
Härte *f*

2203 PERMANENT LOAD
f charge *f* permanente
d Dauerlast *f*; Nennlast *f*

2204 PERMANENT WELL
well completely equipped and
developed for a long productive life
(as opposed to an observation or
exploratory well)
f puits *m* permanent
d endgültige Bohrung *f*

2205 PERMANENT WILTING POINT
saturation at which permanent
wilting occurs
f point *m* de flétrissure permanente
d permanenter Welkepunkt *m*

PERMEABILITY, effective see 622
-, intrinsic see 1071
-, relative see 2384
-, transverse see 2829

2206 PERMEABILITY BARRIER
geologic or petrographic feature in
a bed obstructing free flow
f barrière *f* de perméabilité
d Permeabilitätsbarriere *f*

2207 PERMEABILITY TENSOR
permeability in an anisotropic
medium
f tenseur *m* de perméabilité
d Permeabilitätstensor *m*

2208 PERMEAMETER
device to measure permeability
f perméamètre *m*
d Permeameter *n*; Vorrichtung *f*
zur Durchlässigkeitsmessung

2209 PERMIAN
most recent geologic period of the
Paleozoic era
f Permien *m*
d Perm *n*

2210 PERMISSIBLE LOAD
f charge *f* admissible
d zulässige Belastung *f*

2211 PERVIOUS
permitting fluids to pass
f perméable
d durchlässig

2212 PETROGRAPHY
science of describing and
identifying rocks
f pétrographie *f*
d Petrographie *f*; Gesteinskunde *f*

2213 PHOTOGEOLOGY
interpretation of aerial photographs
for geological purposes
f photogéologie *f*
d Photogeologie *f*

2214 PHOTOGRAMMETRY
preparation of maps and measureme
from (stereoscopic) aerial photographs
f photogrammétrie *f*
d Photogrammetrie *f*

2215 PHOTOMULTIPLIER
f photomultiplicateur *m*
d Photoelektronenverstärkerröhre

2216 PHREATIC DECLINE
downward movement of water table
f abaissement *m* phréatique
d Grundwasserspiegelabfall *m*

2217 PHREATIC FLUCTUATION
fluctuation of the water table
f fluctuation *f* phréatique
d Schwankung *f* des Grundwasserspiegels

2218 PHREATIC RISE
upward movement of water table
f remontée *f* phréatique
d Grundwasserspiegelanstieg *m*

2219 PHREATIC SURFACE
free water surface at atmospheric
pressure
f surface *f* de la nappe phréatique
d Grundwasseroberfläche *f*

2220 PHREATIC WATER
see ground water

2221 PHREATIC ZONE
zone in soil profile saturated with
ground water; a zone of saturation
f zone *f* de l'eau soutenue;
zone *f* phréatique
d Grundwasserzone *f*

2222 PHREATOPHYTE
desert plants with deeply penetratin

roots reaching the water table,
growing mainly along stream course
(word proposed by E.O. Meinzer)
f phréatophythe *m*
d Phreatophyte *f*

2223 pH VALUE
negative exponent of hydrogen ion
concentration
f valeur *f* du pH
d pH-Wert *m*; Wasserstoff
exponent *m*

2224 PHYLLITE
metamorphic argillaceous rock
f phyllade *m*
d Phyllit *m*

2225 PHYSICAL ANALYSIS
f analyse *f* physique
d physikalische Untersuchung *f*

2226 PHYSIOGRAPHY
science of the origin and evolution
of land forms
f physiographie *f*
d Physiographie *f*

2227 PHYTOMETER
device to measure transpiration of
plants embedded in soil
f phytomètre *m*
d Pflanzenverdunstungsmesser *m*

2228 PIEDMONT PLAIN
plain extending outwards from the
base of a mountain system
f plaine *f* de piémont
d Bergfussebene *f*

2229 PIEZOMETER
pressure reading and measuring
instrument
f piézomètre *m*
d Druckmesser *m*

2230 PIEZOMETRIC HEAD
sum of pressure and elevation head
f hauteur *f* piézométrique;
énergie *f* potentielle
d piezometrische Druckhöhe *f*

2231 PIEZOMETRIC POTENTIAL
piezometric head
f potentiel *m* piézométrique
d Druckpotential *n*

2232 PIEZOMETRIC SURFACE
defined by elevation to which water
will rise in artesian wells or wells

penetrating confined aquifers,
determined by water pressure and
elevation of aquifer
f surface *f* piézométrique
d Druckfläche *f*; piezometrisches
Niveau *n*

2233 PILLOW LAVA
lava showing structure resembling
pillows
f lave *m* en coussins
d Kissenlava *f*

2234 PILOT BIT
f outil-pilote *m*
d Vorbohrmeissel *m*

2235 PINGO;
HYDROLACCOLITH
see hydrolaccolith
f laccolith *m* de glace
d Eislakkolith *m*

2236 PIPE
closed tubular conduit for fluid
transport
f tuyeau *m*; tubage *m*
d Rohr *n*

PIPE, discharge see 518
-, riser see 2414
-, screen see 2486
-, seamless see 2489
-, slotted see 2574
-, stove see 2656
-, tile see 2788
-, water see 2946

2237 PIPE CASING
lining of a well in form of tubular
steel or cast iron pipe
f tubage *m*
d Verrohrung *f*

2238 PIPE COUPLING
f manchon *m* de tubage
d Rohrverbinder *m*

2239 PIPE LINE
f conduit *m*; pipeline *m*
d Pipeline *f*; Fernleitung *f*

PIPE LINE, gas see 819

2240 PIPE MANIFOLD
f collecteur *m*
d Verteilerrohr *n*

2241 PIPE WRENCH
f clé *f* à tubes
d Rohrzange *f*

2242 PIT
    f fosse *f*
    d Grube *f*

    PIT, gravel see 874
    -, recharge see 2359
    -, settling see 2517
    -, slush see 2577
    -, test see 2764
    -, well see 2997

2243 PITCHER PUMP
    a type of piston pump
    f pompe *f* à plongeur
    d Tauchkolbenpumpe *f*

2244 PITOT TUBE
    device to measure flow velocity
    through pressure differences
    f tube *m* de Pitot
    d Staudruckmesser *m*;
       Pitot'sche Röhre *f*

    PLAIN, alluvial see 60
    -, coastal see 315
    -, flood see 748
    -, outwash see 2151
    -, piedmont see 2228

    PLANE, bedding see 167
    -, contact see 366
    -, datum see 442
    -, fault see 708
    -, hodograph see 934
    -, joint see 1101

2245 PLANIMETER
    instrument for the automatic
    determination of irregular areas on
    a map
    f planimètre *m*
    d Planimeter *n*

    PLATE, base see 154
    -, slotted see 2575

2246 PLATEAU
    elevated level land surface
    f plateau *m*
    d Plateau *n*; Hochebene *f*

    PLATEAU, lava flow see 1139

2247 PLATY
    f en forme de plaquette
    d plättchenförmig

2248 PLEISTOCENE
    geologic epoch in the Quaternary
    period

    f Pléistocène *m*
    d Pleistozän *n*

2249 PLIOCENE
    most recent geologic epoch in the
    Tertiary period
    f Pliocène *m*
    d Pliozän *n*

2250 PLUGGING AGENT
    mud additive that seals off a very
    permeable layer by clogging of the
    borehole walls
    f colmatant *m*
    d Dichtungsmittel *n*

2251 PLUNGER PUMP
    f pompe *f* à piston; pompe *f* à
       plongeur
    d Kolbenpumpe *f*; Tauchkolben-
       pumpe *f*

2252 PLUTONIC WATER
    water in or derived from magma at
    considerable depth
    f eaux *f pl* plutoniques
    d plutonisches Wasser *n*

2253 POCKET STORAGE
    water storage in depressions on the
    land surface
    f emmagasinement *m* dans les
       dépressions du sol
    d Wasserspeicherung *f* an der
       Bodenoberfläche

2254 PODSOL
    light colored soil (forest regions)
    f podzol *m*
    d Podsolboden *m*

    POINT, concentration see 337
    -, drive see 592
    -, freezing see 787
    -, match see 1197
    -, melting see 2021
    -, neutrality see 2107
    -, node see 2111
    -, reference see 2376
    -, saturation see 2472
    -, shock see 2536
    -, shot see 2540
    -, stagnation see 2636
    -, triple see 2842
    -, wilting see 3016

2255 POINT-BAR DEPOSIT
    sedimentation on inside of meander
    loop
    f banc *m* de sable à l'intérieur de l
       boucle

d Sandbank *f* am Gleithang;
   Anlandung *f*

2256 POINT OF INFLECTION
point where curve changes slope
f point *m* d'inflexion
d Wendepunkt *m*

2257 POINT OF RISE
f point *m* de montée
d Anstiegspunkt *m*

2258 POISE
measure of viscosity
f poise *f*
d Poise *n*

2259 POLARIZATION
migration and separation of ions to
the electrodes in a direct current
electrolyte process giving rise to
higher overall resistance
f polarisation *f*
d Polarisierung *f*

2260 POLLUTANT
substance causing pollution
f matière *f* polluante
d Verunreinigung *f*;
   Schmutzstoff *m*

2261 POLLUTED WATER
water containing sewage or other
contaminants
f eaux *f pl* polluées
d verunreinigtes Wasser *n*;
   Abwasser *n*; Schmutzwasser *n*

2262 POLLUTION
contamination of the environment
with undesirable or obnoxious
substances
f pollution *f*
d Verschmutzung *f*;
   Verunreinigung *f*

POLLUTION, organic see 2138

2263 POLLUTION ABATEMENT
all measures taken to prevent or to
protect against pollution
f protection *f* contre la pollution
d Gewässerschutz *m*

2264 POND
small body of surface water
f étang *m*
d Teich *m*

2265 PONDED WATER
water held in depression by a barrier

f eaux *f pl* retenues
d eingedämmtes Wasser *n*

2266 PORE
small void space in rock or
unconsolidated aggregate of soil
particles
f pore *m*
d Pore *f*; Hohlraum *m*

2267 PORE ENTRY RADIUS
radius of flow channel at pore entry,
smaller than average pore radius
f rayon *m* d'entrée de pore;
   rayon *m* d'étranglement de pore
d Poreneintrittsradius *m*

2268 PORE PRESSURE
pressure of water in pores of
saturated medium
f pression *f* de pore
d Porendruck *m*; Porenwasserdruck *m*

2269 PORE SPACE
space occupied by voids, containing
gases or liquids, in a rock sample
f volume *m* des pores
d Porenraum *m*

PORE SPACE, vugular see 2910

2270 POROSIMETER
device to measure porosity
f porosimètre *m*
d Porosimeter *n*

2271 POROSITY
ratio of void volume to bulk volume
of rock sample
f porosité *f*
d Porosität *f*; Porengehalt *m*

POROSITY, absolute see 6
-, effective see 623, 624
-, practical see 623
-, secondary see 2493

2272 POROUS MEDIUM
any medium containing interdispersed
void space
f milieu *m* poreux
d poröses Medium *n*

2273 POTABILITY
f potabilité *f*
d Trinkbarkeit *f*

2274 POTABLE WATER
f eau *f* potable
d Trinkwasser *n*

2275 POTAMOLOGY
study of streams
f potamologie *f*
d Potamologie *f*; Flusskunde *f*

2276 POTASSIUM
K
f potasse *m*
d Kalium *n*

2277 POTENTIAL
f potentiel *m*
d Potential *n*

POTENTIAL, contact see 367
-, electrochemical see 635
-, force see 775
-, membrane see 2024
-, junction see 1102
-, piezometric see 2231
-, redox see 2371
-, spontaneous see 2626
-, streaming see 2668
-, velocity see 2891
-, zeta see 3030

2278 POTENTIAL ELECTRODE
f électrode *f* de potentiel
d Potentialelektrode *f*;
Messelektrode *f*

2279 POTENTIAL EVAPOTRANSPIRATION
evapotranspiration occurring under
adequate soil-moisture supply at all
times for given temperature and
humidity conditions
f évapotranspiration *f* potentielle
d mögliche Evapotranspiration *f*;
potentielle Evapotranspiration *f*

2280 POTENTIAL FLOW
irrotational flow occurring in a
conservative force field or
potential field
f écoulement *m* potentiel
d Potentialströmung *f*

2281 POTENTIOMETER
instrument to measure voltage
differences
f potentiomètre *m*
d Potentiometer *n*; Spannungsmesser *m*

2282 POTHOLE
hole formed by the erosive action
of whirling water
f marmite *f* torrentielle
d Kolk *m*; Erosionskessel *m*

2283 PRACTICAL POROSITY
see effective porosity

2284 PRE-CAMBIAN
geologic era preceding Cambrain
period
f Antécambrien *m*
d Präkambrium *n*

2285 PRECIPITATION
water precipitating in liquid or solid
form from atmosphere
f précipitation *m*
d Niederschlag *m*

PRECIPITATION, accumulated
see 13
-, channel see 279
-, convective see 379
-, cyclonic see 434
-, effective see 625
-, orographic see 2142

2286 PRECIPITATION-EVAPORATION
RATIO
f rapport *m* précipitation-évaporation
d Niederschlags-Verdunstungs-
verhältnis *n*

2287 PRECIPITATION EXCESS
part of precipitation contributing
directly to runoff
f précipitation *f* excédentaire
d Niederschlagsüberschuss *m*

2288 PRECIPITATION GAGE
instrument to measure amount of
precipitation per unit area
f appareil *m* de mesure de la
précipitation
d Niederschlagsmesser *m*

PRECIPITATION INDEX,
antecedent see 88

2289 PRESSURE
f pression *f*
d Druck *m*

PRESSURE, absolute see 7
-, air see 44
-, barometric see 142
-, differential see 501
-, discharge see 519
-, flowing see 757
-, gage see 804
-, hydrostatic see 986
-, initial see 1035
-, osmotic see 2145
-, overburden see 2155

-, pore see 2268
-, saturation see 2473
-, working see 3023

2290 PRESSURE BUILDUP CURVE
f courbe *f* de remontée de
pression
d Druckaufbaukurve *f*

2291 PRESSURE CELL
pressure measuring and
transducing device
f cellule *f* piézométrique
d Druckdose *f*

2292 PRESSURE DROP
pressure difference occurring
between two points along a stream
line in a flow system
f chute *f* de pression
d Druckabfall *m*; Druckverlust *m*

2293 PRESSURE HEAD
f énergie *f* de pression
d Druckhöhe *f*

PRESSURE OF VAPOR, partial
see 2173

2294 PRESSURE SURGE
f à-coup *m* de pression
d Druckstoss *m*

2295 PRESSURE TRANSMITTER
f transducteur *m* de pression
d Druckgeber *m*

2296 PRISM STORAGE
storage of water in river channel
or reservoir in prism above
original water level
f emmagasinement *m* prismatique
d prismatisch gespeichertes Fallwasser *n*

2297 PROBE
sensing instrument to take
measurements at the interior of
a relatively unaccessible system
f sonde *f*
d Sonde *f*

PROCESS, congealing see 354
-, erosional see 669
-, geomorphic see 836
-, transportational see 2828

PROFILE, flood see 749
-, hydraulic see 957
-, seismic see 2503

-, soil see 2596
-, stream see 2671
-, zonal soil see 3032

2298 PROTECTIVE CASING
f tubage *m* de protection
d Schutzverrohrung *f*

2299 PSYCHROMETER
apparatus to measure relative
humidity indirectly
f psychromètre *m*
d Psychrometer *n*

2300 PUDDLE
water collecting in very small
surface depressions
f flaque *f* d'eau
d Pfütze *f*

2301 PULLEY
f moufle *m*
d Flaschenzugblock *m*

2302 PULSE GENERATOR
f générateur *m* de pulsations
d Pulsgenerator *m*

2303 PUMICE
glassy, very porous lava
f pierre *f* ponce
d Bimsstein *m*

PUMP, centrifugal see 273
-, deep well turbine see 449
-, displacement see 526
-, double acting see 540
-, gear see 823
-, jet see 1097
-, metering see 2036
-, mud see 2092
-, pitcher see 2243
-, plunger see 2251
-, sand see 2464
-, submersible see 2684
-, suction see 2698

PUMPAGE, water see 2947

2304 PUMP DISCHARGE
f refoulement *m* de la pompe
d Pumpenförderung *f*

2305 PUMP HOUSE
f abri *m* des pompes
d Pumpenkammer *f*

2306 PUMPING PATTERN
arrangement of pumping wells
f disposition *f* des puits de pompage
d Entnahmeanordnung *f*

2307 PUMPING STATION
f station f de pompage
d Pumpstation f

2308 PUMPING TEST
test to determine aquifer
characteristics by pumping well
and plotting drawdown curves
f essai m de pompage; essai m de
puits
d Pumpversuch m

2309 PUMPING UNIT
f groupe m de pompes
d Pumpanlage f

2310 PUMP LINER
liner of pump cylinder
f chemise f de pompe
d Pumpenauskleidung f

2311 PYCNOMETER
bottle with accurately determined
volume for density determinations
f pycnomètre m

d Pyknometer n

2312 PYRITE
mineral FeS_2, sometimes source
of sulfuric contaminations
f pyrite m
d Schwefelkies m; Pyrit m

2313 PYROCLASTIC BLOCK
detrital volcanic block
f bloc m pyroclastique
d pyroklastischer Block m

2314 PYROCLASTIC FLOW
dense, viscous lavaflow containing
clastic material; ignimbrite
f tuf m soudé; ignimbrite m
d geschweisster Tuff m;
Schmelztuff m

2315 PYROXENE
mineral group of common rock-
forming constituents
f pyroxène m
d Pyroxen n

Q

2316 QUAGMIRE
  wet and unstable land area
  f bourbe *f*
  d Morast *m*

2317 QUARTERNARY
  geologic period of the Cenozoic era
  f Ère *f* Quaternaire
  d Quartär *n*

2318 QUARTZ
  crystal form of SiO_2

  f quartz *m*
  d Quarz *m*

2319 QUICKSAND
  f sable *m* mouvant
  d Schwimmsand *m*

2320 QUIET REACH
  reach of river with no features
  disturbing flow pattern
  f section *f* tranquille
  d ruhige Strecke *f*

R

2321 RADIAL FLOW
radial flow into or out of a well
under ideal circular boundary
conditions
f écoulement *m* radial circulaire
d radialer Fluss *m*

2322 RADIOACTIVE CONTAMINATION
f contamination *f* radioactive
d Strahlenverseuchung *f*

2323 RADIOACTIVE TRACER
tracer used in hydrological velocity
determinations
f traceur *m* radioactif
d radioaktive Markierung *f*;
radioaktiver Tracer *m*

2324 RADIOACTIVITY LOG
log measuring radioactivity in a
borehole
f diagraphie *f* de radioactivité
d Aufnahme *f* der Radioaktivität

2325 RADIOISOTOPE
f radio-isotope *m*; isotope *m*
radioactif
d radioaktives Isotop *n*

RADIUS, drainage see 556
-, hydrualic see 958
-, pore entry see 2267

2326 RADIUS OF INFLUENCE
radial distance to points around well
affected by pumping
f rayon *m* d'appel; rayon *m* d'action
d Absenkungsradius *m*

2327 RAIN
liquid precipitation of atmospheric
water in form of drops and droplets
f pluie *f*
d Regen *m*

RAINFALL, effective see 626

2328 RAIN FALL EXCESS
portion of rainfall contributing
directly to runoff
f pluie *f* excédentaire
d Regenüberschuss *m*

2329 RAINFALL INTENSITY
volume or depth of rainfall per unit
time

f intensité *f* de la pluie
d Regenintensität *f*; Regenstärke *f*

2330 RAINFALL SIMULATOR
laboratory device to simulate
rainstorms
f simulateur *m* pluviométrique
d Regensimulator *m*; Berieselungsanlage *f*

2331 RAIN GAGE
instrument to measure height of
rainfall
f pluviomètre *m*
d Regenmesser *m*

2332 RAIN GAGE NETWORK
areal distribution of rain gages
f réseau *m* pluviométrique
d Niederschlagsbeobachtungsnetz *n*

2333 RAIN INTENSITY
intensity of rain fall expressed in
depth per time (inch hour)
f intensité *f* de pluie
d Regenintensität *f*

2334 RANDOM DISTRIBUTION
f distribution *f* aléatoire
d Zufallsverteilung *f*

2335 RANDOM SAMPLE
f échantillon *m* instantané
d Stichprobe *f*

2336 RAPID
stream section with notably higher
flow velocity than in adjoining parts
f rapide *m*
d Stromschnelle *f*

2337 RAPID FLOW
open channel flow with Froude
number greater than unity
f débit *m* rapide; écoulement *m*
rapide
d Schiessen *n*

RATE, drilling see 581
-, flow see 761
-, lapse see 1129
-, penetration see 2187
-, seepage see 2500
-, swelling see 2736

2338 RATE OF DRAFT
      rate at which water is required
      for use; demand
      f débit *m* d'écoulement
      d Verbrauchsrate *f*

2339 RATE OF DRYING
      f taux *m* de dessèchement
      d Trocknungsrate *f*

2340 RATE OF INFILTRATION
      maximum rate at which soil can
      absorb water
      f capacité *f* d'infiltration
      d Eindringungsrate *f*

2341 RATE OF PRODUCTION
      f taux *m* de production
      d Förderrate *f*

2342 RATING CURVE
      graphic relationship of stage to
      discharge
      f courbe *f* de tarage
      d Abflusskurve *f*

      RATIO, bifurcation see 178
      -, drainage see 557
      -, mixing see 2057
      -, precipitation-evaporation see
        2286
      -, relief see 2387
      -, transpiration see 2827
      -, void see 2899

2343 RATIONAL FORMULA
      equation relating runoff intensity
      and area to a runoff coefficient
      f équation *f* rationelle
      d rationale Abflussformel *f*

2344 RAVINE
      small erosional depression
      f ravin *m*
      d Tobel *m*; kleine Schlucht *f*

2345 RAW WATER
      untreated water
      f eaux *f pl* non-traitées
      d unbehandeltes Wasser *n*;
         Rohwasser *n*

      REACH, quiet see 2320

2346 REAMED WELL
      well that has been enlargened by
      reaming the original hole
      f puits *m* alésé; puits *m* élargi
      d nachgeräumter Brunnen *f*;
         erweiterte Bohrung *f*

2347 REAMER
      cutting tool to enlargen the diameter
      of existing holes
      f outil *m* aléseur
      d Nachschneider *m*; Räumer *m*

2348 REAMING OF A SLIM HOLE
      enlarging of a test hole to a pumping
      or permanent well
      f élargissement *m* d'une sonde à
         faible diamètre
      d Ausräumen *n* einer kleinen
         Bohrung; Erweiterungsbohrung *f*

2349 RECEIVER
      part of a remote measuring system
      receiving incoming data or impulses
      f récepteur *m*
      d Empfänger *m*

2350 RECEIVING SURFACE
      surface receiving precipitation
      or radiation
      f surface *f* de réception
      d Auffangfläche *f*

2351 RECEIVING WATER COURSE
      f cours *m* d'eau récepteur
      d Vorfluter *m*

      RECESSION, groundwater see 907

2352 RECESSIONAL MORAINE
      moraine deposited by a retreating
      glacier
      f moraine *f* de retrait
      d Rückzugsmoräne *f*

2353 RECESSION CONSTANT
      f constante *f* de récession
      d Rückgangskonstante *f*

2354 RECESSION CURVE
      falling limb of hydrograph curve
      f courbe *f* de décrue; courbe *f*
         de tarissement
      d abfallender Kurvenast *m* der
         Ganglinie; Rückgangskurve *f*

2355 RECESSION FLOW
      flow after rainfall stops
      f écoulement *m* en décrue
      d Abflussrückgang *m*

2356 RECESSION SEGMENT
      part of hydrograph representing
      withdrawal of water from storage
      f segment *m* de tarissement
      d Trockenwetterlinie *f*

2357 RECHARGE
artificial replenishment of a depleted
aquifer by injection or infiltration
of water from the surface
f recharge f; alimentation f
   artificielle
d künstliche Grundwasseranreicherung f; Wiederauffüllung f

RECHARGE, artificial see 117
-, induced see 1016

2358 RECHARGE LINE
recharge wells arranged in linear
fashion to approximate line source
f ligne f de recharge
d Versickerungsbrunnenkette f

2359 RECHARGE PIT
large diameter well or shaft for
recharge under gravity
f fossé m de recharge
d Versickerungschacht m; Senkschacht m; Sickerschacht m

2360 RECHARGE WATER
water used for replenishment
f eaux f pl de recharge
d künstliches Grundwasser n

2361 RECHARGE WELL;
DIFFUSION WELL; INVERTED
WELL
well into which recharge water
is introduced
f puits m de recharge
d Versickerungsbrunnen m;
   Senkbrunnen m

2362 RECIPIENT
vessel receiving liquids in volume
measurements
f récipient m
d Auffanggefäss n

2363 RECLAMATION
improve land use, eliminate ill
effects for this purpose
f récupération f
d Rückgewinnung f; Wiederherstellung f; Melioration f

RECLAMATION, water see 2949

RECORD, stage see 2635
-, well see 2999

2364 RECORDER
instrument continuously or intermittently recording measurements

f enregistreur m
d Schreiber m; Registriergerät n

RECORDER, water-stage see 2959

2365 RECORDING DRUM
f tambour m enregistreur
d Registriertrommel f;
   Registrierwalze f

2366 RECORDING GAGE
f pluviographe m
d Niederschlagsschreiber m;
   Schreibregenmesser m

2367 RECORDING OSCILLOGRAPH
f oscillographe m enregistreur
d Oszillograph m

2368 RECOVERY
f récupération f
d Ausbeute f

2369 RECOVERY METHOD
pumping test in which both drawdown
and recovery of head after pumping
has stopped are observed in the
same well
f méthode f par remontée
d Druckaufbauverfahren n

2370 RECRYSTALLIZATION
new formation of crystals from
solid rock material
f recristallisation f
d Rekristallisation f

2371 REDOX POTENTIAL (Eh)
oxidation-reduction potential
f potentiel m redox
d Redoxpotential n

2372 REDUCER
pipe or casing connector reducing
the diameter
f réducteur m
d Reduzierstück n

2373 REDUCING JOINT
f raccord m réducteur
d Reduzierverbindung f

2374 REDUCTION
mechanical device to reduce speed
or length of a trace
f démultiplication f
d Untersetzung f

REDUCTION, evaporation see 682
-, surface area see 2712

2375 REEF
      dissected ridge of rocks totally or
      partially submerged in sea water,
      often of organic origin
      f récif *m*
      d Riff *n*

2376 REFERENCE POINT
      f point *m* de référence
      d Bezugspunkt *m*

2377 REGELATION
      melting of ice under pressure and
      subsequent freezing
      f regelation *f*
      d Regelation *f*

      REGIME, fumicular see 801
      -, pendular see 2184
      -, saturation see 2474

      REGIMEN, flow see 762

2378 REGION OF DISPERSED WATER
      diffuse interface between fresh-
      water and sea water caused by
      mixing in a coastal aquifer
      f zone *f* de transition saumâtre
      d Brackwasserzone *f* im
         Grundwasserleiter

2379 REGOSOL
      dry sandy soil
      f sol *m* sablonneux
      d Sandboden *m*

2380 REGRESSION LINE
      curve fitted to all mean values of
      one variable
      f courbe *f* de régression
      d Ausgleichskurve *f*

2381 REGULATION RESERVOIR
      f réservoir *m* de compensation
      d Ausgleichbehälter *m*

2382 REJUVENATION
      occurrence of young morphologic
      forms in a mature relief
      f rajeunissement *m*
      d Verjüngung *f*

2383 RELATIVE HUMIDITY OF
      ATMOSPHERE
      ratio of absolute humidity to
      maximum possible saturation at
      given conditions
      f humidité *f* relative
      d relative Luftfeuchte *f*

2384 RELATIVE PERMEABILITY
      ratio of permeability of one
      immiscible phase to intrinsic
      permeability in multiphase flow
      f perméabilité *f* relative
      d relative Durchlässigkeit *f*;
         relative Permeabilität *f*

2385 RELIEF
      elevation differences in topography
      of a land surface
      f relief *m*
      d Relief *n*

      RELIEF, maximum basin see 1198

2386 RELIEF INTENSITY
      average altitude difference between
      the highest point of a basin and the
      valley bottom
      f vigueur *f* du relief
      d Reliefenergie *f*

2387 RELIEF RATIO
      ratio of basin relief to horizontal
      distance along which it is measured
      f indice *m* du relief
      d Reliefenergie *f*; Geländeneigung *f*

2388 REPLENISHMENT
      restoration of water in depleted
      aquifer
      f alimentation *f*; ralimentation *f*
      d Anreicherung *f*

2389 RESEQUENT RIVER
      river flowing according to consequent
      drainage pattern, however, at lower
      level than original slope
      f rivière *f* réséquente
      d resequenter Fluss *m*

2390 RESERVOIR
      a) recipient for the collection of
         small amount of liquid
      b) surface water impoundment
      f réservoir *m*
      d a) Sammelbehälter *m*
         b) Stausee *m*; Speichersee *m*

      RESERVOIR, groundwater see 909
      -, oil see 2126
      -, regulation see 2381

2391 RESERVOIR EVAPORATION
      evaporation from the free surface
      of impounded water bodies
      f évaporation *f* sur les retenues
      d Seeverdunstung *f*;
         Stauseeverdunstung *f*

2392 RESERVOIR LAKE
lake obtained by the impoundment
of water for storage purposes
f lac *m* de barrage
d Stausee *m*

2393 RESIDUAL DRAWDOWN
drawdown measured after stopping
of pumping in a single well test
f rabattement *m* résiduel
d Restabsenkung *f*

2394 RESIDUE
solids remaining after evaporation
f résidu *m* après évaporation;
résidu *m*
d Verdunstungsrückstand *m*;
Rückstand *m*; Abdampfrückstand *m*; Rest *m*

RESIDUE, dry see 604

RESISTANCE, acoustic see 19
-, flow see 763
-, wear see 2973

2395 RESISTANCE-CAPACITY NETWORK
electrical analog model simulating
viscous flow by flow of electricity
through resistors and capacitors
f réseau *m* à résistances -
capacitances
d Widerstands-Kapazitätsnetz *n*

2396 RESISTANCE THERMOMETER
thermometer based on the principle
that the resistivity of a platinum
wire is proportional to its temperature
f thermomètre *m* à résistance
d Widerstandsthermometer *n*

2397 RESISTANCE TO FLOW
f résistance *f* à l'écoulement
d Fliesswiderstand *m*

2398 RESISTIVITY
f résistivité *f*
d spezifischer Widerstand *m*

RESISTIVITY, apparent see 95
-, electrical see 632

2399 RESISTIVITY LOG
recording of electrical resistivity
versus depth
f diagraphie *f* de résistivité
d Widerstandslog *n*

2400 RESISTIVITY-SPACING CURVE
plot of apparent resistivity against
electrode spacing

f courbe *f* résistivité-espacement
d Widerstand-Elektrodenabstands-
kurve *f*

2401 RESISTIVITY SURVEY
complete study of a well or well
field by resistivity methods
f étude *f* des résistivités
d Widerstandsmessung *f*

2402 RESURGENT WATER
magmatic water of external origin
f eaux *f pl* résurgentes
d wiederkehrendes Grundwasser *n*

2403 RETENTION
detention of water on surface
depressions or in subsurface void
space; retention of water in pores
against gravity
f rétention *f*
d Haltungsvermögen *n*;
Rückhaltevermögen *n*

RETENTION, sieve see 2545
-, specific see 2619
-, surface see 2720

2404 RETURN FLOW
f reflux *m*
d Rückfluss *m*

2405 REVERSE CIRCULATION
method of circulating drilling fluid
downwards through the annulus and
upwards through the drill pipe
f circulation *f* inverse
d Gegenstromspülung *f*

2406 REVERSE FAULT
fault where relative movement of the
hanging wall has been in the upward
direction
f faille *f* inverse
d Wechsel *m*

2407 REVERSE ROTARY
rotary drilling with reverse circula
f forage *m* rotary inverse
d Rotaryverfahren *n* mit Gegen-
spülung

2408 RHYOLITE
very dense fine grained granitic roc
f rhyolite *m*
d Rhyolith *m*

2409 RIDGE
elongated narrow elevation
f dorsale *m*; crête *f*
d Rücken *m*; Kamm *m*

2410 RIFT VALLEY
      surface depression due to the
      formation of graben block
      faulting
      f vallée f d'effondrement
      d Grabental n; Bruchtal n

2411 RINSE, TO
      f rincer
      d spülen

2412 RIPPEL MARK
      wavelike sculpture on water
      covered sand surfaces obtained
      by wave action
      f ride f de fond
      d Ripplemarke f

      RISE capillary see 242
      -, phreatic see 2218

2413 RISER
      pipe through which liquid rises in
      a well
      f colonne f montante
      d Steigrohr n

2414 RISER PIPE
      pipe through which water is raised
      in a production well
      f colonne f montante
      d Steigrohr n

2415 RISING SEGMENT
      part of hydrograph describing curve
      during precipitation
      f courbe f de concentration
      d steigender Kurvenast m

2416 RISING VELOCITY
      f vitesse f ascensionnelle
      d Steiggeschwindigkeit f

2417 RIVER
      natural water course through which
      runoff reaches sea
      f rivière f; fleuve m
      d Fluss m; Strom m

      RIVER, aggrading see 34
      -, consequent see 358
      -, obsequent see 2120
      -, resequent see 2389
      -, tidal see 2786

2418 RIVER BED
      channel of a river covered by its
      water
      f lit m d'une rivière
      d Flussbett n

2419 RIVER BEND
      f tournant m d'une fleuve
      d Flusschleife f

2420 RIVER BOTTOM
      f fond m de la rivière
      d Flussohle f

2421 RIVER REACH
      particular segment of a river
      f cours m d'un fleuve; bief m
      d Flusslauf m; Flussstrecke f

2422 RIVER SWAMP
      swamp in lowlands adjoining river
      f marécage m fluvial
      d Flussmorast m

2423 RIVER SYSTEM
      system of main river with all
      branches and tributaries
      f réseau m fluvial
      d Flusssystem n; Stromnetz n

2424 RIVER TERRACE
      level land terraces formed in a
      valley by fluviatile erosion or
      aggradation
      f terrasse f fluviale
      d Flussterrasse f

2425 RIVULET
      very small stream
      f ruisseau m
      d Rinnsal n

2426 ROCK
      consolidated mineral matter of
      igneous, sedimentary or chemical
      origin
      f roche f
      d Stein m; Gestein n

      ROCK, cavernous see 262
      -, clastic see 298
      -, consolidated see 359
      -, crystalline see 421
      -, detrital see 298
      -, extrusive see 698
      -, igneous see 998
      -, indurated see 1019
      -, intrusive see 1073
      -, unaltered see 2856

      ROCKS, carbonate see 248
      -, evaporite see 685

2427 ROCKFALL
      falling of bedrock from cliff or
      steep slope

f   éboulement *m* de roches
d   Steinfall *m*; Bergrutsch *m*

2428   ROCKFILL
f   enrochement *m*
d   Steinpackung *f*

2429   ROCK FORMATION
lithologically or structurally
distinct part of lithosphere
f   formation *f*
d   Gesteinsformation *f*

2430   ROCK SYSTEM
rocks deposited during a given
geologic time period
f   système *m* lithologique
d   Gesteinsfolge *f*

2431   ROCK TERRACE
terrace due to erosional action and
denudation
f   terrasse *f* rocheuse
d   Felsterrasse *f*

2432   ROCK TEXTURE
geometrical aspects and arrangement
of component particles of a rock
f   texture *f* des roches
d   Gesteinstextur *f*

2433   ROLLER BIT
drilling tool with a set of rotating
toothed rollers or cones
f   outil *m* à molettes
d   Rollenmeissel *m*

2434   ROOF DRAINAGE
precipitation runoff from roofs
f   évacuation *f* des eaux de toiture
d   Dachentwässerung *f*

2435   ROOT ZONE
zone in soil profile penetrated by
plant roots
f   zone *f* radiculaire
d   Wurzelzone *f*

2436   ROPE SOCKET
f   cosse *f* de câble
d   Kausche *f*; Kabelschuh *m*

ROTARY, hydraulic see 959
-, reverse see 2407

2437   ROTARY MOTION
f   mouvement *m* de rotation
d   Drehbewegung *f*

2438   ROTATING METER
stream velocity meter transforming

stream momentum into angular
momentum by vanes and rotor
f   moulinet *m*
d   Messflügel *m*

2439   ROTATING TABLE
horizontal round table that
transmits rotary movement to the
kelley and the drill pipe
f   table *m* de rotation
d   Drehtisch *m*

2440   ROUGHNESS
unevenness of surfaces giving rise
to high flow resistances
f   rugosité *f*
d   Rauhigkeit *f*

ROUGHNESS, bed see 170

2441   ROUGHNESS COEFFICIENT
coefficient describing roughness of
channel bed
f   coefficient *m* de rugosité
d   Rauhigkeitsbeiwert *m*;
Bettrauhigkeitszahl *f*

2442   ROUNDNESS
degree to which a sand grain approa
spherical shape
f   arrondi *m*
d   Abrundung *f*

2443   ROUT, TO
action of predicting and directing
of flood waves through a channel
system
f   propager
d   weiterleiten

2444   RUNAROUND
working platform in rotary drilling
f   passerelle *f* de derrick
d   Arbeitsbühne *f*

2445   RUN DRY, TO
to cease to flow of a well or spring
f   tarir
d   versiegen

2446   RUNOFF
discharge of water through surface
streams of a drainage basin; sum of
surface runoff and ground water flo
that reaches the streams
f   écoulement *m* de base; débit *m* de
base; écoulement *m* total
d   Abfluss *m*; Oberflächenabfluss *m*

RUNOFF, base see 149
-, direct (surface) see 514

RUNOFF, groundwater see 910
-, peak see 2179
-, storm see 514
-, subsurface see 2690
-, surface see 2721
-, total see 2810

2447   RUNOFF COEFFICIENT
        dimensionless coefficient to
        estimate runoff as a certain
        percentage of storm rainfall
        f   coefficient *m* de l'écoulement
            total
        d   Abflussbeiwert *m*

S

2448 SAFETY VALVE
    f clapet *m* de sécurité
    d Sicherheitsventil *n*

2449 SAFE YIELD
    amount of water withdrawn from
    basin without producing undesired
    result
    f débit *m* de sécurité
    d sichere Ausbeute *f*; sichere
       Entnahme *f*; sicheres Grund-
       wasserdargebot *n*

2450 SAFE YIELD OF STREAM
    lowest dry weather flow of a stream
    f débit *m* de sécurité
    d Sicherheitswert *m* der Entnahme

2451 SALINE SPRING
    spring water having high salt content
    f source *f* chlorurée
    d Solquelle *f*; Saline *f*

2452 SALINE WATER
    f eau *f* salée
    d Salzwasser *n*

2453 SALINITY LEVEL
    f degré *m* de salinité
    d Höhe *f* des Salzgehaltes

2454 SALINITY STRATIFICATION
    stratification of water in estuaries
    due to salinity-density difference
    f stratification *f* par salinité
    d Schichtung *f* nach dem Salz-
       gehalt

2455 SALTATION LOAD
    solid matter transported by stream
    by leaping movement over stream
    bed
    f charge *f* en saltation
    d Geröllfrachtung *f*; hüpfende
       Geschiebefrachtung *f*

2456 SALT DOME
    domelike intrusion of a mobile salt
    core into sedimentary rock
    f dôme *m* de sel
    d Salzdom *m*; Salzstock *m*

2457 SALT LAKE
    lake containing high salt concentra-
    tion usually with no outflow

    f lac *m* salé
    d Salzsee *m*

2458 SALT TOLERANCE
    resistance of crops to salt
    concentration
    f résistance *f* à la salinité;
       résistance *f* au sel
    d Salzfestigkeit *f*

2459 SALTY WATER
    water containing from 10,000 to
    100,000 ppm of total dissolved
    solids
    f eau salée *f*
    d Salzwasser *n*

    SAMPLE, disturbed see 531
    -, random see 2335
    -, soil see 2597
    -, water see 2953

    SAMPLER, snow see 2585

2460 SAMPLING
    taking of small quantities of water
    or porous media for further
    analysis
    f prise *f* d'échantillon
    d Probenahme *f*

2461 SAND
    unconsolidated detrital rock materia
    f sable *m*
    d Sand *m*

    SAND, clayey see 300
    -, clean see 305
    -, course see 3121
    -, drift see 566
    -, dune see 607
    -, fine see 728
    -, fine grained see 726
    -, medium see 2018
    -, shaly see 2525
    -, very fine see 2893

2462 SAND LINE;
    BOILING LINE
    cable operating the bailer
    f câble *m* de curage
    d Schöpfseil *n*

2463 SAND MODEL
    scaled down physical model of
    aquifer simulating boundary conditi

f   modèle *m* en sable
d   Sandkastenmodell *n*; Sandmodell *n*

SAND POINT, see drive point

2464   SAND PUMP
bailing device with a bottom valve
f   cuiller *f*
d   Sandpumpe *f*

2465   SAND SEPARATOR
device to remove sand granules
from well water
f   séparateur *m* de sable
d   Sandabscheider *m*

2466   SANDSTONE
f   grés *m*
d   Sandstein *m*

2467   SANITARY WELL PROTECTION
sealing of well to prevent entry of
pathogenic organisms
f   protection *f* sanitaire d'un puits
d   sanitärer Brunnenschutz *m*

2468   SAPROLITE
highly weakened metamorphic rock
f   saprolite *m*
d   Saprolith *m*

2469   SATURATED FLOW
(single phase) flow when all voids
are filled
f   régime *m* d'écoulement saturé
d   gesättigte Strömung *f*

SATURATION, gas see 820
-, irreducible see 1080
-, threshold see 2779

2470   SATURATION DEFICIENCY
f   déficit *m* de saturation
d   Sättigungsdefizit *n*

2471   SATURATION DISTRIBUTION
f   distribution *f* de saturation
d   Sättigungsverteilung *f*

2472   SATURATION POINT
f   point *m* de saturation
d   Sättigungspunkt *m*

2473   SATURATION PRESSURE
f   pression *f* de saturation
d   Sättigungsdruck *m*

2474   SATURATION REGIME
flow regime in completely
saturated porous medium

f   régime *m* de saturation
d   Sättigungsregime *n*

SATURATION VAPOR PRESSURE
see 2883

2475   SCALAR QUANTITY
f   quantité *f* scalaire
d   Skalare *f*; skalare Grösse *f*

2476   SCALE
very thin and flat rock fragment
f   écaille *f*
d   Schuppe *f*

2477   SCALE
accumulation of precipitated solid
material
f   dépôt *m*
d   Ansatz *m*

2478   SCALE
ratio of prototype to model
dimensions
f   échelle *f*
d   Masstab *m*

2479   SCALING FACTOR
ratio of characteristics of model to
those of prototype
f   facteur *m* d'échelle
d   Masstabbeiwert *m*

2480   SCHIST
foliated metamorphic rock
f   schiste *m*
d   Schiefer *m*

SCHIST, mica see 2040

2481   SCHISTOSITY
foliation of metamorphic rock
f   schistosité *f*
d   Schieferung *f*

2482   SCINTILLOMETER
f   scintillomètre *m*
d   Szintallationszähler *m*

2483   SCOUR
erosive action of running water in
streams
f   affouillement *m*
d   Tiefenschurf *m*

2484   SCREEN
f   tamis *m*
d   Sieb *n*

2485 SCREENING PLANT
f installation *f* de tamisage
d Siebanlage *f*

2486 SCREEN PIPE
slotted casing section positioned
opposite the producing horizon to
prevent inflow of sand into well
f crépine *f*
d Siebrohr *n*; Filterrohr *n*

2487 SEA LEVEL
averaged height of the surface of
the sea used as datum for elevations
f niveau *m* de la mer
d Meeresspiegel *m*; Seehöhe *f*

2488 SEALING-GROUT
cement grout injected between casing
and bore hole wall to seal off aquifer
from external contamination
f laitier *m* de ciment
d Abdichtungszementbrühe *f*

2489 SEAMLESS PIPE
f tube *m* sans soudure
d nahtloses Rohr *n*

2490 SEASONAL VARIATION
f variation *f* saisonnière
d jahreszeitliche Schwankung *f*

2491 SEA WATER INTRUSION
encroachment of sea water into a
coastal aquifer
f invasion *m* des eaux salées
d Eindringen *n* von Meerwasser

2492 SECONDARY INTERSTICES
voids formed after rocks had
been formed
f interstices *mpl* secondaires
d sekundäre Hohlräume *mpl*

2493 SECONDARY POROSITY
porosity created after deposition
of sediment due to fracturing,
leaching etc.
f porosité *f* secondaire
d sekundäre Porosität *f*

2494 SEDIMENTARY DEPOSIT
f dépôt *m* sédimentaire
d Sedimentablagerung *f*

2495 SEDIMENTATION
deposition of solid disintegrated
rock material by water, wind or
gravity transport
f sédimentation *f*
d Sedimentation *f*

2496 SEDIMENT TRANSPORT
all transport of eroded rock materia
by moving water or wind
f transports *mpl* solides;
transport *m* de sédiments
d Sedimenttransport *m*;
Sedimentfrachtung *f*

2497 SEEPAGE
slow flow through a filter, small
opening or porous medium; moveme
of water in unsaturated soil
f suintement *m*; écoulement *m* par
infiltration
d Sickerung *f*; Sickerströmung *f*

SEEPAGE, storm see 2690
-, surface see 2722

2498 SEEPAGE COEFFICIENT
f coefficient *m* d'infiltration
d Filterkoeffizient *m*

SEEPAGE LOSS, canal see 233

2499 SEEPAGE PATH
trajectory of fluid particles in
seepage flow
f chemin *m* d'infiltration
d Sickerweg *m*

2500 SEEPAGE RATE
velocity of seepage flow
f vitesse *f* d'infiltration
d Sickerrate *f*; Sickergeschwindigkeit *f*

2501 SEEPAGE SPRING;
FILTRATION SPRING
spring where surface discharge
occurs from numerous small openin
f source *f* de ruissellement;
source *f* d'infiltration
d Sickerquelle *f*; flächenhafter
Grundwasseraustritt *m*

2502 SEEPAGE SURFACE
outflow surface between water level
and intersection of the phreatic sur
with well
f surface *f* de suintement
d Sickerfläche *f*; Sickerstrecke *f*

SEEPAGE VELOCITY
see Darcy velocity

SEGMENT, approach see 96
-, crest see 405
-, recession see 2356
-, rising see 2415

2503   SEISMIC PROFILE
      f   profil *m* sismique; coupe *f*
          sismique
      d   seismisches Profil *n*

2504   SEISMIC REFLECTION
      reflection of a seismic ray on a
      lithologic interface
      f   réflexion *f* sismique
      d   seismische Reflextion *f*

2505   SEISMIC REFRACTION
      refraction of a seismic wave at a
      lithologic interface
      f   réfraction *f* sismique
      d   seismische Refraktion *f*;
          seismische Brechung *f*

2506   SEISMIC WAVE
      wave generated by a seismic
      impulse or explosion
      f   onde *f* sismique
      d   seismische Welle *f*;
          Erschütterungswelle *f*

2507   SEISMOMETER
      detector of seismic waves
      f   sismomètre *m*
      d   Seismometer *n*

2508   SELECTIVE ABSORPTION
      f   absorption *f* sélective
      d   Selektivabsorption *f*;
          selektive Absorption *f*

2509   SELF-CLEANING CAPACITY
      capacity of a river to clean its
      water from pollutants over a given
      length of water course
      f   pouvoir *m* auto-épurateur
      d   Selbstreinigungskraft *f*

2510   SELF-POTENTIAL
      natural electric potential occurring
      in a well
      f   potentiel *m* spontané
      d   Eigenpotential *n*

2511   SENSIBLE HEAT
      f   chaleur *f* sensible
      d   wahrnehmbare Wärme *f*

2512   SEPARATION
      f   séparation *f*
      d   Loslösung *f*; Trennung *f*

      SEPARATION, hydrograph see 970
      -, sand see 2465
      -, water see 2954

2513   SERIES
      subdivision of rock according to
      age at which they were laid down
      in a geologic epoch
      f   série *f* lithologique
      d   Schichtenfolge *f*

2514   SERPENTINE
      metamorphic product of peridotites
      f   serpentine *f*
      d   Serpentin *m*

2515   SETTING OF CEMENT
      process of hardening of cement
      f   prise *f* du ciment
      d   Abbinden *n* des Zements

2516   SETTLING BASIN
      basin used for settling out of solids
      from suspensions
      f   bassin *m* de décantation
      d   Absetzbecken *n*

2517   SETTLING PIT
      f   bac *m* de décantation
      d   Klärbecken *n*

2518   SETTLING VELOCITY
      terminal velocity at which a
      particle will fall through a fluid
      f   vitesse *f* limite de sédimentation;
          vitesse *f* de décantation
      d   Absetzgeschwindigkeit *f*

2519   SEWAGE
      domestic and municipal wastes
      f   eaux *f pl* d'égouts
      d   Abwasser *n*

2520   SEWAGE TREATMENT
      f   traitement *m* des eaux d'égouts;
          épuration *f* des eaux d'égouts
      d   Abwasserreinigung *f*;
          Abwasserbehandlung *f*

2521   SHAFT
      vertical and usually large diameter
      hole penetrating geologic formations
      for access of subsurface points
      f   puits *m*
      d   Schacht *m*

2522   SHAFT
      axis transmitting or receiving
      rotational movement
      f   arbre *m*
      d   Welle *f*

      SHALE, bentonitic see 174

2523 SHALE LINE
line connecting points of zero
potential in a self potential log
f ligne *f* de base des marnes
d Basislinie *f*

2524 SHALLOW WELL
f puits *m* peu profond
d Flachbrunnen *m*

2525 SHALY SAND
sand containing considerable
amounts of clay and shales
f sable *m* argileux
d toniger Sand *m*

SHAPE, basin see 161
-, grain see 863
-, spherical see 2624

2526 SHATTERED FAULT ZONE
f zone *f* de broyage; zone *f*
fracturée d'un système de failles
d Rüschelzone *f*

2527 SHEAR
f cisaillement *m*
d Scherung *f*

2528 SHEAR INTENSITY
f intensité *f* de cisaillement
d Scherintensität *f*

2529 SHEAR STRENGTH
f résistance *f* au cisaillement
d Scherfestigkeit *f*

2530 SHEAR VELOCITY
f vitesse *f* de cisaillement
d Schergeschwindigkeit *f*

2531 SHEAR WAVE
f onde *f* transversale
d Transversalwelle *f*; Scherwelle *f*

2532 SHEAVE
f poulie *f*
d Scheibe *f*

2533 SHEET EROSION
erosion occurring over widespread
tabular sedimentary or effusive rock
f érosion *f* en nappe
d Flächenerosion *f*

2534 SHEET FLOW
shallow flow of extrusive lava over
wide area
f épanchement *m* effusif en couche
d Flächenerguss *m*; Arealeruption *f*

2535 SHIELD
geologically stable and undisturbed
continental block
f bouclier *m*
d Schild *m*

2536 SHOCK POINT
point at which seismic impulse is
applied to system under study
f point *m* de choc
d Schockpunkt *m*

2537 SHOCK WAVE
f onde *f* de choc
d Stosswelle *f*

SHOE, casing see 256
-, guide see 912

2538 SHORE
zone of separation between land and
moving water
f rivage *m*
d Ufer *n*

2539 SHOT DRILLING
method of drilling where shot dropped
into the bore hole through the drill
pipe exercises abrasive action on the
bottom hole
f sondage *m* à la grenaille
d Schrotbohren *n*

2540 SHOT POINT
point where explosive charge is set
off in seismic survey
f point *m* de tir
d Schusspunkt *m*

2541 SIDE WALL
wall of a well
f paroi *f* d'un puits
d Brunnenwandung *f*

2542 SIEVE
f tamis *m*
d Sieb *n*

2543 SIEVE ANALYSIS
mechanical grain size analysis by
sieving
f granulométrie *f* mécanique
d Siebanalyse *f*

2544 SIEVE OPENING
opening between mesh wires of a
sieve
f ouverture *f* de maille
d lichte Maschenweite *f*

2545 SIEVE RETENTION
material retained on a sieve
f retenue *f* au tamis
d Siebrückstand *m*

SILICA, see silicon dioxide

SILICA, amorphous see 66

2546 SILICATE ROCK
rock containing silica in predomi-
nant proportions
f roches *f pl* siliceuses
d Silikatgestein *n*

2547 SILICIC ACID
H_4SiO_4 monomeric
f acide *m* silicique
d Kieselsäure *f*

2548 SILICON BRASS
f laiton *m* siliceux
d Siliziummessing *m*

2549 SILICON BRONZE
f bronze *m* siliceux
d Siliziumbronze *f*

2550 SILICON DIOXIDE
silica, SiO_2
f silice *f*; oxyde *m* de silicium
d Siliziumdioxyd *n*; Kieselerde *f*;
Silikat *n*

2551 SILL
concordant magma intrusion between
sedimentary beds
f filon-couche *m*
d Lagergang *m*

2552 SILL
submarine separation of different
basins
f seuil *m*
d Schwelle *f*

2553 SILT
particle diameter 0.05 to 0.005 mm
(USBS)
f silt *m*
d Schluff *m*

2554 SILTING
deposition of silt, especially in
reservoirs
f envasement *m*
d Anschwemmung *f*; Verschlickung *f*

2555 SILTSTONE
f phtanite *m*
d Tongestein *n*

2556 SILURIAN
geologic period of the Paleozoic era
f Silurien *m*
d Silur *n*

2557 SILVER IODIDE
AgI, chemical substance used as
condensation nuclei in weather
modification experiments
f iodure *m* d'argent
d Silberjodit *m*

SIMILARITY, dynamic see 611
-, geometric see 835
-, kinematic see 1111

2558 SIMILARITY CRITERIA
conditions indicating under what
circumstances a model and prototype
are similar
f conditions *f pl* de similitude
d Ähnlichtkeitsbedingungen *f pl*

2559 SIMPLE HYDROGRAPH
single peaked hydrograph
f hydrogramme *m* simple
d einfache Abflussganglinie *f*

2560 SINGLE OUTLET
stream cutting through divide
(tributary basin); outflow into sea
(major basin)
f exutoire *m* unique
d Auslass *m*

2561 SINK
(mathematical)
f puits *m*
d Senke *f*

2562 SINKER BAR
heavy bar rod above bit in cable
drilling
f tige *f* de battage
d Schwerstange *f*

2563 SINK HOLE
hole in karstic limestone terrane
through which water escapes
underground
f doline *f*
d Doline *f*; Karsttrichter *m*

2564 SIPHON
f siphon *m*
d Siphon *m*; Saugheber *m*

2565 SIPHONING
f siphonnage *m*
d Saughebewirkung *f*

SIZE, grain see 864
-, mesh see 2030

2566 SKIN EFFECT
effect of the zone of reduced
permeability immediately around
the borehole on transient flow
phenomena (in pumping tests)
f effet *m* pariétal
d Hauteffekt *m*

2567 SLAG
congealed lava, scoria
f scorie *f*
d Schlacke *f*; vulkanische
Schlacke *f*

2568 SLATE
metamorphic rock showing well
developed cleavage
f ardoise *f*
d Schiefer *m*; Plattenschiefer *m*

2569 SLEDGE
heavy hammer
f maillet *m*; masse *f*
d Fäustel *m*

2570 SLICKENSIDE
polished fault plane with grooves
due to relative motion of fault
blocks
f miroir *m* de faille
d Rutschspiegel *m*

2571 SLIDING
downslope movement of rock and
earth material
f glissement *m*
d Abgleiten *n*

2572 SLIPS
wedges to hold drill pipe while
adding a new length of pipe in
rotary drilling
f coins *mpl* de retenue
d Fangkeile *mpl*

2573 SLOPE
inclination of a surface
f pente *f*
d Gefälle *n*; Hang *m*

SLOPE, continental see 371
-, ground see 890
-, water surface see 2961

2574 SLOTTED PIPE
f crépine *f* à fentes
d Siebrohr *n*

2575 SLOTTED PLATE
f tôle *f* perforée
d Siebblech *n*

2576 SLUSH BUCKET
bucket shaped bailer
f cuiller *f*
d Sandpumpe *f*; Schmandlöffel *m*

2577 SLUSH PIT
settling pit for drilling mud
f bac *m* de décantation
d Absetzbecken *n*

2578 SNOW
solid crystalline form of water
f neige *f*
d Schnee *m*

2579 SNOW COVER;
SNOWPACK
accumulated height of snow covering
a given area
f couche *f* de neige
d Schneedecke *f*

2580 SNOW DENSITY
f densité *f* de la neige
d Schneedichte *f*

2581 SNOWDRIFT
snow accumulation due to wind
transport
f congère *f*
d Schneewehe *f*

2582 SNOW GAGE
f nivomètre *m*
d Schneeniederschlagsmesser *m*

2583 SNOW LINE
line connecting elevations above
which snowpack remains throughout
the year
f limite *f* des neiges éternelles
d Schneegrenze *f*

2584 SNOW MELT
f fonte *f* de neige
d Schneeschmelze *f*

SNOWPACK, see snow cover

2585 SNOW SAMPLER
tube taking cylindrical samples
through the snow profile
f échantillonneur *m* de neige
d Schneeprobenehmer *m*;
Schneeausstecher *m*

2586 SNOW STAKE
f échelle *f* de neige
d Schneepegel *m*

SOCKET, bell see 171
-, rope see 2436

2587 SOD
root system in the soil
f système *m* de racines
d Wurzelwerk *n*

2588 SODIUM
Na
f sodium *m*
d Natrium *n*

SOIL, azonal see 126
-, halomorphic see 918
-, lateritic see 1137

2589 SOIL AGGREGATE
loosely cemented cluster of soil
particles
f agrégat *m* des particules de sol
d Bodenaggregat *n*

2590 SOILCOVER
layer of soil material covering the
bedrock
f couverture *f* de sol
d Bodendecke *f*; Bodenkrume *f*

2591 SOIL MECHANICS
science dealing with the mechanical
properties of soils
f mécanique *f* des sols
d Bodenmechanik *f*

2592 SOIL-MOISTURE METER
device to record soil moisture in situ
f appareil *m* de mesure de l'humidité
du sol
d Bodenfeuchtemessgerät *n*

2593 SOIL-MOISTURE SUCTION
negative pore pressure exerted by
capillary forces
f succion *f* de l'eau dans le sol
d Saugwirkung *f* des Bodenwassers

2594 SOIL MOISTURE TENSION
negative pore pressure
f tension *f* de l'eau dans le sol
d Bodenfeuchtesaugspannung *f*

2595 SOIL PARTICLE
f particule *f* de sol
d Bodenpartikel *n*; Bodenteilchen

2596 SOIL PROFILE
vertical section of soil mantle
usually with distinguishable soil
horizons (A,B,C)
f section *f* du sol
d Bodenprofil *n*

SOIL PROFILE, zonal see 3032

2597 SOIL SAMPLE
sample of soil on which soil
properties are to be determined
f échantillon *m* de sol
d Bodenprobe *f*

2598 SOIL STRUCTURE
f structure *f* du sol
d Bodenstruktur *f*

2599 SOIL SURFACE
f surface *f* du sol
d Bodenoberfläche *f*

2600 SOIL SWELLING
volume increase of soil due to
swelling of unsaturated clay
particles when in contact with water
f gonflement *m* du sol
d Bodenquellung *f*

2601 SOIL WATER
gravity and pellicular water
contained in the soil zone
f eau *f* du sol
d Bodenfeuchte *f*; Bodenwasser *n*

2602 SOILWATER ZONE
upper portion of the zone of aeration
containing soil water; belt of soil
water
f zone *f* d'évaporation; zone *f*
au voisinage du sol
d bodennahe Zone *f*; Bodenwassergürtel *m*

2603 SOLAR RADIATION
f irradiation *f* solaire
d Sonnenstrahlung *f*

2604 SOLID MATRIX
assembly of interconnected solid
mineral grains surrounded by voids
f phase *f* solide
d Festkörpergerüst *n*

2605 SOLID VOLUME
volume of the solid particles in a
porous sample
f volume *m* de la phase solide;
volume *m* des pleins
d Festkörpervolumen *n*

2606 SOLIFLUCTION
slow flowage of mud streams in
arctic regions
f solifluction *f*
d Solifluktion *f*

2607 SOLUBILITY
f solubilité *f*
d Löslichkeit *f*

2608 SOLUM
top layers of soil profile
f sol *m* arrable
d Ackerkrume *f*

SOLUTION, analog see 71
-, buffered see 208
-, numerical see 2118

SONDE, monoelectrode see 2072

2609 SONDE SPACING
distance between measuring and
current electrodes
f espacement *m* de la sonde
d Messlänge *f* einer Anordnung

2610 SONIC GENERATOR
f générateur *m* de son
d Schallerzeuger *m*

2611 SOUND VELOCITY
f vitesse *f* du son
d Schallgeschwindigkeit *f*

2612 SOURCE
(mathematical)
f source *f*
d Quellpunkt *m*

SOURCE, neutron see 2109

2613 SOURCE CHAMBER
f chambre *f* de captage
d Quellstube *f*

SPACE, pore see 2269
-, total pore see 2808
-, vugular pore see 2910

SPACING, electrode see 636
-, sonde see 2609
-, well see 3001

2614 SPECIFIC CAPACITY
ratio of well discharge to
corresponding drawdown
f débit *m* spécifique
d Brunnenergiebigkeitsmass *n*;
  spezifische Ergiebigkeit *f*

2615 SPECIFIC DENSITY
f densité *f*
d Dichte *f*

SPECIFIC DISCHARGE
see Darcy velocity

2616 SPECIFIC DRAWDOWN
amount of drawdown per unit
discharge in a well
f rabattement *m* spécifique
d spezifische Absenkung *f*

2617 SPECIFIC ELECTRICAL
CONDUCTANCE
conductance of a cube of solution
(1 cm^3)
f conductivité
d spezifische Leitfähigkeit *f*

2618 SPECIFIC GRAVITY
f poids *m* spécifique
d spezifisches Gewicht *n*

2619 SPECIFIC RETENTION;
WATER RETAINING CAPACITY
water held against gravity forces
f eau *f* de rétention; capacité *f*
  de rétention; pouvoir *m* de
  rétention d'eau
d spezifisches Wasserhaltungsvermögen *n*; Wasserrückhaltevermögen *n*

2620 SPECIFIC SURFACE
ratio of grain particle surface to
volume of grain particles
f surface *f* spécifique
d spezifische Oberfläche *f*

2621 SPECIFIC VOLUME
f volume *m* spécifique
d spezifisches Volumen *n*

2622 SPECIFIC YIELD
water drained from soil under
gravity flow
f débit *m* spécifique; eau *f* de
  gravité; capacité *f* de libre
  écoulement
d spezifische Ergiebigkeit *f*

2623 SPELEOLOGY
exploration and study of undergroun
caverns
f spéléologie *f*
d Höhlenkunde *f*

2624 SPHERICAL SHAPE
f forme *f* sphérique
d kugelförmige Gestalt *f*

2625 SPILLWAY
device for the escape of excess
water
f déversoir *m*
d Überfallwehr *n*; Wehr *n*

2626 SPONTANEOUS POTENTIAL
natural electrical potential
measured in well; self-potential
f potentiel *m* spontané
d Eigenpotential *n*

2627 SPRING
localized natural hydraulic discharge
of water at surface resulting in a
small rivulet
f source *f*
d Quelle *f*

SPRING, artesian see 114
-, barrier see 144
-, boundary see 197
-, carbonated see 247
-, channel see 280
-, contact see 368
-, cool see 385
-, depression see 468
-, dimple see 507
-, filtration see 2501
-, fracture see 783
-, gravity see 885
-, intermittant see 1062
-, medicinal see 2017
-, mineral see 2048
-, perennial see 2195
-, saline see 2451
-, seepage see 2501
-, subaqueous see 2681
-, thermal see 2769
-, tubular see 2849
-, unconformity see 2861
-, valley see 2880
-, warm see 2914

2628 SPRING, TO
action of water originating or
rising from a spring
f jaillir
d entspringen; hervorquellen

2629 SPUDDER
f installation *f* de forage pour
l'avant-trou
d Vorbohrer *m*

2630 STAFF GAGE
fixed graduated scale
f échelle *f* limnimétrique
d Messlatte *f*; Lattenpegel *m*

2631 STAGE
water surface elevation at a point
(along stream, in lake, etc.) above
an arbitrary datum
f hauteur *f* d'eau
d Wasserstand *m*; Höhe *f* des
Wasserspiegels

STAGE, water see 2958

2632 STAGE-DISCHARGE RELATION
see rating curve
f courbe *f* de tarage
d Bezugskurve *f*; Abflusskurve *f*

2633 STAGE HYDROGRAPH
elevation of stage plotted against
time
f relation *f* hauteur – temps
d Wasserstandsganglinie *f*

2634 STAGE INDICATOR
f indicateur *m* limnimétrique
d Standanzeiger *m*; Wasserstandsanzeiger *m*

2635 STAGE RECORD
stage discharge relations presented
in tabulated form
f tableau *m* des hauteurs
d Abflusstafel *f*

2636 STAGNATION POINT
foremost point on streamline
dividing area of pumping depression
from zone of influence in a tilted
aquifer being pumped by one well
f point *m* de stagnation
d untere Scheitelung *f*;
Kulminationspunkt *m*

2637 STAINLESS STEEL
f acier *m* inoxydable
d rostfreier Stahl *m*

2638 STALACTITE
dripstone hanging from cavern roof
f stalactite *m*
d Stalaktit *m*

2639 STALAGMITE
dripstone column rising from cavern
floor
f stalagmite *m*
d Stalagmit *m*

STANDARD COEFFICIENT OF
PERMEABILITY
see laboratory coefficient

2640 STANDARD DEVIATION
measure of variability of square
of individual deviations from
their mean
f écart-type *m*
d Standardabweichung *f*

2641 STANDARD TOOL
percussion, cable tool in cable
drilling
f installation *f* de forage
standard
d Standardbohrgerät *n*

2642 STATE OF SOLUTION
degree to which a mineral or rock
has gone into solution
f degré *m* de dissolution
d Lösungszustand *m*

STATION, gaging see 808
-, hydrometric see 980
-, pumping see 2307

2643 STATISTICAL ANALYSIS
f analyse *f* statistique
d statistische Analyse *f*

2644 STEADY FLOW
flow where velocity at a point
remains constant with respect to
time
f écoulement *m* permanent
d stetige Strömung *f*

2645 STEEP
property of inclination with very
great gradient
f à pente raide; abrupt
d steil

2646 STEMFLOW
rain water flowing down stem
of plants
f ruissellement *m* le long du tronc
d Stammabfluss *m*

2647 STEREOGRAM
block diagram, three dimensional
diagram
f diagramme *m* stéréoscopique
d Blockbild *n*

2648 STILLING WELL
well connected to a flowing stream
through a bottom conduit permitting
elevation measures to be taken in
quiescent water
f puits *m* de mesure
d Beruhigungsschacht *m*

2649 STOMATAL TRANSPIRATION
transpiration by escape of water
through pores (stomata) of leaves
f transpiration *f* par stomata
d stomatäre Transpiration *f*

STORAGE, aquifer see 101
-, bank see 138
-, pocket see 2253
-, prism see 2296
-, wedge see 2976

2650 STORAGE CAPACITY
a) ability of an aquifer to store
water;
b) capacity of rivers to store water
in their own channel
f capacité *f* d'emmagasinement
d Speicherfähigkeit *f*; Wasseraufnahmefähigkeit *f*; Speichervermögen *n*; Rückhaltevermögen

2651 STORAGE COEFFICIENT
volume of water stored or released
from a column of aquifer with unit
cross section under unit pressure
decline
f coefficient *m* d'emmagasinement;
storativité *f*; coefficient *m* de
stockage
d Speicherkoeffizient *m*;
Speicherungsbeiwert *m*

2652 STORAGE GAGE
precipitation gage collecting and
storing total amount of inflowing
water to be read at long intervals
f pluviomètre *m* totalisateur
d Niederschlagssammler *m*;
Totalisator *m*

2653 STORAGE IN DEPRESSIONS
water retention in surface depressio
f stockage *m* dans les dépressions
du sol
d Wasserspeicherung *f* in Senken

2654 STORM
a) disturbance of average meteoro-
logical conditions usually connec
with precipitation
b) period of precipitation over a
specific drainage basin
f averse *f*; grain *m*; orage *m*; tem
d Niederschlagsfall *m*, Regenfall *m*
Schauer *m*; Gewitter *n*; Sturm *m*

STORM, design see 481

2655 STORM INTENSITY PATTERN
      f hyétogramme *m*
      d Verteilung *f* der Niederschlags-
         intensität

      STORM RUNOFF, see direct
      runoff

      STORM SEEPAGE, see subsurface
      runoff

2656 STOVE PIPE
      double wall casing, as introduced
      by California stove pipe drilling
      method
      f tubage *m* double
      d Doppelverrohrung *f*

      STRAINER, micro see 2043
      -, suction see 2699

2657 STRATH TERRACE
      erosional remnant of elevated
      broad river valley
      f terrasse *f* du replat de versant
      d Erosionsterrasse *f* im
         Vorrumpf

2658 STRATIFICATION
      depositional structure of sedi-
      mentary rocks in beds and layers
      f stratification *f*
      d Schichtung *f*

      STRATIFICATION, salinity see
      2454
      -, thermal see 2770

2659 STRATIGRAPHY
      study of stratified rock
      f stratigraphie *f*
      d Stratigraphie *f*

2660 STRATUM
      sedimentary bed or layer
      f couche *f*; lit *m*
      d Schicht *f*

      STRATUM, confining see 350

2661 STRAY CURRENTS
      random electrical currents
      originating from leaks in electrical
      circuits
      f courants *mpl* vagabonds
      d Streuströme *fpl*

2662 STREAM
      a body of flowing water

      f fleuve *m*; rivière *f*
      d Strom *m*; Fluss *m*

      STREAM, adjusted see 26
      -, antecedent see 90
      -, continuous see 372
      -, effluent see 628
      -, ephemeral see 659
      -, gaining see 628
      -, influent see 1032
      -, insulated see 1045
      -, intermittent see 1063
      -, interrupted see 1066
      -, losing see 1032
      -, natural see 2102
      -, subterranean see 2692

      STREAMS, perennial see 2196

2663 STREAM BED
      bottom of stream covered by water
      f lit *m* d'une rivière
      d Flussbett *n*

2664 STREAM CHANNEL
      f chenal *m*
      d Rinne *f*; Flusslauf *m*

2665 STREAM DEVELOPMENT
      ratio of actual tortuous stream
      length between two points on straight
      line connecting these points
      f développement *m* du cours
      d Stromentwicklung *f*

2666 STREAM FLOW
      total runoff confined in stream and
      channels
      f écoulement *m* total
      d Gesamtabfluss *m*

2667 STREAM FREQUENCY
      channel frequency, number of stream
      segments per unit area
      f fréquence *f* des éléments du réseau
      d Flussstreckenhäufigkeit *f*

2668 STREAMING POTENTIAL
      electrical potential difference
      created by flow through a porous
      medium
      f potentiel *m* électrocinétique
      d Strömungspotential *n*

2669 STREAMLINE
      line to which flow velocity vectors
      are tangent
      f ligne *f* de courant
      d Stromlinie *f*

2670 STREAM ORDER
hierarchic order of stream segments
according to tributaires
f numéro *m* d'ordre d'un cours
d'eau
d Ordnungsstufe *f* eines Flusses

2671 STREAM PROFILE
elevation of main stream bed as a
function of distance from outflow
f profil *m* en long d'une rivière
d Flussprofil *n*; hydrologischer
Längsschnitt *m*

2672 STREAMTUBE
imaginary tube of fluid bounded by
streamlines
f filet *m* fluide
d Stromfaden *m*

STRENGTH, breaking see 200
-, compressive see 335
-, sheer see 2529
-, tensile see 2757

STRESS, intergranular see 1061

2673 STRESS LIMIT
f tension *f* limite
d Grenzbelastung *f*

2674 STRIKE
direction of the line of intersection
of a bed or other structural
feature with the horizontal
f direction *f*
d Streichen *n*

2675 STRIKE VALLEY
valley following strike of underlying strata
f vallée *f* subséquente
d Nachfolgetal *n*; subsequentes
Tal *n*

2676 STRINGER
irregular vein cutting through a
rock mass
f filet *m* irrégulier
d unregelmässiger Gang *m*;
Erzschnur *f*

2677 STRUCTURAL DOME
f dôme *m* de structure
d Strukturdom *m*

2678 STRUCTURAL FACTOR
features modifying or interrupting
continuity of rock types
f facteur *m* de structure
d Strukturfaktor *m*

2679 STRUCTURAL GEOLOGY
part of geology dealing with the
structures of rock
f géologie *f* structurale;
tectonique *f*
d Strukturgeologie *f*; tektonische
Geologie *f*

STRUCTURE, chaotic see 281
-, massive see 1194
-, soil see 2598

2680 STUFFING BOX
f presse - étoupe *m*
d Stopfbüchse *f*

2681 SUBAQUEOUS SPRING
springs discharging below surfaces
of water bodies such as oceans,
lakes and rivers
f exutoire *m* subaquatique
d subaquatische Quelle *f*;
Grundquelle *f*

2682 SUBARTESIAN WELL
artesian well (cf.) with insufficient
head to raise water above land
surface
f puits *m* artésien sans écoulemen
libre
d subartesischer Brunnen *m*

2683 SUBLIMATION
direct conversion of water from its
solid state to the vapor phase
f sublimation *f*
d Sublimation *f*

2684 SUBMERSIBLE PUMP
f pompe *f* immergée; pompe *f*
submersible
d Tauchpumpe *f*; Unterwasserpumpe *f*

2685 SUBPERMAFROST WATER
groundwater below the permafrost
f eau *f* sous la zone de pergelisol
d Grundwasser *n* unter der Gefror

2686 SUBSEQUENT RIVER
river flowing along strike of a weak
formation; tributary of a consequen
river
f rivière *f* subséquente
d Nachfolgefluss *m*; subsequenter
Fluss *m*

2687 SUBSIDING WATER
f eau *f* en décrue
d fallendes Wasser *n*

2688 SUBSOIL
      f sous-sol *m*
      d Untergrund *m*

2689 SUBSURFACE FLOW
      see subsurface runoff
      f écoulement *m* souterrain
      d unterirdischer Abfluss *m*

2690 SUBSURFACE RUNOFF;
      STORM SEEPAGE; SUBSURFACE
      FLOW; SUBSURFACE STORM
      FLOW
      runoff due to infiltrated precipitation
      moving laterally under surface
      f écoulement *m* hypodermique
      d unechter Grundwasserabfluss *m*

2691 SUBTERRANEAN
      beneath the surface of the earth
      f souterrain
      d unterirdisch

2692 SUBTERRANEAN STREAM
      stream flowing through very large
      caves and caverns underground
      f fleuve *m* souterrain
      d unterirdischer Fluss *m*

2693 SUCCESSION OF FORMATIONS
      f succession *f* stratigraphique;
         suite *f* de couches
      d Schichtenfolge *f*

      SUCTION, soil-moisture see 2593

2694 SUCTION HEAD
      f hauteur *f* d'aspiration
      d Saughöhe *f*

2695 SUCTION LIFT
      height to which a pump can aspire
      a liquid
      f hauteur *f* d'aspiration
      d Saughöhe *f*

2696 SUCTION LIMIT
      f limite *f* de succion
      d Grenzsaugfähigkeit *f*

2697 SUCTION LINE
      tubular connection line through
      which liquid is aspired into pump
      f tuyau *m* d'aspiration
      d Saugleitung *f*

2698 SUCTION PUMP
      f pompe *f* aspirante
      d Saugpumpe *f*

2699 SUCTION STRAINER
      f crépine *f* filtrante
      d Filterkorb *m*

2700 SULFATE
      SO_4
      f sulfate *m*
      d Sulfat *n*

2701 SULFURIC ACID
      H_2SO_4
      f acide *m* sulfurique
      d Schwefelsäure *f*

2702 SUMMATION CURVE
      curve of cumulated values
      f courbe *f* cumulative
      d Summenkurve *f*

2703 SUMMIT
      highest point of a physiographic
      feature
      f sommet *m*
      d Gipfel *m*

2704 SUMP
      pumping pit from where pump lifts
      water by suction
      f puisard *m*
      d Pumpensumpf *m*; Sumpf *m*

2705 SUNKEN PAN
      evaporation pan buried in the ground
      for equal elevation of water surface
      and ground surface
      f bac *m* enterré
      d versenkter Landverdunstungskessel *m*

2706 SUPERIMPOSED VALLEY
      valley established on surface in
      pattern independent of underlying
      rock structure
      f vallée *f* surimposée; percée *f*
         épigénétique
      d aufgesetztes Tal *n*; epigenetisches
         Tal *n*

2707 SUPERPOSITION
      f superposition *f*
      d Superposition *f*

2708 SUPERSATURATION
      f supersaturation *f*; saturation *f*
         excédentaire; sursaturation *f*
      d Übersättigung *f*

      SUPPLY, surface water see 2726
      -, water see 2960

2709 SUPPLY SYSTEM
 f réseau *m* d'alimentation
 d Versorgungsnetz *n*

2710 SUPRAPERMAFROST WATER
 ground water above permafrost
 f eau *f* au dessus de la zone de
  pergelisol
 d Grundwasser *n* über der Gefrornis

2711 SURF
 f déferlement *m*
 d Brandung *f*

 SURFACE, erosion see 670
 -, land see 1127
 -, phreatic see 2219
 -, piezometric see 2232
 -, receiving see 2350
 -, seepage see 2502
 -, soil see 2599
 -, specific see 2620

2712 SURFACE AREA REDUCTION
 f réduction *f* de la superficie
 d Oberflächenverkleinerung *f*

2713 SURFACE CASING
 part of well casing extending above
 land surface; standpipe
 f colonne *f* de surface
 d Standrohr *n*

2714 SURFACE DETENTION
 sheet flow of water in overland
 flow before channel is reached
 f stockage *m* de surface;
  rétention *f* provisoire
 d Oberflächenrückhaltung *f*;
  Oberflächenspeicherung *f*

2715 SURFACE ENTRY
 opening immediately at land
 surface permitting infiltration to
 take place
 f entrée *m* de surface
 d Eindringöffnung *f*

2716 SURFACE EQUIPMENT
 f appareillage *m* de surface
 d Übertageausrüstung *f*

2717 SURFACE FILM
 (monomolecular) film of organic
 compounds forming on water or
 grain surface
 f film *m* de surface; pellicule *f*
  de surface
 d Oberflächenfilm *m*

2718 SURFACE MAPPING
 topographic and geodetic mapping
 of an area (as opposed to geologic
 mapping)
 f levée *f* topographique
 d topographische Kartierung *f*

2719 SURFACE MINE
 strip mine
 f exploitation *f* minière à ciel
  ouvert
 d Tagebau *m*

2720 SURFACE RETENTION
 water held on land surface
 f rétention *f* dans les dépressions
  du sol
 d Oberflächenrückhaltung *f*;
  Wasserspeicherung *f* an der
  Bodenoberfläche

2721 SURFACE RUNOFF
 part of runoff travelling over groun
 surface and through channels
 f ruissellement *m* de surface
 d Oberflächenabfluss *m*

2722 SURFACE SEEPAGE
 surface discharge of ground water
 not important enough to form
 rivulet
 f suintement *m* de surface
 d Flächensickerung *f*; flächenhaft
  Wasseraustritt *m*

2723 SURFACE SPREADING
 method of artificial recharge of
 water by spreading on surface
 f épandage *m* en surface
 d Flächenberieselung *f*

2724 SURFACE TENSION
 free specific surface energy
 occurring at the interface between
 a liquid and its own vapor phase
 f tension *f* superficielle
 d Oberflächenspannung *f*

2725 SURFACE WATER
 water obtained from surface
 supplies
 f eau *f* de surface
 d Oberflächenwasser *n*

2726 SURFACE WATER SUPPLY
 f alimentation *f* en eau de surfac
 d Oberflächenwasservorräte *mpl*

2727 SURGING
 rapid upward and downward moven
 of a plunger in a well (developmen
 method)

f   décolmatage *m* d'un puits
d   Stöpseln *n* eines Brunnens

2728   SURVEY
f   levé *m*
d   Vermessung *f*

SURVEY, dipmeter see 511
-, field see 718
-, magnetic see 1179
-, resistivity see 2401

2729   SURVEYING
f   arpentage *m*
d   Vermessung *f*; Landvermessung *f*

2730   SUSPENDED LOAD
sedimentary matter transported
in suspension by a moving stream
f   charge *f* en suspension
d   Schwebefrachtung *f*;
     Schwebstoffbelastung *f*

2731   SUSPENDED MATTER
solid matter small enough to be held
in suspension by moving or stagnant
water
f   matière *f* en suspension
d   Schwebstoff *m*

SUSPENDED SUBSURFACE WATER
see vadose water

2732   SUSPENDED WATER
water in zone of aeration kept in
suspension by capillary forces
f   eau *f* de suspension
d   Wasser *n* in der luftbeeinflussten
     Zone; schwebendes Wasser *n*

2733   SUSTAINED YIELD
rate at which water can be with-
drawn from an aquifer without
depleting the supply
f   débit *m* permanent
d   Dauerspende *f*

2734   SWALE
marshy depression or depression in
groundmoraine
f   mare *f*
d   Grundmoränetümpel *m*

2735   SWELLING
volume increase due to intake and
absorption of water (especially
clays)
f   gonflement *m*
d   Quellen *n*; Anschwellen *n*

SWELLING, soil see 2600

2736   SWELLING RATE
time rate of volume increase
f   vitesse *f* de gonflement
d   Anschwellrate *f*

2737   SWIVEL
rotating head of drillstem through
which the drilling fluid is injected
f   tête *f* d'injection
d   Bohrkopf *m*

2738   SYENITE
igneous rock with no quartz
content
f   syénite *f*
d   Syenit *m*

2739   SYNCLINAL VALLEY
valley following the axis of a
syncline
f   vallée *f* synclinale
d   Muldental *n*

2740   SYNCLINE
downfolded stratum
f   synclinal *m*
d   Mulde *f*

2741   SYNOPTIC NETWORK
network of first order stations
permitting the regular observation
of weather for all points at the
same time
f   réseau *m* synoptique
d   synoptisches Beobachtungsnetz *n*

2742   SYNTHETIC UNIT HYDROGRAPH
unit hydrograph constructed by
assuming reaction of a drainage
basin based on its physical
characteristics
f   hydrogramme *m* unitaire synthétique
d   synthetische Einheitskurve *f*
     der Abflussganglinie; theoretischer
     Einheitshydrograph *m*

SYSTEM, drainage see 558
-, open see 2132
-, river see 2423
-, rock see 2430
-, supply see 2709
-, well point see 2998

T

TABLE, permafrost see 2201
-, rotating see 2439
-, water see 2962

2743 TABLE MOUNTAIN
flat topped mountain; mesa
f montagne f tabulaire
d Tafelberg m

2744 TAILWATER
lower course of a river with
respect to a given point or structure
f cours m inférieur; eau f d'aval
d Unterlauf m; Unterwasser n

2745 TALC
soft silica rock containing
magnesium
f talc m
d Talk m

2746 TALUS CONE
conelike collecyion of disintegrated
rock material originating from and
adjacent to a steeper slope
f cône m de déjection
d Schuttkegel m

2747 TALUS FAN
f cône m d'alluvions
d Schuttfächer m

TANK, air separating see 46
-, gage see 805
-, holding see 939

2748 TAPE GAGE
f ruban m de mesure; décamètre m
en ruban
d Messband n; Bandmasspegel m

2749 TAPPING WELL
well completed at top of aquifer (no
penetration)
f puits m imparfait effleurant la
nappe
d unvollkommener Brunnen m
(nur bis zur Grundwasserdeck-
fläche vordringend)

2750 TECTONIC
pertaining to structural features
due to the deformation of the crust
f tectonique
d tektonisch

2751 TECTONIC VALLEY
valley formed by tectonic forces
f vallée f structurale
d tektonisches Tal n

2752 TELEMETERING
method of transmitting measurements
from point of measure to a distant
reading or recording device
f télémesure f
d Fernmessung f

TEMPERATURE, formation see 779

2753 TEMPERATURE EFFICIENCY
efficiency factor defined by
Thornthwaite for different climates
f efficacité f de température
d Temperaturwirksamkeit f

2754 TEMPERATURE LOG
recording of curve of groundwater
temperature in a well
f diagraphie f de température
d Temperaturlog n

2755 TEMPORARY CASING
f tubage m temporaire
d vorläufige Verrohrung f

2756 TEMPORARY HARDNESS
carbonate hardners
f dureté f temporaire; dureté f
carbonatée
d vorübergehende Härte f;
temporäre Härte f

TENSION, interfacial see 1059
-, soil moisture see 2594
-, surface see 2724

2757 TENSILE STRENGTH
f résistance f à la traction
d Zugfestigkeit f

TENSOR, permeability see 2207

2758 TENSOR QUANTITY
f quantité f tensorielle
d Tensorgrösse f

TERMINAL, ground see 891

2759 TERMINAL MORAINE
glacial deposit accumulated in front
of glacier

f   moraine *f* frontale
d   Endmoräne *f*

2760   TERRACE
flat surface bounded by steplike
steep slopes
f   terrasse *f*
d   Terrasse *f*; Absatz *m*

TERRACE, fill see 722
-, river see 2424
-, rock see 2431
-, strath see 2657

2761   TERRANE
area with some specific characteristics (e.g. limestone terrane)
f   terrain *m*
d   Gelände *n*

2762   TERTIARY
geologic period of the Cenozoic era
f   Ère *f* Tertiaire
d   Tertiär *n*

TEST, field see 719
-, infiltrometer see 1030
-, model see 2061
-, pumping see 2308

2763   TEST HOLE
hole to test depth of ground water,
water quality or geological
conditions; exploratory drillhole
f   puits *m* d'essai; sondage *m* d'essai
d   Versuchsbohrung *f*;
Untersuchungsbohrung *f*;
Testbohrung *f*

2764   TEST PIT
f   fouille *f* de recherche
d   Schürfloch *n*

TEXTURE, rock see 2432

2765   TEXTURE OF SOIL
f   texture *f* de sol
d   Bodentextur *f*

2766   THALWEG
line of maximum depth of stream
cross section
f   thalweg *m*; talweg *m*
d   Talweg *m*

2767   THEIS EQUATION
nonequilibrium equation of radial
flow towards well
f   équation *f* de Theis
d   Theis'sche Brunnengleichung *f*

2768   THERMAL CONDUCTIVITY
f   conductibilité *f* thermique
d   Wärmeleitfähigkeit *f*

2769   THERMAL SPRING
spring with temperature of spring
water above average temperature
of superficial rock
f   source *f* thermale
d   Thermalquelle *f*

2770   THERMAL STRATIFICATION
stratification of water in reservoirs
due to thermal-density differences
f   stratification *f* thermique
d   Wärmeschichtung *f*;
Temperaturschichtung *f*

2771   THERMOCLINE
intermediate layer in stratified water
f   thermocline *m*
d   Sprungschicht *f*

2772   THERMOCOUPLE
temperature measuring device
based on proportionality between
thermoelectric current and temperature
difference between thermojunctions
f   thermocouple *m*
d   Thermoelement *n*

2773   THERMOMETER
f   thermomètre *m*
d   Thermometer *n*

THERMOMETER, resistance see
2396

2774   THICKNESS
width of a bed
f   épaisseur *f*; puissance *f* d'une
couche
d   Mächtigkeit *f*; Schichtmächtigkeit

2775   THIEF ZONE
zone through which drilling fluid is
lost into formation through borehole
wall
f   zone *f* de perte de boue
d   Verlustzone *f*; Diebszone *f*

2776   THIEM EQUATION
equation describing steady state
equilibrium radial flow into well
f   formule *f* de Thiem
d   Thiem'sche Brunnenformel *f*

2777   THIXOTROPY
property of a gel to become fluid
under application of shear stresses

f thixotropie *f*
d Thixotropie *f*

2778 THREADED JOINT
f joint *m* fileté
d Gewindeverbinder *m*

2779 THRESHOLD SATURATION
saturation below which no flow
occurs
f saturation *f* de seuil
d Schwellensättigungswert *m*

2780 THROTTLE VALVE
f clapet *m* étrangleur
d Drosselventil *n*

2781 THROUGHFALL
part of precipitation that reaches
ground by falling through vegetative
cover
f pluie *f* tombant directement sur
le sol (à travers le feuillage)
d Tropfendurchfall *m*

2782 THROW
vertical displacement of stratum
along a fault plane
f rejet *m* vertical
d seigere Sprunghöhe *f*

2783 TIDAL CURRENT
current produced by tidal action
f courant *m* de marée
d Gezeitenstrom *m*

2784 TIDAL EFFICIENCY
ratio of piezometric level amplitude
to tidal amplitude
f coefficient *m* de fluctuation par
marées
d Gezeitenwirkungsgrad *m*

2785 TIDAL FLUCTUATION
fluctuation of water level due to
tidal motion
f fluctuation *f* dûe aux marées
d Gezeitenschwankung *f*

2786 TIDAL RIVER
river strongly influenced and
subject to tidal currents
f rivière *f* à marées
d Tidefluss *m*

2787 TIGHTEST PACKING
arrangement of particles
allowing only minimum void space
in unit cell of sample
f arrangement *m* le plus compact;
empilement *m* le plus serré
d dichteste Packung *f*

TILE, drain see 559

2788 TILE PIPE
f tuyeau *m* en terre cuite
d Dränagerohr *n*; Tonrohr *n*

2789 TILL
glacial deposit
f argile *m* à blocaux; depôt *m*
glacial
d Geschiebemergel *m*

TILL, glacial see 849
-, lodgement see 1162

2790 TILTED AQUIFER
dipping aquifer, inclined aquifer
f nappe *f* aquifère inclinée
d einfallender Grundwasserleiter *m*

TIME, arrival see 112
-, lag see 1119
-, transit see 2821
-, travel see 2821

2791 TIME BASE
sum of storm duration time and
concentration time in hydrograph
f temps *m* de base
d Basiszeit *f*

2792 TIME-DRAWDOWN CURVE
plot of drawdown variation with time
f courbe *f* rabattement-temps
d Absenkungsganglinie *f*

2793 TIME LAG
time elapsed between the onset of a
certain event and the reaction to this
event
f retard *m*
d Verzögerung *f*; Verspätung *f*

2794 TIME OF CONCENTRATION
time required for surface runoff
produced in farthest part of basin
to reach concentration point under
consideration
f temps *m* de concentration
d Konzentrationszeit *f*

2795 TIME OF RISE
time between first arrival of runoff
and arrival of the peak flow
f temps *m* de montée
d Steigdauer *f*

2796 TIMER
time indicator
f minuterie *f*
d Zeitzähler *m*

2797 TIPPING BUCKET
revolving measuring reservoirs
in a recording rain gage
f auget *m* basculeur
d Wippe *f*; Hornersche Wippe *f*

TOOL, cable see 220
-, fishing see 731
- standard see 2641

2798 TOOL BODY
main body of a drilling tool on
which cutting edges are mounted
f matrice *f* d'outil
d Meisselkörper *m*

2799 TOOL JOINT
drill pipe connection
f joint *m* de tige
d Gestängeverbinder *m*

2800 TOPOGRAPHIC DIVIDE
crest line dividing one drainage
basin from another
f ligne *f* de partage topographique
d topographische Wasserscheide *f*

2801 TOPOGRAPHY
physical features of a geographical
area
f topographie *f*
d Topographie *f*; Lagebeschreibung *f*

2802 TOPSOIL
topmost portion of soil profile
f couverture *f* de sol
d Mutterboden *m*

2803 TORSION
f torsion *f*
d Torsion *f*; Verdrehung *f*;
Verdrillung *f*

2804 TORSION BALANCE
f balance *f* de torsion
d Torsionswaage *f*; Drehwaage *f*

2805 TORTUOSITY
ratio of actual length of pore
channel to over all length of sample;
sinuosity of actual flow path in
porous medium
f tortuosité *f*
d Tortuosität *f*

2806 TOTAL CAPACITY
maximum rate of yield of a well
f débit *m* maximum
d maximale Schüttung *f*

2807 TOTAL HARDNESS
sum of permanent and temporary
hardness
f dureté *f* totale
d Gesamthärte *f*

2808 TOTAL PORE SPACE
sum of interconnected and non-
interconnected pore space
f volume *m* total des pores
d Gesamtporenvolumen *n*;
Gesamtporenraum *m*

2809 TOTAL POROSITY
see absolute porosity
f porosité *f* totale
d totale Porosität *f*

2810 TOTAL RUNOFF
sum of all components of runoff
into a stream
f écoulement *m* total
d Gesamtabfluss *m*

2811 TOURMALINE
borosilicate mineral
f tourmaline *f*
d Turmalin *m*

TRACE, pen see 2189

2812 TRACE CONSTITUENTS
f constituant *m* en trace
d Spurenelement *n*; Spurenbestandteil *n*

2813 TRACE ELEMENT
f élément *m* en trace
d Spurenelement *n*

2814 TRACER
substance introduced into a flow
system at a very low concentration
for the observation of velocity
patterns
f traceur *m*
d Indikator *m*

TRACER, radioactive see 2323

2815 TRACER FLOW METHOD
method of determining flow
velocities and directions by intro-
ducing tracers or indicators into
ground water stream
f méthode *f* des traceurs
d Tracerverfahren *n*;
Immissionsverfahren *n*

TRACTION LOAD, see bed load

2816 TRANQUIL FLOW
open channel flow with Froude
number smaller than unity
f écoulement *m* tranquille
d ruhige Strömung *f*

2817 TRANSDUCER
f transducteur *m*
d Geber *m*

TRANSFER, energy see 653
-, heat see 928
-, mass see 1195

2818 TRANSGRESSION
spreading of the sea over level
areas
f transgression *f*
d Transgression *f*

2819 TRANSITION
f transition *f*
d Übergang *m*

2820 TRANSITION ZONE
zone in which properties of two
adjacent units change gradually
f zone *f* de transition
d Übergangszone *f*

**2821 TRANSIT TIME;
TRAVEL TIME**
travel time of a sonic impulse
through a given length of rock
f temps *m* de propagation;
temps *m* de parcours; durée *f* de
parcours
d Laufzeit *f*

2822 TRANSMISSION
f transmission *f*
d Durchleitung *f*; Weiterleitung *f*

2823 TRANSMISSION CAPACITY
property of porous medium to
conduct fluid
f capacité *f* de transmission
d Leitvermögen *n*

**2824 TRANSMISSIVITY;
COEFFICIENT OF TRANS-
MISSIBILITY**
product of coefficient of
permeability and thickness of
aquifer
f transmissivité *f*
d Einheitsergiebigkeit *f*

2825 TRANSPIRATION
evaporation of water absorbed by
plants
f transpiration *f*
d Transpiration *f*; Pflanzenverdunstung *f*

TRANSPIRATION, cuticular see 430
-, stomatal see 2649

2826 TRANSPIRATION DEPTH
depth of water consumed annually
by plants
f hauteur *f* de transpiration
d Transpirationshöhe *f*

2827 TRANSPIRATION RATIO
ratio of water weight transpired to
weight of dry matter produced
(exclusive of roots)
f coefficient *m* de transpiration
d Transpirationskoeffizient *m*

2828 TRANSPORTATIONAL PROCESS
all processes contributing to the
transport of eroded material
f procédé *m* de transport
d Verfrachtung *f*; Transportvorgang *m*

2829 TRANSVERSE PERMEABILITY
permeability measured perpendicula
to axis of core sample
f perméabilité *f* transversale
d quergerichtete Permeabilität *f*

2830 TRANSVERSE WAVE
wave generated by shearing displace
ments where wave motion is perpenc
ular to direction of propagation
f onde *f* de cisaillement
d Scherungswelle *f*

TRAVEL TIME, see transit time

2831 TRAVERTINE
porous calcium carbonate
concretionary deposit
f travertin *m*
d Travertin *m*

2832 TREE MOLD
hollow mold left by a tree trunk in
a lava flow
f eisomorphose *f*
d Baumgussform *f*; Lavamatrix *f*

2833 TRELLIS
geometrical arrangement of inter-
woven pattern

f   treillis *m*
d   Flechtmuster *n*

2834   TRELLIS DRAINAGE PATTERN
arrangement of stream and
tributaries in a rectangular fashion
f   configuration *f* en espalier
d   gitterförmige Anordnung *f*

2835   TREMOLITE
silicate mineral of the amphibole
group
f   trémolite *m*
d   Tremolit *m*

2836   TRIASSIC
oldest geologic period of the
Mesozoic era
f   Trias *m*
d   Trias *n*

2837   TRIBUTARY
stream contributing its waters to
another stream of higher order
f   tributaire *m*; affluent *m*
d   Nebenfluss *m*

2838   TRIBUTARY RIVER
smaller stream entering and
contributing to flow of a bigger
river
f   affluent *m*
d   Nebenfluss *m*

2839   TRIBUTARY VALLEY
less important valley joining bigger
valley
f   vallée *f* tributaire
d   Seitental *n*

2840   TRICKLING
f   ruissellement *m*
d   Rinnsal *n*

2841   TRICONE ROCK BIT
rotary drilling bit with three
cone shaped rollers
f   tricône *m*
d   Dreirollenmeissel *m*

2842   TRIPLE POINT
point at which solid, liquid and
vapor phase are in equilibrium
f   point *m* triple
d   Tripelpunkt *m*

2843   TRIPOLY
very fine grained silica sand
f   tripoli *m*
d   Kieselgur *m*

2844   TRITIUM
isotope of water H_3O (HTO) of
special usefulness in hydrologic
tracer studies
f   tritium *m*
d   Tritium *n*

2845   TROUGH
surface depression
f   dépression *f*; bassin *m*
d   Trog *m*; Senke *f*; Mulde *f*

2846   TRUCK-MOUNTED
f   mobile
d   fahrbar

2847   TRUE VELOCITY
in ground water flow: velocity in
porous interstice; interstitial
velocity
f   vitesse *f* interstitielle;
vitesse *f* dans les pores
d   Porenfliessgeschwindigkeit *f*;
Bahngeschwindigkeit *f*

2848   TRUNCATION
horizontal or vertical clean cut of
a topographic feature
f   rabotage *m*
d   Abschleifung *f*

TUBE, lava see 1140
-, measuring see 2013

2849   TUBULAR SPRING
spring issuing from round channel
such as a lava tube
f   source *f* tubulaire
d   Rundnischenquelle *f*

2850   TUFF
porous rock formed by compaction
of volcanic ashes
f   tuf *m*
d   Tuff *m*

2851   TURBIDITY
diminishing of light penetration
through water sample due to
suspended and colloidal materials
f   trouble *m*; turbidité *f*
d   Trübung *f*

2852   TURBINE PUMP
f   pompe *f* à turbine
d   Turbinenpumpe *f*

TURBINE PUMP, deep well
see 449

2853   TURBODRILL
       drill where rotary movement is
       generated in a turbine directly
       above the bit
       f   turboforeuse *f*
       d   Bohrturbine *f*

2854   TURBULENCE
       irregular motion of fluid particles
       in an inertia dominated flow
       regimen

       f   turbulence *f*
       d   Turbulenz *f*

2855   TYPE CURVE
       plot of well function versus lower
       limit of integral used in Theis'
       graphical solution method
       f   courbe *f* standard
       d   Bezugskurve *f* der Brunnen-
           funktion W(u)

U

2856 UNALTERED ROCK
rock that has not experienced
physical or chemical erosion
f roche *f* saine
d gewachsener Fels *m*

2857 UNCASED HOLE
f puits *m* ouvert
d unverrohrte Bohrung *f*

2858 UNCONFINED FLOW
flow displaying free surface
f écoulement *m* en nappe libre
d ungespannter Grundwasserfluss *m*

2859 UNCONFINED WATER
ground water vertically in direct
contact with atmosphere
f eau *f* libre; nappe *f* libre
d ungespanntes Grundwasser *n*;
freies Grundwasser *n*

2860 UNCONFORMITY
fossil land surface representing
absence of a sequence of sediments
f discontinuité *f* stratigraphique
d Diskordanz *f*; Schichtlücke *f*

2861 UNCONFORMITY SPRING
spring issuing at contact of
aquifer with an unconformity
f source *f* de faille
d Verwerfungsquelle *f*

2862 UNCONTAMINATED ZONE
in electrical logging practice zone
around borehole not contaminated
by mud filtrate
f zone *f* non-contaminée
d unberührte Zone *f*

2863 UNDERDRAINAGE
drainage from under a hydrologic
feature such as river, barrier,
lake etc.
f infradrainage *m*
d Unterströmung *f*

2864 UNDERGROUND WATERS
subsurface waters, waters below
the ground
f eaux *fpl* souterraines
d unterirdische Wässer *npl*

2865 UNIFORM
f uniforme
d einheitlich; gleichmässig

2866 UNIFORM FLOW
flow with constant velocity at all
points and at all times
f écoulement *m* uniforme
d gleichförmige Strömung *f*

UNCONFORMITY, angular see 81

2867 UNIFORMITY COEFFICIENT
ratio of the 60 percentile grain
size to the 10 percentile, indicating
degree of sorting of granular
material; (Hazen uniformity
coefficient)
f coefficient *m* d'uniformité
d Gleichförmigkeitsziffer *f*
(nach Hazen)

UNIT, geohydrologic see 826
-, pumping see 2309

2868 UNIT-HYDROGRAPH
hypothetical discharge hydrograph
for a given point resulting from
unit rainfall which produces unit
runoff
f hydrogramme *m* unitaire
d Einheitskurve *f* der Abflussganglinie; Einheitshydrograph *m*

2869 UNSATURATED COEFFICIENT OF
PERMEABILITY
apparent coefficient of permeability
in flow through an unsaturated medium
f coefficient *m* de perméabilité
relative
d relativer Durchlässigkeitsbeiwert *m*;
ungesättigte Durchlässigkeitsziffer *f*

2870 UNSATURATED FLOW
two phase flow through pores only
partially filled with water and air
f écoulement *m* en régime non-
saturé
d Strömung *f* in der belüfteten
Zone; ungesättigter Fluss *m*

2871 UNSTEADY FLOW
flow with finite local acceleration
term; streamlines vary with time
f écoulement *m* non-permanent
d unstetige Strömung *f*

2872 UPLIFT
relative upward movement of a part
of the earth's crust

f   soulèvement *m*
d   Erhebung *f*; Hebung *f*

2873   UPPER CONFINING BED
       impermeable bed overlying
       an aquifer
       f   toit *m* imperméable d'un
           aquifère
       d   Deckschicht *f*

2874   UPSTREAM
       f   en amont
       d   flussaufwärts

USE, conjuctive see 356
-, consumptive see 363
-, water see 2963

2875   U.S. WEATHER BUREAU CLASS
       A LAND PAN
       evaporimeter developed by U.S.
       Weather Bureau, recommended as
       standard device by the World
       Meteorological Organization
       f   bac *m* de classe A
       d   Landkessel A *m* (Standardgerät)

V

2876 VADOSE WATER;
SUSPENDED SUBSURFACE WATER
water suspended in the unsaturated
zone of aeration between surface
waters and ground water
f eaux *f pl* suspendues; eaux *f pl*
   vadoses
d vadoses Grundwasser *n*;
   schwebendes Grundwasser *n*

2877 VALLEY
f vallée *f*
d Tal *n*

VALLEY, anticlinal see 92
-, antecedent see 91
-, buried see 212
-, rift see 2410
-, strike see 2675
-, superimposed see 2706
-, synclinal see 2739
-, tectonic see 2751
-, tributary see 2839

2878 VALLEY FILL
unconsolidated debris accumulated
on the valley bottom
f remblaiement *m* de vallée
d Talschutt *m*

2879 VALLEYSIDE-SLOPE
f versant *m* d'une vallée
d Talhang *m*

2880 VALLEY SPRING
springs occurring at valley sides
where water table intersects
surface
f source *f* de vallée
d Talquelle *f*

VALUE, discrete see 522
-, limiting see 1153
-, mean see 2005

2881 VALVE
f vanne *f*
d Ventil *n*

VALVE, air release 45
-, ball see 135
-, butterfly see 214
-, check see 283
-, control see 378
-, drain see 560

VALVE, foot see 774
-, gate see 822
-, safety see 2448
-, throttle see 2780

2882 VAPORIZATION
process by which liquid or solid
water changes into gaseous state
f vaporisation *f*
d Verdampfung *f*

2883 VAPOR PRESSURE (SATURATION......)
f pression *f* de vapeur
d Dampfdruck *m*

2884 VARIANCE
square of standard deviation
f variance *f*
d Streuung *f*

2885 VARVE
alternating coarse and fine
grained layer in glacial lake
sediments
f varve *f*
d Warve *f*

2886 VECTOR FIELD
f champ *m* vectoriel
d Vektorfeld *n*

2887 VEGETATION COVER
cover of living vegetation on top
of upper soil horizon
f couverture *f* végétale
d Pflanzendecke *f*

2888 VEIN
opening filled with mineral matter
f filon *m*
d Gang *m*

2889 VELOCITY
f vitesse *f*
d Geschwindigkeit *f*

VELOCITY, Darcy see 440
-, field... of groundwater see 720
-, rising see 2416
-, seepage see 440, 2502
-, settling see 2518
-, shear see 2530
-, sound see 2611
-, true see 2847
-, wave see 2972

2890 VELOCITY HEAD
f énergie f cinétique
d Geschwindigkeitshöhe f

2891 VELOCITY POTENTIAL
f potentiel m de vélocité
d Geschwindigkeitspotential n

2892 VERNIER
part of measuring device to obtain
very fine adjustment
f vernier m
d Nonius m

2893 VERY FINE SAND
grain diameter 0.1 to 0.05 mm
(USBS)
f sable m très fin
d Feinstsand m

2894 VESICULAR
containing small circular cavities
f vésiculeux
d bläschenförmig

2895 VIRGIN FLOW
flow unaffected by artificial
diversions, impoundments, or
channels
f écoulement m vierge
d unbeeinflusste Strömung f

2896 VISCOSIMETER
f viscosimètre m
d Viskosimeter n

2897 VISCOSITY
resistance of liquid to flow; property
of a real fluid creating shear
forces between two fluid elements
and giving rise to fluid friction
f viscosité f
d Viskosität f; Zähigkeit f

2898 VISCOUS FORCE
f force f de viscosité
d Reibungskraft f

2899 VOID RATIO
ratio of volume of voids to volume
of solids in a porous sample
f indice m des vides
d relativer Porenraum m

2900 VOIDS
open space between solid material
in a porous medium
f vides mpl
d Hohlräume mpl

2901 VOLATILE COMPONENTS
f composants mpl volatils
d flüchtige Bestandteile mpl

2902 VOLCANIC ACTIVITY
igneous activity near or at the
surface of the earth with outflow
of the igneous material on the
surface
f activité f volcanique;
volcanisme m
d Vulkanismus m (im engeren
Sinne)

2903 VOLCANIC ASH
fine grained material resulting
from explosion of magma
f cendre f volcanique
d Vulkanasche f

2904 VOLCANIC LAKE
lake formed in the impermeable
part of a volcanic crater
f lac m volcanique
d Vulkansee m; Mar n

2905 VOLCANIC VENT
chimney like conduit from body of
magma to the place of eruption
f diatrème m; évent m
d Vulkanschlot m

2906 VOLCANIC WATER
water in or derived from shallow
magma
f eaux fpl volcaniques
d vulkanisches Wasser n

2907 VOLTMETER
f voltmètre m
d Spannungsmesser m; Voltmeter n

VOLUME, solid see 2605
-, specific see 2621

2908 VOLUMETRIC FLOWMETER
apparatus to measure volume flow
rate
f débimètre m volumétrique
d Volumenflussmessgerät n

2909 VOLUMETRIC MOISTURE CONTEN
concentration of water in soil by
volume
f teneur f en eau par volume
d volumetrischer Feuchtegehalt m

2910   VUGULAR PORE SPACE
       void space due to solution cavities
       of small size
       f   espace *m* des vides par solution
       d   Lösungshohlraum *m*

W

2911 WADING MEASUREMENT
discharge measurement during
which hydrographer can take
readings standing in the river
f jaugeage *m* à gué
d Furtmessung *f*

2912 WALKING BEAM
oscillating beam used to produce
the rise and fall of the tools in
cable-tool drilling
f balancier *m*
d Bohrschwengel *m*

2913 WALL OF A WELL
f paroi *f* d'un puits
d Bohrlochswand *f*

2914 WARM SPRING
f source *f* chaude
d Arkatotherme *f*

2915 WASH
small ravine due to outwash by
flow in desert regions
f oued *m*
d Wadi *m*

2916 WASHER
f rondelle *f*
d Unterlegscheibe *f*

2917 WASH LOAD
incoming load of suspended
sediment passing through river
network without depositing
f charge *f* de ruissellement
d eingeleitete Materialfrachtung *f*

2918 WASHOVER
liberating a stuck tool by drilling
over it with an overshot
f surforage *m*
d Überbohren *n*

2919 WASTE DISPOSAL
f élimination *f* des résidus
d Abfallbeseitigung *f*

2920 WASTE LOAD
content of wastes by weight of
volume transported by or discharged into a river
f charge *f* en résidus
d Abwasserlast *f*

2921 WASTE PRODUCTS
f déchets *mpl*
d Abfälle *mpl*; Abfallstoffe *mpl*

2922 WASTE WATER
water containing sewage and waste
products
f eaux *fpl* d'égouts
d Abwasser *n*

2923 WATER
f eau *f*
d Wasser *n*

WATER, active see 22
-, available see 124
-, backwash see 131
-, brackish see 199
-, capillary see 243
-, cavern see 263
-, compensation see 328
-, confined see 349
-, connate see 357
-, cooling see 384
-, dead see 443
-, drinking see 586
-, flood see 751
-, fresh see 791
-, gravitational see 878
-, head see 924
-, hygroscopic see 992
-, imported see 1008
-, industrial see 1021
-, infiltration see 1028
-, interstitial see 1069
-, intrapermafrost see 1070
-, juvenile see 1103
-, low see 1174
-, magmatic see 1178
-, marine see 1187
-, metamorphic see 2033
-, meteoric see 2034
-, mine see 2049
-, natural see 2103
-, oceanic see 2124
-, oil field see 2125
-, pellicular see 2183
-, phreatic see 2220
-, plutonic see 2252
-, polluted see 2261
-, ponded see 2265
-, potable see 2274
-, raw see 2345
-, recharge see 2360
-, resurgent see 2402

WATER, saline see 2452
-, salty see 2459
-, soil see 2601
-, subsiding see 2687
-, subpermafrost see 2685
-, suprapermafrost see 2710
-, surface see 2725
-, suspended see 2732
-, suspended subsurface see 2876
-, unconfined see 2859
-, vadose see 2876
-, volcanic see 2906
-, waste see 2922
-, well see 3005

2924 WATER-BALANCE
instrument to measure evaporation
by gravimetry (developed by Wild)
f évaporomètre *m* (de Wild)
d Verdunstungswaage *f* (nach
Wild)

2925 WATER-BEARING
containing water
f aquifère
d wasserhaltig; wasserführend

2926 WATER-BORNE DISEASE
disease spread by organic contaminants contained in the water supply
f maladie *f* d'origine hydrique
d Wasserkrankheit *f*

2927 WATER BUDGET
quantitative accounting of water
volumes involved in hydrologic
cycle
f bilan *m* hydrologique
d Wasserbilanz *f*

2928 WATER CATCHMENT
intake of water from an aquifer or
a surface reservoir
f puisage *m* d'eau; captage *m* d'eau
d Wasserfassung *f*; Wassergewinnung *f*

2929 WATER CONSERVATION
all measures to reduce quantitative
or qualitative spoilage of water
f conservation *f* d'eau
d Wasserbewirtschaftung *f*

2930 WATER CONTENT
f teneur *f* en eau
d Wassergehalt *m*

2931 WATER COURSE
any channel conveying water
f cours *m* d'eau
d Wasserlauf *m*

WATER COURSE, receiving see
2351

2932 WATER CYCLE
f cycle *m* d'eau
d Wasserkreislauf *m*

2933 WATER DEMAND
f besoin *m* en eau
d Wasserbedarf *m*

2934 WATER EQUIVALENT
depth of water resulting from
melting of snow
f hauteur *f* d'eau équivalente
d Wasserwert *m* des Schnees

2935 WATER GAGING
f hydrométrie *f*
d Wassermessung *f*

2936 WATER HAMMER
abnormally high pressure rise in a
pipe when sudden changes in flow
occur
f coup *m* de bélier
d hydraulischer Stoss *m*;
Wasserhammer *m*

2937 WATER INVASION
sudden invasion of water into well
or bore
f invasion *f* d'eau
d Wassereinbruch *m*

2938 WATER LAW
f législation *f* des eaux
d Wasserrecht *n*

2939 WATER LEVEL
level of free surface of a water
body or water column
f niveau *m* d'eau
d Wasserspiegel *m*

2940 WATERLOGGED
water saturated
f noyé
d durchtränkt

2941 WATERLOGGING
water accummulation on top of
soil where water table and ground
surface coincide
f imbibition *f* d'eau (sous forme
de marais)
d Wasserdurchtränkung *f*

2942 WATER METER
f compteur *m* d'eau
d Wasseruhr *f*

2943 WATER OF CONSTITUTION
chemically bound water
f eau *f* de constitution
d Konstitutionswasser *n*

2944 WATER OF CRYSTALLIZATION
water embodied in crystal structure
f eau *f* de cristallisation
d Kristallisationswasser *n*

2945 WATER OF DEHYDRATION
water freed from hydrous
minerals by chemical changes
f eau *f* de constitution
d Dehydrationswasser *n*;
Konstitutionswasser *n*

2946 WATER PIPE
f conduite *f* d'eau
d Wasserleitung *f*

2947 WATER PUMPAGE
f élévation *f* de l'eau;
pompage *m* de l'eau
d Wasserhebung *f*

2948 WATER QUALITY
physical chemical and biological
characteristics of water
f propriétés *fpl* caractéristiques
de l'eau
d Wasserbeschaffenheit *f*;
Wassergüte *f*

2949 WATER RECLAMATION
process waste water purification
to acceptable standards for further
use
f récupération *f* d'eau
d Wasserrückgewinnung *f*;
Abwasserrückgewinnung *f*

2950 WATER REQUIREMENT
quantity of water needed for crop
regardless of source
f demande *f* en eau
d Wasserbedarf *m*

2951 WATER RESOURCES
total supply of surface ground and
reclaimed water that can be used
f ressources *fpl* en eau
d Wasservorräte *mpl*;
Wasserschatz *m*

2952 WATER RESOURCES
MANAGEMENT
f économie *f* des eaux
d Wasserwirtschaft *f*

WATER RETAINING
see specific retention

WATERS, underground see 2864

2953 WATER SAMPLE
f échantillon *m* d'eau
d Wasserprobe *f*

2954 WATER SEPARATOR
f séparateur d'eau *m*
d Wasserabscheider *m*

2955 WATERSHED
a) drainage basin;
b) divide separating one drainage
basin from another
f a) bassin *m* hydrologique
b) ligne *f* de partage
d a) Einzugsgebiet *n*
b) Wasserscheide *f*

2956 WATER SHORTAGE
f pénurie *f* d'eau
d Wassermangel *m*

2957 WATER SOLUBLE
f soluble dans l'eau
d wasserlöslich

2958 WATER STAGE
height of the water level
f hauteur *f* d'eau
d Wasserstand *m*

2959 WATER-STAGE RECORDER
f limnigraphe *m*
d Schreibpegel *m*

2960 WATER SUPPLY
f alimentation *f* en eau;
approvisionnement *m* en eau
d Wasserversorgung *f*;
Wasserdarbietung *f*

2961 WATER SURFACE SLOPE
see also hydraulic gradient for
free surface waters
f pente *f* de la ligne d'eau
d Wasserspiegelgefälle *n*

2962 WATER TABLE
surface separating ground water
zone from capillary fringe in
unconfined aquifer conditions
f niveau *m* phréatique; surface *f*
hydrostatique; surface *f* libre
des eaux souterraines
d Grundwasserspiegel *m*;
Grundwasseroberfläche *f*

WATER TABLE perched see 2191

2963 WATER USE
f utilisation *f* de l'eau
d Wassernutzung *f*

2964 WATER VAPOR
f vapeur *f* d'eau
d Wasserdampf *m*

2965 WATERWAY
artificial or natural watercourse
fit for navigation
f canal *m*; cours *m* d'eau
d Wasserweg *m*

WATER WITCHING, see dowsing

2966 WATER WORKS
plant where water is treated and
prepared for municipal consumption
f usine *f* d'eau
d Wasserwerk *n*

2967 WATER YEAR
12 month period for streamflow
computation (adopted by U.S.
Geological Survey, Oct. 1 to Sept. 30)
f année *f* hydrologique
d hydrologisches Jahr *n*

2968 WATER-YIELD
f débit *m* d'exploitation
d Wasserspende *f*; Wasserergiebigkeit *f*

WAVE, compression see 334
-, flood see 752
-, longitudinal see 1169
-, seismic see 2506
-, shear see 2531
-, shock see 2537
-, transverse see 2830

2969 WAVE FRONT
f front *m* d'onde
d Wellenfront *f*

2970 WAVE PATH
f trajectoire *f* des ondes;
rayon *m*
d Wellenweg *m*

2971 WAVE PROPAGATION
f propagation *f* des ondes
d Wellenausbreitung *f*

2972 WAVE VELOCITY
f célérité *f* d'une onde
d Wellengeschwindigkeit *f*

2973 WEAR RESISTANCE
f résistance *f* à l'usure
d Verschleissfestigkeit *f*

2974 WEATHERING
disintegration and decomposition of
rocks by different geological
processes
f altération *f* des roches
d Verwitterung *f*

2975 WEATHER MODIFICATION
f modification *f* artificielle du
temps
d künstliche Wetterbeeinflussung *f*

2976 WEDGE STORAGE
storage in form of a wedge
overlying prism; storage in flooded
river segment
f stockage *m* en forme de coin
d keilförmige Fallwasserspeicherung *f*

2977 WEIGHING FACTOR
f coefficient *m* de pondération
d Gewichtszahl *f*

WEIGHT, bit see 182

2978 WEIGHT DENSITY
f poids *m* spécifique
d Wichte *f*; spezifisches Gewicht *n*

2979 WEIR
dam across a water course to
control, raise or measure water
flow
f déversoir *m*
d Wehr *n*

WEIR, measuring see 2014

2980 WEIR COEFFICIENT
coefficient used in transforming
water depths into discharge volumes
in weir measurements
f coefficient *m* du déversoir
d Wehrbeiwert *m*

2981 WELDED JOINT
f joint *m* soudé
d Schweissverbindung *f*

WELL, abandonded see 1
-, absorbing see 8
-, artesian see 115
-, collector see 325
-, diffusion see 2361
-, disposal see 527
-, draw see 564

WELL, driven see 591
-, dug see 605
-, eccentric see 618
-, failing see 701
-, flowing artesian see 756
-, gage see 806
-, image see 1000
-, inverted see 2361
-, jetted see 1098
-, multiaquifer see 2094
-, observation see 2121
-, oil see 2127
-, partially penetrated see 2172
-, permanent see 2204
-, reamed see 2346
-, recharge see 2361
-, shallow see 2524
-, stilling see 2648
-, subartesian see 2682
-, tapping see 2749

2982 WELL-ALIGNMENT
orderly arrangement of wells in a
linear fashion to produce straight
injection or withdrawal fronts
f alignement *m* des puits
d Reihenbildung *f* von Bohrungen;
   Brunnenausrichtung *f*

2983 WELL CAPACITY
rate at which water will be yielded
from a well
f débit *m* d'un puits
d Brunnenergiebigkeit *f*;
   Schüttung *f*

2984 WELL COMPLETION
final cleaning and construction
operations to put well in production
f complétion *f* des puits
d Inbetriebsetzung *f* eines Brunnens

2985 WELL CONSTRUCTION
f construction *f* d'un puits
d Brunnenbau *m*

2986 WELL CURB
concrete wall around well for
sanitary protection
f bordure *f* d'un puits
d Brunnenumrandung *f*

2987 WELL DEVELOPMENT
operations to assure and increase
production of a well before
completing well
f développement *m* d'un puits
d Brunnenentwicklung *f*

2988 WELL DIAMETER
f diamètre *m* du puits
d Brunnendurchmesser *m*

2989 WELL FIELD
tract of land especially devoted to
wells
f champ *m* de puits
d Brunnenfeld *n*

2990 WELL FRACTURING
method of creating fractures around
well by explosion or high pressure
injection
f fracturation *f* hydraulique des
   puits
d hydraulische Rissbildung *f* in
   Brunnen

2991 WELL FUNCTION
exponential integral as used in
Theis' non equilibrium equation;
W(u)
f fonction *f* caractéristique (de
   puits pompé)
d Brunnenfunktion *f*

2992 WELL HYDROGRAPH
graph of water level fluctuations
in well
f hydrogramme *m* du puits
d Wasserstandsganglinie *f* im
   Brunnenschacht

2993 WELL INTERFERENCE
effect of overlap of areas of
influence of two or more wells
pumping from the same aquifer
f interférence *f* de puits
d Brunnenbeeinflussung *f*;
   Übergreifen *n* der Brunnen-
   senkflächen

2994 WELL KNIFE
tool to cut perforations or slots
into plain casing
f coupe-tubage *m*
d Rohrschneider *m*

2995 WELL LOSS
head loss caused by flow through
screen and inside well
f perte *f* de charge dans un puits
d Reibungsverlust *m* im Brunnen

2996 WELL PERFORATOR
tool to produce holes in casing to
permit the entry of water into the
well
f perforateur *m*
d Perforiergerät *n*

2997 WELL PIT
well bore, hollow shaft of a well
f trou *m* de puits
d Brunnenschacht *m*

2998 WELL POINT SYSTEM
battery of wells connected by
suction header
f batterie *f* de puits
d Brunnenkette *f*

2999 WELL RECORD
body of data regarding well
f rapport *m* sur le puits
d Brunnenprotokoll *n*;
Brunnenaufzeichnung *f*

3000 WELL SORTED GRAINS
assortment of grains having the
same diameter
f granulométrie *f* uniforme
d gut sortierte Kornklasse *f*

3001 WELL SPACING
distance between wells in a well
field
f espacement *m* entre les puits
d Brunnenabstand *m*

3002 WELL STIMULATION
well treatment methods to increase
yield
f traitement *m* des puits
d Bohrlochsbehandlung *f* zur
Erhöhung der Schüttung

3003 WELL TOP
f tête *f* de puits
d Brunnenkopf *m*

3004 WELL TREATMENT
special mechanical or chemical
treatment of a well to increase
yield
f traitement des puits *m*
d Bohrlochsbehandlung *f*

3005 WELL WATER
water produced by a well
f eau *f* de puits
d Brunnenwasser *n*

3006 WELL YIELD
quantity of water produced by a well
f débit *m* d'un puits
d Brunnenergiebigkeit *f*;
Brunnenschüttung *f*

3007 WET LINE
portion of line submerged under
water in stream measurements
f câble *m* immergé
d Unterwasserseil *n*

3008 WETTABILITY
property of a solid substance to

be wetted by a liquid such as water
f mouillabilité *f*
d Benetzbarkeit *f*

3009 WETTED AREA
cross sectional area of that portion
of a channel that is filled with water
f surface *f* mouillée
d benetzter Querschnitt *m*

3010 WETTED PERIMETER
perimeter over which the flowing
water is in actual contact with the
channel walls and bottom
f périmètre *m* mouillé
d benetzter Umfang *m*

WETTING ANGLE, see angle of contact

3011 WETTING PERIOD
period of contact between a liquid
and a solid surface during which
wetting occurs
f temps *m* de mouillage
d Benetzungsdauer *f*

3012 WHIPSTOCK
wedge-like tool placed in a well in
order to change the direction of
further drilling
f sifflet *m* déviateur
d Ablenkkeil *m*

3013 WHIRL
f tourbillon *m*
d Wirbel *m*; Strudel *m*

WIDTH, base see 155

3014 WIDTH OF CONTRIBUTION
width of the contributing region
between the ground water divide
from which water enters a well
(case of originally inclined
piezometric surface)
f front *m* d'appel; front *m* d'emprunt
d Entnahmebreite *f*

3015 WILT, TO
shrinking of cell walls due to loss
in turgor as a result of water
deficiency in plant
f flétrir
d welken

3016 WILTING COEFFICIENT;
WILTING POINT
f soil moisture content at which
plants wilt
f point *m* de flétrissure
d Welkepunkt *m*

WILTING POINT, permanent
see 2205

3017 WIND FACTOR
factor containing a monthly mean
wind velocity in evaporation
equations
f   facteur *m* de vent
d   Windfaktor *m*

3018 WIND FIELD
air velocity field above ground due
to wind action
f   champ *m* des vitesses du vent
d   Windfeld *n*

WIRE, gay see 915

3019 WIRE GAGE
f   jaugeur *m* à câble
d   Seilpegel *m*

3020 WIRE LINE
wire cable
f   câble *m*
d   Seil *n*; Kabel *n*

3021 WITHDRAW, TO
to draw water from an aquifer or
reservoir
f   soustraire
d   entnehmen

3022 WOLLASTONITE
silicate mineral in contact-
metamorphosed limestone
f   wollastonite *m*
d   Wollastonit *m*

3023 WORKING PRESSURE
f   pression *f* de service
d   Betriebsdruck *m*

3024 WORKOVER
reworking of a well that has
declined in yield
f   reconditionnement *m*
d   Wiederaufwältigung *f*

3025 XEROPHYTE
f   xérophyte *f*
d   Trockenpflanze *f*

Y

3026 YIELD
quantity of water discharged
from an aquifer
f rendement *m*
d Ausbeute *f*; Dargebot *n*

YIELD, perennial see 2197
-, safe see 2449
-, specific see 2622

-, sustained see 2733
-, well see 3006

3027 YOUNG'S MODULUS
elastic or stretch modulus giving
ratio of force per unit area to strain
f module *m* d'élasticité
d Elastizitätsmodul *m*

Z

ZERO, gage see 807

3028 ZERO ADJUSTMENT
adjustment of a scale or a
measuring circuit to an original
point of departure
f   mise *f* à zéro
d   Nullpunkteinstellung *f*

3029 ZERO DATUM
f   niveau *m* de référence zéro
d   Nullhöhe *f*

3030 ZETA POTENTIAL
f   potentiel *m* zeta
d   Zeta-Potential *n*

3031 ZIRCON
mineral
f   zircon *m*
d   Zirkon *n*

3032 ZONAL SOIL PROFILE
normal horizontal distribution of
soil zones
f   profil *m* de sol à horizons
d   zonales Bodenprofil *n*

ZONE, dispersion see 524
-, fault see 710
-, ferrito see 714
-, flushed see 771
-, invaded see 1075
-, littoral see 1160
-, phreatic see 2221
-, root see 2435
-, shattered fault see 2526
-, soilwater see 2602
-, thief see 2775
-, transition see 2820
-, uncontaminated see 2862

3033 ZONE OF ACCUMULATION
second horizon of soil profile (B)
usually zone of clay accumulation
subjacent to zone (A)
f   horizon *m* d'apport; horizon *m*
d'accumulation
d   Ausfällungszone *f*; Illuvialhorizont *m*; B-Horizont *m*

3034 ZONE OF AERATION
zone in ground profile with
considerable saturation in air where
isolated water moves under gravity
against capillary forces
f   zone *f* d'aération; zone *f*
de rétention
d   Überwasserspiegelzone *f*;
Haftwasserzone *f*; luftbeeinflusste Zone *f*

3035 ZONE OF INVESTIGATION
zone over which a given
measuring device is able to obtain
information
f   zone *f* d'investigation
d   untersuchte Zone *f*

3036 ZONE OF LEACHING
top horizon of soil profile (A) most
intensely weathered
f   horizon *m* éluvial; horizon *m* de
lessivage
d   Auslaugungszone *f*;
Eluvialhorizont *m*; A-Horizont *m*

3037 ZONE OF RAINFALL
f   zone *f* de pluie
d   Regenstrich *m*

3038 ZONE OF ROCK FLOWAGE
deep zone of earth's crust where
rocks deform by plastic flowage
f   zone *f* plastique de la lithosphère
d   plastische Zone *f* der Gesteinshülle

3039 ZONE OF ROCK FRACTURE
upper zone of lithosphere where
rocks react to strain by fracture
f   zone *f* supérieure de la
lithosphère
d   obere Zone *f* der Gesteinshülle

3040 ZONE OF SATURATION
zone completely saturated with
water, ground water zone
f   zone *f* de saturation
d   Sättigungszone *f*; Unterwasserspiegelzone *f*

FRENCH

abaissement de la nappe
   phréatique 907
- phréatique 2216
abîme 9
ablation 2
abri des pompes 2305
abrupt 2645
absorption sélective 2508
accélération de la pesanteur
   879
accident 530
accumulation 14
- d'humidité 2062
acide hydrochlorique 961
- silicique 2547
- sulfurique 2701
acidité 15
acier inoxydable 2637
à-coup de pression 2294
activité induite 1014
- magmatique 997
- volcanique 2902
additif de boue de forage 2084
adhérence du ciment 268
adiabatique 25
adsorption 28
advection 29
aération 30
aérobique 32
affaissement de la surface 1126
affleurement 2146
affluence 1031
affluent 2837, 2838
afflux 1031
- latéral 1134
affouillement 2483
agrégat 35
- des particules de sol 2589
agressif 36
air comprimé 332
aire de drainage 548
- d'influence 107
air-lift 42
albedo 48
alcalinité 54
alimentation 2388
- artificielle 2357
- en eau 2960
- en eau de surface 2726
- initiée 1016
alignement des puits 2982
alios 229
- ferrugineux 714
allochtone 55
alluvion 62
altération des roches 2974
alvéolaire 64
amortissement 67, 436
ampèremètre 65
amphibole 68
amplitude 69
analogie par cuve électrolytique 342
- par tissu conducteur 343
analyse chimique 284
- complète 330
- de carotte 388
- de l'hydrogramme 970
- fréquentielle 789
- hypsométrique 2078

analyse physique 2225
- statistique 2643
andésite 73
anémomètre 74
angle de contact 75
- de réflexion 77
- de réfraction 78
- de repos 79
- d'incidence 76
anguleux à arêtes vives 80
anhydrite 82
anisotropique 83
année hydrologique 2967
anomalie 87
- de la courbe PS 464
- de la gravité 880
Antécambrien 2284
anticlinal 93
apatite 94
à pente raide 2645
aplanissement 859
appareil de Hele-Shaw 929
- de mesure de la précipitation
   2288
- de mesure de l'humidité du
   sol 2592
appareillage de surface 2716
approvisionnement en eau 2960
aqueduc 98
aquiclude 99
aquifère 2925
aquifuge 102
aquitard 103
aragonite 104
arborescent 460
arbre 2522
ardoise 2568
argile 299, 302
- à blocaux 194, 849, 1162, 2789
argileux 108
argilite benthonique 174
aride 110
arpentage 2729
arrache-carotte 391
arrangement 2166
- des grains 862
- le plus compact 2787
- le plus lâche 1170
arrondi 2442
ascension capillaire 242
atmomètre 118
atmosphère 119
- absolue 4
- physique 4
attraction moléculaire 2066
attrition 120
auget basculeur 2797
augite 122
autochtone 123
avalanche 125
avant-montagne 797
averse 2654
- utilisée dans les calculs 481
azote 2110

bac de classe A 2875
- de décantation 2517, 2577
- de jaugeage 805
- d'évaporation au dessus du
   terrain 1124

bac enterré 2705
- évaporatoire 681
- flottant 741
- intercepteur 939
bactéries pathogènes 2177
baguette divinatoire 537
baisse du niveau dynamique 562
balance de torsion 2804
balancier 2912
banc de sable à l'intérieur de
   la boucle 2255
barographe 139
baromètre 140
barrage 435
- déversoir 2158
- souterrain 894
- souterrain en eau douce 792
- souterrain naturel 899
barrière 143
- de perméabilité 2206
- hydrologique 973
- naturelle dans un aquifère
   894, 899
basalte 147
basses-eaux 1174
bassin 2845
- clos 309
- de décantation 2516
- d'entremont 1064
- d'épandage 1024
- échantillon 691
- hydrogéologique 895
- hydrologique 2955
- versant 156, 257, 549
batholite 162
bathomètre 163
batterie de puits 2998
berge 136, 643
besoin en eau 2933
béton 338
bicarbonate 176
bief 2421
bifurcation 177
bilan des nappes souterraines
   903
- énergétique 649
- hydrologique 974, 2927
- régional 662
biotite 180
bloc affaissé 858
blocage 187
bloc pyroclastique 2313
- surélevé 946
bobine de mesure 2008
bordure d'un puits 2986
borne de mise à la terre 891
- repère 172
bouchon argileux 303
bouclier 2535
boue 2083
- de forage 579
bourbe 2316
brèche 201
bronze siliceux 2549
bruit de fond 128
by-pass 215

cabestan 245
câble 3020
- d'ancrage 915

câble de cabestan 259
- de curage 2462
- de diagraphie 1165
- de forage 578
- de levage 936
- de manoeuvre 573
- de tubage 255
- exondé 43
- immergé 3007
- porteur 251
caillou 2181
caisson 223
cake de boue 724
calcaire 1152
- argileux 109
- d'algues 50
calcareux 224
calcite 225
caldère 226
calibration 227
calotte glaciaire 996
Cambrien 232
camion de diagraphie 1166
- d'enregistrement 1166
canal 277, 2965
- de jaugeage 2009
cannelure glaciaire 848
cañon 234
cap 244
capacité 235
- au champ 716
- capillaire 716
- d'absorption 1025
- de libre écoulement 2622
- d'emmagasinement 2650
- de pénétration 655
- de rétention 2619
- de transmission 2823
- de transport 252, 382
- d'infiltration 1022, 2340
- effective d'absorption 623
capillarité 236
captage d'eau 2928
- des eaux souterraines 896
caractéristiques du bassin 157
- du lit 278
carapace figée 353
carbonate 246
Carbonifère 250
- inférieur 2055
- supérieur 2188
carottage 392
- électrique 633
carotte 387
carte 1185
carter 948
cascade souterraine 897
casque de battage 589
cassure 397
- fragile 205
caverne 260
célérité d'une onde 2972
cellule piézométrique 2291
cendre volcanique 2903
Cénozoïque 272
centre de gravité d'une pluie 274
cercle d'influence 295
chaille 289
chaîne de montagnes 2080

chaleur de condensation 926
- de vaporisation 927
- de vaporisation latente 1130
- sensible 2511
chambre d'aspiration 1040
- de captage 2613
champ de puits 2989
- des vitesses du vent 3018
- vectoriel 2886
changement de faciès 700
charge 922
- accidentelle 697
- admissible 2210
- de dynamite 612
- de la couche du lit 364
- de ruissellement 2917
- du lit 168
- en résidus 2920
- en saltation 2455
- en suspension 2730
- extérieure 697
- normale 153
- permanente 2203
- stabilisée 2101
- sur l'outil 182
- totale 651
charnière 173
charriage 168
chef foreur 576
chemin d'infiltration 2499
chemise de pompe 2310
chenal 913, 2664
- alluvial 57
chevauchement 2162
chloration 291
chlore 292
chott 52
chute 702
- de pression 2292
ciment 265
cimentation 267
ciment d'injection 269
cimenter 266
ciment illuvial 898
circuit de mesure 2007
- intégrant 1049
circulation de boue 2085
- inverse 2405
cisaillement 2527
citerne 296
clapet à échappement d'air 45
- à billes 135
- de fermeture 283
- de fond 774
- de sécurité 2448
- étrangleur 2780
clé à tubes 2241
clivage 306
cloche de repêchage 171
coefficient barométrique 141
- d'activité 23
- d'écoulement 557
- de Darcy 951
- de diffusion 503
- de fluctuation par marées 2784
- de frottement 795
- de fuite 1146
- de l'écoulement total 2447
- de mélange 2057

coefficient d'emmagasinement 2651
- de perméabilité 319
- de perméabilité Darcy sur le terrain 717
- de perméabilité du laboratoire 1113
- de perméabilité relative 2869
- de pondération 2977
- de réduction d'un bac 2170
- de rugosité 2441
- de ruissellement 557
- de stockage 2651
- de traînée 546
- de transpiration 2827
- d'infiltration 2498
- du bac 2170
- du déversoir 2980
- d'uniformité 2867
- hygroscopique 989
coins de retenue 2572
col de cygne 856
colibacille 322
collecteur 2240
- principal 324
collier de battage 590
colmatant 2250
colmater 308
colonne de battage 594
- de boue 2086
- de mercure 2026
- de pierre formée par des concrétions calcaires 587
- de surface 2713
- montante 2413, 2414
compaction 327
complétion des puits 2984
composant 361
composante de gravitation 881
composants volatils 2901
composition 331
compressibilité 333
compteur d'eau 2942
concentration en ions d'hydrogène 965
concession 97
concrétion 229, 339
condensation 340
conditions à la limite 195
- géologiques 830
- de Ghyben-Herzberg 844
- de similitude 2558
- initiales 1034
conducteur 344
conductibilité hydrodynamique 962
- thermique 2768
conductivité 2617
- hydraulique 951
conduit 2239
conduite 345
- d'eau 2946
cône d'alluvions 56, 58, 2747
- d'appel 346
- de déjection 2746
- de recharge 347
- de sondage 592
configuration de drainage 555
- en espalier 2834

confluent 351
congélation 354
congère 2581
conglomérat 355
- basal 146
conservation d'eau 2929
- massique 1190
consolidation 360
consommation totale 363
constante de récession 2353
- diélectrique 499
constituant en trace 2812
construction d'un puits 2985
contamination 369
- radioactive 2322
contre-courant 396
contrepression 129
convergence 380
corrasion 393
corrélation géologique 832
corrosif 395
cosse 217
- de câble 2436
côte 422
couche 165, 1141, 2660
- aquifère 100
- aquifère à fuites 1147
- aquifère artésienne 113
- aquifère littorale 314
- caractéristique 1188
- de lave 1138
- de neige 2579
- imperméable 350
- intercalaire 1053
- intercalée 1052
- limite 196
- monomoléculaire 2073
coulée de boue 2089
couler 754
coulisse de forage 1094
coup de bélier 2936
coupe géologique 829
- lithologique 828, 833
- sismique 2503
- transversale 417
coupe-tubage 2994
courant alternatif 63
- de densité 462
- de marée 2783
- direct 512
courants vagabonds 2661
courant tellurique 614
courbe cumulative 2702
- d'abaissement 908
- d'ajustage 27
- de concentration 336, 2415
- de décrue 2354
- de dépression 563
- de désorption 482
- de durée 609
- de durée des débits 755
- de masse 1191
- de niveau 374
- de régression 2380
- de remontée de pression 2290
- de remous 133
- de retenue 133
- des débits classés 609
- des valeurs cumulées 1191
- d'étalonnage 228

courbe de tarage 2342, 2632
- de tarissement 908, 2354
- du débit cumulé 758
- isohyète 1086
- rabattement-distance 563
- rabattement-temps 2792
- résistivité-espacement 2400
- standard 2855
cours d'eau 2931, 2965
- d'eau récepteur 2351
- d'un fleuve 2421
- inférieur 1172, 2744
- supérieur 924
couverture 2154
- de sol 2590, 2802
- mécanique 2015
- végétale 2887
craie 276
crépine 2486
- à fentes 2574
- filtrante 2699
Crétacé 407
crête 2409
creuser 504, 687
crevasse 408, 409, 733
cric 1093
crochet de forage 577
croûte calcaire 229
crue 743, 933
- utilisée pour un calcul 480
cryologie 420
cuiller 134, 2464, 2576
curie 426
cycle 433
- d'eau 2932
- hydrologique 975

Darcy 439
débimètre 759
- massique 1193
- volumétrique 2908
débit 761
- de base 2446
- d'écoulement 2338
- d'écoulement pérenne 2197
- de crue 932
- de pointe 1199
- de sécurité 2449, 2450
- d'étiage 1173
- d'évaporation 678
- d'exploitation 2968
- d'un puits 2983, 3006
- en eau souterraine 900
débiter 516
débit hydraulique 952
- jaugé 803
- maximum 2806
- permanent 2733
- rapide 2337
- spécifique 2614, 2622
déblais de forage 432
déborder 2157
débris 444
décamètre en ruban 2748
déchargement 515
déchets 2921
décolmatage 446
- d'un puits 2727
décomposer 447

décomposition de
  l'hydrogramme 970
décrue souterraine 907
déferlement 2711
déficit de saturation 2470
- en humidité 2064
déformation 450
dégazage 817
dégradation 451
degré 860
- d'aération 452
- de dissolution 2642
- de lapidifaction 453
- de salinité 2453
- de saturation 454
délaissés de crue 747
délitement 2175
delta 456
demande biochimique en
  oxygène (D.B.O) 179
- chimique en oxygène 288
- en eau 458, 2950
- en eau d'irrigation 610, 1082
- en oxygène 2164
déminéralisation 459
demi-vie 916
démultiplication 2374
dendritique 460
dénoyage 490
dénoyer 489
densité 461, 2615
- de drainage 550
- de la neige 2580
- du réseau 550
- massique 1192
dénudation 463
déplacement 525
- miscible 2054
dépôt 2477
- chimique 285
- d'eau de fonte 2149
- d'éboulis 59
- de filtration 724
- éolien 658
- glaciaire 845
- morainique 2077
- organogène 2136
dépôts deltaiques 457
dépôt sédimentaire 2494
dépression 467, 2845
- de la surface 561
dérivée directionnelle 513
derrick 475
désémulsifiant 645
désert 478
dessableur 477
dessalage 476
dessiccation 479
de surface 3
détecteur de fuites 1144
détonateur 184, 485
détritus 486
développement du cours 2665
- d'un puits 2987
déverser 535
déversoir 2625, 2979
- à mesure 2014
- de trop-plein 2156
déviation 487
Dévonien 488

diaclase 1100
diagénèse 494
diagramme fonctionnel 186
- latéral 1132
- stéréoscopique 2647
diagraphie 1164
- à espacement normal 2113
- de contact 365
- de diamétreur 231
- de l'avancement 582
- de la vitesse d'écoulement 767
- de microrésistivité 365
- de paroi 365
- de radioactivité 2324
- de rayons gamma 810
- de résistivité 2399
- de température 2754
- du foreur 570
- géologique 833
- neutron 2108
- par induction 1018
- sonique 18
diamant industriel 1020
diamétrage 231
diamètre du puits 2988
- effectif 621
- extérieur 696
- intérieur 1042
diamétreur 230
diastrophisme 497
diatomite 498
diatrème 2104, 2905
différence du rayonnement 2105
diffusion 502
- moléculaire 2067
digue 505, 1148
diopside 508
diorite 509
dioxyde carbonique 249
- de carbone 249
direction 2674
discontinuité 520, 521
- stratigraphique 2860
discordance 81
disjonction en colonnes 326
dispersion 523
- hydrodynamique 963
disponibilité en eau (pour l'évaporation) 680
disposition des puits de pompage 2306
dissoudre 528
distribution aléatoire 2334
- de fréquence 790
- de saturation 2471
- granulométrique 865
diurne 534
doline 538, 2563
dolomie 539
dôme de sel 2456
- de structure 2677
données 441
- de laboratoire 1114
- expérimentales 1114
dorsale 2409
doseur 711
drague à grappin 297
drainage d'eau 490
- endoréique 1065

drainage par gravité 882
drainer 489
drill-stem-test 585
drumlin 599
durée de parcours 2821
dureté 920
- carbonatée 2756
- non-carbonatée 2202
- permanente 2202
- temporaire 2756
- totale 2807
dynamomètre 613

eau 2923
- active 22
- angulaire 1069
- au dessus de la zone de pergelisol 2710
- capillaire 243
- captive 349
- corrosive 22
- cunéiforme 1069
- dans la zone du pergelisol 1070
- d'aval 2744
- de capillarité 243
- de compensation 328
- de constitution 2943, 2945
- de cristallisation 2944
- de fonte 2022
- de gravité 878, 2622
- de mer 1187, 2124
- de mine 2049
- de puits 3005
- de refroidissement 384
- de rétention 2619
- de rinçage 131
- de surface 2725
- de suspension 2732
- de tension superficielle 2183
- disponible (pour les plantes) 124
- douce 791
- du sol 2601
- en décrue 2687
- gravifique 878
- hygroscopique 992
- libre 2859
eau-mère 2079
eau morte 443
- naturelle 2103
- pelliculaire 2183
- phréatique 892
- phréatique indigène 2097
- potable 586, 2274
- salée 2452, 2459
- saumâtre 199
- sous la zone de pergelisol 2685
eaux connées 357
- de cavernes 263
- d'égouts 2519, 2922
- de mine 2045
- de recharge 2360
- de remous 132
- des gisements pétrolifères 2125
- d'importation 1008
- d'infiltration 1028
- d'usage 1021
- en crue 751

eaux juvéniles 1104
- magmatiques 1178
- météoriques 2034
- non-traitées 2345
- plutoniques 2252
- polluées 2261
- régénérées (par le métamorphisme) 2033
- résurgentes 2402
- retenues 2265
- souterraines 892, 2864
- suspendues 2876
- vadoses 2876
- volcaniques 2906
éboulement 264
- de roches 2427
éboulis glaciaire 846, 1162
écaille 2476
écart moyen 2003
écart-type 2640
échange de base 148
- de chaleur 925
- de gaz 815
échantillon d'eau 2953
- de sol 2597
- instantané 2335
échantillonneur de neige 2585
échantillon perturbé 531
échelle 2012, 2478
- à maximums 406
- de neige 2586
- limnimétrique 2630
économie des eaux 2952
écoulement 515, 2147
- critique 412
- dans un canal 2131
- de base 2446
- de la nappe captive 348
- de pointe 2179
- du cours principal 1182
- en décrue 2355
- en nappe libre 2858
- en nappe phréatique 765
- en régime non-saturé 2870
- hypodermique 1060, 2690
- irrotationnel 1083
- laminaire 1121
- non-permanent 2871
- par infiltration 2497
- permanent 2644
- potentiel 2280
- radial circulaire 2321
- rapide 2337
- souterrain 910, 2689
- total 2446, 2666, 2810
- tranquille 2816
- très lent 402
- uniforme 2866
- vierge 2895
écrasement 323
effet d'amortissement 437
- d'arc-boutement 203
- de bouts 647
- électrocinétique 638
- Klinkenberg 1112
- pariétal 2566
efficacité barométrique 141
- de température 2753
effluent 627, 2147
- acide (venant d'une mine) 17

effondrement 323
effusion 630
eisomorphose 2832
élargissement d'une sonde à
    faible diamètre 2348
électrode de courant 427
- de potentiel 2278
- écran 911
- mobile 2082
électrofiltration 637
électrolyte 639
élément en trace 2813
élévation 640
- de l'eau 2947
élimination des résidus 2919
élutriation 642
embouchure 644
emmagasinement dans la rive
    138
- dans les dépressions du sol
    2253
- prismatique 2296
emmagasiner 1009
empilement 2166
- le plus lâche 1170
- le plus serré 2787
en amont 2874
en aval 541
encroûtement 229
endogène 648
endroit exposé 695
endurcissement 919
énergie cinétique 2890
- de position 641
- de pression 2293
- hydraulique 955
- libre de surface 786
- potentielle 2230
enfoncer 588
en forme de plaquette 2247
enregistreur 2364
enrochement 2428
enthalpie 654
entrée de surface 2715
- du puits 2081
entrophie 656
envahissement 646
envasement 2554
enveloppe de gravier 871
Eocambrien 51
Eocène 657
épaisseur 2774
épanchement 630
- effusif en couche 2534
épandage en surface 2723
épilimnion 660
épissure de câble 219
époque 661
éprouvette 2013
épuisement 465
épuration des eaux d'égouts
    2520
équation de continuité 373
- d'état 663
- de Theis 2767
- hydrologique 976
- rationelle 2343
équipe de foreurs 574
équipotentielle 664
équivalent chimique 286

équivalent d'humidité 2065
- par million 665
ère 666
Ere Mésozoïque 2032
- Paléozoïque 2169
- Quaternaire 2317
- Tertiaire 2762
érodible 667
érosion 668
- de la rive 137
- en nappe 2533
escarpement 672
- de faille 709
esker 673
espace annulaire 86
- des vides par solution 2910
- interstitiel 1067
espacement de la sonde 2609
- des électrodes 636
- entre les puits 3001
essai d'écoulement 764
- de pompage 2308
- de puits 2308
- des couches par les tiges
    de forage 585
- d'infiltromètre 1030
- sur le terrain 719
- sur modèle 2061
estuaire 674
étanchéité 818, 2165
- de ciment 270
étang 2264
étranglement 362
étude des résistivités 2401
- magnétique 1179
- sur terrain 718
étuve 603
eutrophication 675
évacuation des eaux de toiture 2434
évaporation 677
- sur les retenues 2391
évaporit 676
évaporomètre (de Wild) 2924
évapotranspiration 686
- potentielle 2279
événement maximum 2000
- minimum 2050
évent 2905
éventail d'alluvions 58
exhaussement 12
exogène 689
exploitation minière à ciel
    ouvert 2719
exploration géophysique 839
explosif 694
explosion 693
exutoire artificiel 116
- du bassin 159
- naturel (de la nappe
    phréatique) 2898
- souterrain 1050
- subaquatique 2681
- unique 2560

faciès 699
facteur climatique 307
- d'échelle 2479
- de conversion 381
- de déposition 466
- de formation 776, 778
- de forme 780

facteur de fuite 1145
- de structure 2678
- de vent 3017
- d'influence hydrogéologique
    831
- lithologique 1156
facteurs d'influence 376
faille 706
- directe 2115
- inverse 2406
- longitudinale 1168
- perpendiculaire 416
famille de courbes 703
feldspath 712
fente 409
- de dessiccation 2087
ferrugineux 715
filet fluide 2672
- irrégulier 2676
film de surface 2717
filon 506, 2888
filon-couche 2551
filtrat de boue 2088
filtre 723
- de gravier 873, 875
fissure 733
- capillaire 2041
flanc 735
flaque d'eau 2300
flétrir 3015
fleuve 2417, 2662
- intermittent 1063
- souterrain 2692
flexible 737
flexure 738
floculation 742
florescéine 769
flot de base 149
flottation 753
flotteur 739
fluage 401
fluctuation dûe aux marées
    2785
- phréatique 2217
fluide 766
- de forage 575
- homogène 942
fluorine 770
flux 772
fonction caractéristique (de
    puits pompé) 2991
fond de la rivière 2420
- du puits 192
fontaine 781
fonte de neige 2584
forage 571
- à l'air 39
- au câble 216
- au diamant 495
- de reconnaissance 692
- par battage 2194
- par battage au câble 221
- plein diamètre 799
- profond 448
- rotary inverse 2407
force de capillarité 238
- de gravité 883
- de viscosité 2898
- osmotique 2144
forces massiques 189

forer 568
foreuse à percussion 294
formation 2429
- de pluie 777
- de rosée 491
- lacustre 1117
forme du bassin 161
- d'une particule 863
- morphologique 1123
- sphérique 2624
formule de Thiem 2776
fosse 2242
fossé 532
- de drainage 551
- de recharge 2359
fouille de recherche 2764
fracturation 784
- hydraulique 953
- hydraulique des puits 2990
fracture 782
fragile 794
frange capillaire 239
fréquence 788
- des éléments du réseau 2667
friable 794
froid 321
front d'appel 3014
- d'emprunt 3014
- d'onde 2969
fuite 1143
fumerolle 800
fusion 2020

gabbro 802
gaine isolante 1046
galerie de drainage 553
- d'infiltration 1026
galet 2181
galvanomètre 809
garniture 818, 2165
gâteau de boue 724
gaz 812
gazéifère 813
gaz naturel 2099
gazoduc 819
gel dans le sol 798
générateur de pulsations 2302
- de son 2610
géochimie 824
géodésie 825
géohydrologie 827
géologie structurale 2679
géomorphologie 837
géophysique 840
géothermique 841
geyser 843
gisement de pétrole 2126
glace 995
- carbonique 602
- de fond 72
- interstitielle 1068
- profonde 72
glaciation 850
glacier 851
- actif 21
glaciologie 854
glissement 2571
- de terrain 615, 1125
gneiss 855
gonflement 2735

gonflement du sol 2600
gorge 857
gouffre 9
gradient 861
- géothermique 842
- hydraulique 860
- vertical de la température 1129
grain 2654
granodiorite 866
granule 868
granuleux 867
granulométrie mécanique 2543
- uniforme 3000
graphique de distribution 529
grappin 869
grauwacke 886
gravier 870
gravière 874
gravier fluvioglaciaire 2150
gravillon concassé 419
gravimètre 876
grenat 811
grés 2466
grossièreté 313
grotte 260
groupe de pompes 2309
- géohydrologique 826
grue de levage 938

hautes-eaux 933
hauteur d'aspiration 1150, 2694, 2695
- d'eau 2631, 2958
- d'eau équivalente 2934
- de précipitation 472
- de transpiration 2826
- d'évaporation 470
- hydraulique 955
- piézométrique 2230
- pluviométrique 473
hétérogene 930
homogène 941
horizon-C 293
horizon d'accumulation 3033
- d'apport 3033
- de la roche-mère 493
- de lessivage 3036
- durci 921
- éluvial 37, 3036
- ferrugineux 714
- illuvial 175
hornblende 68, 945
huile minérale 2046
humidité 949
- absolue 5
- relative 2383
hydration 950
hydraulique 960
hydroconductibilité 962
hydrogène sulfuré 966
hydrogéochimie 967
hydrogéologie 968
hydrogramme 969
- d'écoulement 517
- du puits 2992
- indiciel 282
- simple 2559
- unitaire 2868

hydrogramme unitaire synthétique 2742
hydrographie 971
hydroisohypse 1087
hydrologie 977
- des nappes souterraines 827
hydrolyse 978
hydromancie 543
hydrométéorologie 979
hydrométrie 981, 2935
hydrophile 982
hydrophobe 983
hydrophyte 984
hydrosphère 985
hyétogramme 987, 2655
hygromètre 988
hypolimnion 993
hypothèses de Dupuit 608
hystérésis 994
- capillaire 240

ignimbrite 2314
illite 999
imbibition 1001
- d'eau (sous forme de marais) 2941
immiscible 1002
impédance 1003
imperméable 1005, 1171
inclinaison du terrain 890
inclinomètre 1010
incompressible 1012
incrustation 1013
indicateur de pointe 406
- limnimétrique 2634
indice d'aération 38
- de bifurcation 178
- de saturation 88
- des vides 2899
- de variation 320
- du relief 2387
- infiltration 1027
induction 1017
infiltration 1023
- provoquée 1015
infiltromètre 1029
Infracambrien 105
infradrainage 2863
inhibiteur de corrosion 394
injecter 1036
injectivité 1038
inondation 743, 1074
inondé 597
insolation 1043
installation de filtration 725
- de forage par battage 220
- de forage pour l'avant-trou 2629
- de forage standard 2641
- de tamisage 248
installations de forage 581
instant de la première arrivée 112
intensité de cisaillement 2528
- de la pluie 2329
- de pluie 2333
intercalé 1051
intercepte 1054
interception 1055
interdigitation 1057

interface 1058
interférence de puits 2993
interprétation des diagraphies 1167
interstice de formation 2141
interstices secondaires 2492
intrusion 1072
invasion 1076
- d'eau 2937
- des eaux salées 2491
inversion 1078
iodure d'argent 2557
irradiation solaire 2603
irrigation 1081
isobathe 1084
isochrone 1085
isopièze 1087
isotherme 1090
isotope 1091
- radioactif 2325
isotropique 1092

jaillir 2628
jauge à chaîne 275
jaugeage à gué 2911
- chimique 634
jauge de profondeur 469
- fluviale 469
jaugeur 2010
- à câble 3019
- Parshall 411
jet 1095
jeu du trépan 181
joint 818, 1099, 1100
- de dessiccation 483
- de refroidissement 383
- de stratification 166
- de tige 2799
- d'expansion 690
- fileté 2778
- isolant 1047
- soudé 2981
Jurassique 1103

kame 1105
kaolin 1106
karst 1107

lac 1120
laccolith 1115
- de glace 972, 2235
lac de barrage 2392
- de cratère 399
- intérieur 1039
- salé 2457
lacustre 1116
lac volcanique 2904
lagune 1118
lait de glacier 852
laitier de ciment 271, 2488
laiton siliceux 2548
lame coupante 431
lamination 1122
lapidification 360
latérite 1136
lave à blocaux 188
- en coussins 2233
législation des eaux 2938
lentille d'eau douce 793
- imperméable 1007

lessivage 1142
levé 2728
levée 1148
- de rive 2100
- topographique 2718
liaison hydrogène 964
ligne de base des marnes 152, 2523
- de charge 650, 652
- de côte 316
- de courant 2669
- de crête 404, 552
- de faille 707
- de partage 536, 552, 2955
- de partage entre deux bassins hydrogéologiques 902
- de partage topographique 2800
- de recharge 2358
- de séparation (des eaux) 536
- isohyète 1086
- isoplèthe 1088
- isopotale 1089
limite des neiges éternelles 2583
- de succion 2696
- fixe 734
- supérieure du pergelisol 2201
limnigraphe 2959
- à bulles 206
- à flotteur 740
limnologie 1154
limon 1161
liquide 1155
lissage 429
lit 165, 2660
- d'une rivière 2418, 2663
lithologie 1157
lithosphère 1159
- , zone plastique de la 3038
- , zone supérieure de la 3039
littoral 1160
lobe du glacier 853
loess 1183
log 1164
Loi de Darcy 438
longueur de mélange 2056
lumachelle 386
lysimètre 1175

macropore 1176
magma 1177
magnétite 1181
maille 2029
maillet 2569
maladie d'origine hydrique 2926
manchon de tubage 254, 2238
manivelle 398
manomètre 1184
- à mercure 2027
marbre 1186
mare 2734
marécage 190
- fluvial 2422
marée terrestre 617
marle 109, 1189
marmite torrentielle 2282
marteau pneumatique 41
masse 2569
- tige 569
mât de forage 581, 1196

matelas de gaz 814
matériel non-consolidé 1011
matière en suspension 2731
- polluante 2260
matrice d'outil 2798
méandre 2001
mécanique des sols 2591
médiane 2016
ménisque 2025
mésophyte 2031
mesure 2006
mesures contre les algues 49
métal alcalin 53
météorologie 2035
méthode d'application 2037
- de lavage par contre-courant 130
- des traceurs 2815
- d'infiltration par fossés 533
- d'infiltration par inondation 746
- gravimétrique 884
- numérique 2117
- par bassins d'infiltration 158
- par compression (Mariotte) 816
- par différences finies 729
- par expansion de gaz 816
- par injection de mercure 2028
- par itération 2039
- par remontée 2369
micaschiste 2040
micropore 2042
microtamis 2043
migration 2044
- capillaire 241
milieu aquifère 100
- poreux 2272
minéral accessoire 10
minéraux 2047
- argileux 301
minuterie 2796
Miocène 2052
miroir de faille 2570
miscible 2053
mise à la terre 888, 891
- à zéro 3028
mobile 2846
mobilité chimique 287
- des ions 1079
mode 2058
modèle 2059
- à membrane élastique 2023
- analogique 70
- en sable 2463
modification artificielle du temps 2975
module d'élasticité 3027
mollisol 2068
moment cinétique 2069
monel 2070
monoclinal 2071
montagne tabulaire 2743
montmorillonite 2074
monture 785
moraine 2076

moraine de retrait 2352
- frontale 2759
- latérale 1135
moufle 2301
- fixe 418
mouillabilité 3008
moulinet 428, 2438
mouton 595
mouvement de rotation 2437
moyenne annuelle 85
- arithmétique 111
- géométrique 834
mur imperméable (d'un
    aquifer) 1171
mylonite 2096

nappe aquifère inclinée 2790
- captive 349
- libre 2859
- perchée 2190
neige 2578
- carbonique 602
nettoyage de la paroi colmatée
    d'un puits 446
névé 730
niveau 1149
- à flotteur 740
- d'eau 2939
- de base 150
- de base d'érosion 151
- de la mer 2487
- de la nappe phréatique 904
- de référence 442
- de référence zéro 3029
- du sol 889
- moyen des mers 2004
- phréatique 2962
- piézométrique (d'une nappe
    libre) 904
nivellement 859
- latérale 1133
nivomètre 2582
noeud 2111
nombre de Horton 947
- de tours 2116
non perméable 1006
normale 2113
noyé 2940
noyau de condensation 341
- hygroscopique 991
nuage 310
numéro d'ordre d'un cours
    d'eau 2670

oasis 2119
obsidienne 2122
océan 2123
Oligocène 2128
olivine 2129
onde de choc 2537
- de cisaillement 2830
- de compression 334
- de crue 752
- longitudinale 1169
- sismique 2506
- transversale 2531
oolithique 2130
optimisation 2134
orage 2654
Ordovicien 2135

orientation 2139
orifice d'adduction 1041
orthogonalité 2143
oscillographe enregistreur 2367
oued 2915
outil à forage 572
- à jet 1096
- à lames 545
- aléseur 2347
- à molettes 2433
- à section en croix 415
- bilame 732
- de repêchage 731
- pilote 2234
- usé 606
ouverture de maille 2544
- des mailles 2030
oxyde de silicium 2550
- ferrique 713
oxygène 2163

packer 2165
palan 185
Paléocène 2168
paroi d'un puits 2541, 2913
particule 2174
- de sol 2595
parties par million 2176
passerelle de derrick 2444
pédiment 2182
pellicule alluviale 61
- de surface 2717
pendage 510
pendagemétrie 511
pendage original 2140
pénéplaine 2185
pénétrable 2186
pénétration complète d'un puits
    329
pente 702, 2573
- ascendante 11
- de la ligne d'eau 2961
pénurie d'eau 2956
percée épigénétique 2706
percolation 2193
percoler 2192
perforateur 2996
- à balles 914
perforation 2198
pergelisol 2200
périmètre d'appel 901
- du bassin 160
- mouillé 3010
période 2199
- glaciaire 847
perméabilité effective 622
- intrinsèque 1071
- relative 2384
- transversale 2829
perméable 2211
perméamètre 2208
Permien 2209
perte de boue 2090
- de charge 796, 923
- de charge dans un puits 2995
- diélectrique 500
- d'interception 1056
- par évaporation 679
- par infiltration 233
pertes initiales 1033

pertes par absorption 620
pétrographie 2212
phase solide 2604
phénomène d'instabilité 1044
photogéologie 2213
photogrammétrie 2214
photographie aérienne 31
photomultiplicateur 2215
phréatophythe 2222
phtanite 2555
phyllade 2224
physiographie 2226
phytomètre 2227
pièce d'ajustage 24
pierre ponce 2303
piézomètre 2229
pile sèche 600
pipeline 2239
plage 164
plaine alluviale 60
- basse 193
- de lavage 2151
- de piémont 2228
- d'inondation 748
- littorale 315
plan de comparaison 442
- de diaclase 1101
- de faille 708
- de stratification 167
- d'hodographe 934
planimètre 2245
plaque de base 154
plateau 2246
- continental 370
plate-forme d'effusion 1139
- de service 2133
Pléistocène 2248
pli 773
Pliocène 2249
ploiement vers le bas 542
pluie 2327
- efficace 626
- excédentaire 2328
- tombant directement sur le
    sol (à travers le feuillage)
    2781
- torrentielle 213, 311
pluviographe 2366
pluviomètre 2331
- standard 2112
- totalisateur 2652
podzol 2254
poids spécifique 2618, 2978
- spécifique apparent 209
point arbitraire 1197
- de choc 2536
- de concentration 337
- de congélation 787
- de flétrissure 3016
- de flétrissure permanente 2205
- de fusion 2021
- de montée 2257
- de référence 2376
- de rosée 492
- de saturation 2472
- de stagnation 2636
- de tir 2540
- d'inflexion 2256
- d'interception 1054
pointe 405, 2178

pointe de crue 745
- de mesure 943
point fixe 172
- neutre 2107
- triple 2842
poise 2258
polarisation 2259
pollution 2262
- organique 2138
pompage de l'eau 2947
pompe à boue 2092
pompe à double effet 540
- à engrenage 823
- à jet 1097
- à piston 2251
- à plongeur 2243, 2251
- aspirante 2698
- à turbine 2852
- à turbine immergée 449
- centrifuge 273
- doseuse 2036
- foulante 526
- immergée 2684
- submersible 2684
ponceau 423
pore 2266
porosimètre 2270
porosité 2271
- absolue 6
- d'interstice primaire 2141
- libre 623
- ouverte 624
- secondaire 2493
- totale 2809
- utile 624
potabilité 2273
potamologie 2275
potasse 2276
potentiel 2277
- de contact 367
- de force 775
- de jonction 1102
- de membrane 2024
- de vélocité 2891
- électrochimique 635
- électrocinétique 2668
- piézométrique 2231
- redox 2371
- spontané 2510, 2626
- zeta 3030
potentiomètre 2281
poulie 2532
poussée d'Archimède 211
pouvoir auto-épurateur 2509
- d'échange ionique 688
- de rétention d'eau 2619
- érosif 671
- évaporant 684
- hygroscopique 990
précipitation 2285
- cyclonique 434
- de convection 379
- de relief 2142
- efficace 625
- excédentaire 2287
précipitations cumulées 13
précipitation sur les surfaces
    d'eau libre 279
prélèvement latéral 1131
presse-étoupe 2167, 2680

pression 2289
- absolue 7
- barométrique 142
- d'air 44
- de pore 2268
- de refoulement 519
- de saturation 2473
- de service 3023
- de vapeur 2883
- différentielle 501
- en débit 757
- excédentaire 2161
- géostatique 2155
- hydrostatique 986
- initiale 1035
- osmotique 2145
- partielle 2173
principe des images 2038
prise d'échantillon 2460
- du ciment 2515
procédé de transport 2828
- géomorphique 836
processus d'érosion 669
production cumulée 424
- d'eau en excès des réserves
    d'exploitation 2051
produit de désintégration radio-
    active 445
profil de crue 749
- de dépression 957
- de sol à horizons 3032
- en long d'une rivière 2671
- sismique 2503
profondeur critique 410
- de la neige 474
- de pénétration 471
- envahie 1077
- normale 2114
propagation de crues 750
- des ondes 2971
propager 2443
propriétés caractéristiques
    de l'eau 2948
- élastiques 631
protection cathodique 258
- contre la pollution 2263
- contre les crues 744
- sanitaire d'un puits 2467
protubérance de la nappe 905
province des eaux souterraines
    906
psychromètre 2299
puisage d'eau 2928
puisard 2704
puissance d'une couche 2774
puits 2521, 2561
- abandonné 1
- absorbant 527
- alésé 2346
- à poulie 564
- artésien 115
- artésien sans écoulement
    libre 2682
- collecteur 325
- creusé 605
- creusé par jets d'eau 1098
- de limnigraphe 806
- de mesure 806, 2648
- de pétrole 2127
- de recharge 8, 2361

puits d'essai 2763
- développé dans plusieurs
    nappes superposées 2094
- d'injection 527
- d'observation 2121
- élargi 2346
- enfoncé 591
- excentrique 618
- fictif 1000
- imparfait 2172
- imparfait effleurant la
    nappe 2749
- incomplet 2172
- ouvert 2857
- permanent 2204
- peu profond 2524
- sec 601
- tarissant 701
pycnomètre 2311
pyrite 2312
pyroxène 2315

quantité scalaire 2475
- tensorielle 2758
quartz 2318

rabattement 562
- résiduel 2393
- spécifique 2616
rabotage 2848
raccord réducteur 2373
radio-isotope 2325
rajeunissement 2382
ralimentation 2388
rapide 2336
rapport précipitation-évapora-
    tion 2286
- sur le puits 2999
ravin 2344
rayon 2970
- d'action 2326
- d'appel 556, 2326
- d'entrée de pore 2267
- d'étranglement de pore 2267
- hydraulique 958
rayonnement net 2105
récepteur 2349
recharge 2357
- artificielle 117
récif 2375
récipient 2362
reconditionnement 3024
recristallisation 2370
récupération 2363, 2368
- d'eau 2949
réducteur 2372
réduction de la superficie 2712
- de l'évaporation 682
réflexion sismique 2504
réflexions multiples 2095
reflux 127, 2404
refoulement de la pompe 2304
refouler 1809
réfraction sismique 2505
regelation 2377
régime 762
- d'eau funiculaire 801
- d'écoulement saturé 2469
- de saturation 2474
- des eaux cunéiformes 2184

région karstique 1108
rejet vertical 2782
relation hauteur-temps 2633
relief 2385
- maximum 1198
remblai de gravier 872
remblaiement 12, 33
- de vallée 2878
remontée phréatique 2218
rendement 3026
répartition hypsométrique 106
réseau 2106
- à résistances - capacitances 2395
- d'alimentation 2709
- de drainage 554, 558
- fluvial 2423
- hydrographique 554, 558
- orthogonal des lignes de courant et des courbes isopièzes 700
- pluviométrique 2332
- synoptique 2741
réservoir 2390
- de compensation 2381
- en eaux souterraines 909
réservoir-jaugeur 805
résidu 2394
- après évaporation 2394
- sec 604
résistance acoustique 19
- à la compression 335
- à la rupture 200
- à la salinité 2458
- à la traction 2757
- à l'écoulement 544, 763, 2397
- à l'usure 2973
- au cisaillement 2529
- au sel 2458
résistivité 2398
- apparente 95
- électrique 632
ressaut hydraulique 956
ressources en eau 2951
retard 455, 1119, 2793
rétention 2403
- dans les dépressions du sol 2720
- de l'écoulement 484
- provisoire 2714
retenue au tamis 2545
revêtement 317, 425
rhyolite 2408
ride de fond 2412
rigole 768
rincer 2411
rivage 2538
rive 136
- haute 931
rivière 2417, 2662
- alimentant la nappe 1032
- alimentée par la nappe 628
- à marées 2786
- antécédente 90
- conséquente 358
- continue 372
- éphémère 659
- interrompue 1066
- isolée 1045
- naturelle 2102

rivière obséquente 2120
- pérenne 2196
- remblayante 34
- réséquente 2389
- subséquente 26, 2686
robinet 318
- de vidange 560
roche 2426
- caverneuse 262
- cristalline 421
- détritique 298
- endurcie 1019
- extrusive 629, 698
- hydatogène 685
- ignée 998
- intrusive 1073
- lapidifiée 359
- mère 2171
- saine 2856
roches carbonatées 248
roche solide 169
roches siliceuses 2546
rondelle 2916
rotary à commande hydraulique 959
roue à aubes 1004
ruban de mesure 2748
rugosité 2440
- du lit 170
ruisseau 400, 2425
ruissellement 2840
- de surface 2159, 2721
- de surface direct 514
- le long du tronc 2646
- sur le terrain 2159

sable 2461
- argileux 300, 2525
- de dune 607
- éolien 536
- fin 726, 728
- grossier 312
- mouvant 2319
- moyen 2018
- propre 305
- pur 305
- très fin 2893
- très gros 727
- vert 887
sabot de guidage 912
- de tubage 256
salina 52
saprolite 2468
saturation de seuil 2779
- en gaz 820
- excédentaire 2708
- irréductible 1080
saumure 204
sceau 207
schéma de pont 202
schiste 2480
schistosité 2481
scintillomètre 2482
scorie 2567
s'ébouler 261
sec à l'air 40
- à l'étuve 2152
séchage 479
sécheresse 596
s'écrouler 261
section du sol 2596

section étranglée 362
- hydraulique 957
- tranquille 2320
sédimentation 2495
segment de tarissement 2356
- non-influencé de l'hydrogramme 96
séisme 616
sel gemme 917
séparateur d'air 46
- d'eau 2954
- de gaz 821
- de sable 2465
séparation 2512
série lithologique 2513
serpentine 2514
seuil 2552
- hydraulique 899
sifflet déviateur 3012
silex impur 289
silice 2550
- amorphe 66
silt 2553
Silurien 2556
similitude cinématique 1111
- dynamique 611
- géométrique 835
simulateur pluviométrique 2330
singularité 521
siphon 2564
siphonnage 2565
sismomètre 838, 2507
socle 145
sodium 2588
sol arrable 2608
- azonal 126
- halomorphe 918
solifluction 2606
sol latéritique 1137
- rocheux 1158
- sablonneux 2379
solubilité 2607
soluble dans l'eau 2957
solution analogique 71
- numérique 2118
solution-tampon 208
sommet 403, 2703
sondage à la grenaille 2539
- d'essai 2763
sonde 940, 2121, 2297
- monoélectrode 2072
- tordue 413
sondeur de la profondeur d'eau 705
sonnette 593
sortie de boue 2091
soulèvement 2872
soupape de commande 378
source 2612, 2627
- artésienne 114
- artésienne en libre débit 756
- chaude 2914
- chlorurée 2451
- de contact 368
- de débordement 144
- de dépression 468
- de déversement 197, 885
- de faille 2861
- de fissures 783

source de fossette 280
- de neutrons 2109
- de ruissellement 2501
- de vallée 2880
- d'infiltration 2501
- froide 385
- gazeuse naturelle (en CO$_2$) 247
- geysérienne 843
- intermittente 1062
- minérale 2048
- pérenne 2195
- ponctuelle 507
- thérapeutique 2017
- thermale 2769
- tubulaire 2849
sous-sol 2688
soustraire 3021
souterrain 2691
spéléologie 2623
spot lumineux 1151
stalactite 2638
stalagmite 2639
station de jaugeage 808
- de pompage 2307
- hydrométrique 980
stockage dans les dépressions du sol 2653
- de gaz dans une couche aquifère 101
- de surface 2714
- en forme de coin 2976
storativité 2651
stratification 2658
- entrecroisée 414
- par salinité 2454
- thermique 2770
stratigraphie 2659
structure chaotique 281
- du sol 2598
- massive 1194
sublimation 2683
subsidence de la surface 1126
substratum imperméable 1171
succession stratigraphique 2693
succion de l'eau dans le sol 2593
suintement 2497
- de surface 2722
suite de couches 2693
sulfate 2700
- de calcium anhydre 82
superposition 2707
supersaturation 2708
suppression de l'évaporation 683
surcharge 2160
surface d'alimentation 1048
- de contact 366
- de la nappe phréatique 2219
- de réception 2350
- d'érosion 670
- de séparation 366
- de suintement 2502
- du lit majeur 2153
- d'une nappe perchée 2191
- du sol 2599
- hydrostatique 2962

surface libre des eaux souterraines 2962
- mouillée 3009
- piézométrique 2232
- spécifique 2620
- terrestre 1127
surforage 2918
surpression atmosphérique 804
sursaturation 2708
susceptibilité magnétique 1180
syénite 2738
synclinal 2740
système de couches aquifères superposées 2093
- de racines 2587
- lithologique 2430
- ouvert 2132

tableau des hauteurs 2635
table de rotation 2439
taille des grains 864
talc 2745
talus continental 371
talweg 2766
tambour 598
- de forage 210
- du câble 218
- enregistreur 2365
tamis 2484, 2542
tarière 121
tarir 2445
tassement 2166
- des grains 862
taux de dessèchement 2339
- de production 2341
technique des modèles 2060
tectonique 2679, 2750
téléférique 222
télémesure 2752
température de formation 779
tempête 2654
temps de base 155, 2791
- de concentration 2794
- de montée 2795
- de mouillage 3011
- de parcours 2821
- de propagation 2821
- de réponse 1119
teneur antécédente d'eau dans le sol 89
- en eau 2930
- en eau par volume 2909
- en humidité 2063
- en humidité par gravimétrie 877
- en matière organique 2137
tenseur de perméabilité 2207
tension aux bornes 2148
- de l'eau dans le sol 2594
- interfaciale 1059
- intergranulaire 1061
- limite 2673
- superficielle 2724
terrain 2761
terrasse 2760
- d'accumulation 722
- de remblaiement 722
- du replat de versant 2657
- fluviale 2424

terrasse rocheuse 2431
terre d'infusoires 498
tête de carottier 390
- de levage 937
- de puits 2081, 3003
- d'injection 1037, 2737
texture de sol 2765
- des roches 2432
thalweg 2766
thermocline 2771
thermocouple 2772
thermomètre 2773
- à résistance 2396
thixotropie 2777
tige carrée 1109
- de battage 2562
tiges de forage 584
tir en éventail 704
toit 2154
- imperméable d'un aquifère 2873
tôle perforée 2575
top 1110
topographie 2801
torrent 736
torsion 2803
tortuosité 2805
tourbe 2180
tourbière 2075
tourbillon 619, 3013
tourmaline 2811
tournant d'un fleuve 2419
trace du stylet 2189
traceur 2814
- radioactif 2323
train de tiges 583
traînée 544
traitement acide de puits 16
- des eaux d'égouts 2520
- des puits 3002, 3004
trajectoire des ondes 2970
tranchant de l'outil 290
transducteur 2817
- de pression 2295
transfert de chaleur 928
- d'énergie 653
- massique 1195
transformation conforme 352
transgression 2818
transition 2819
transmission 2822
transmissivité 2824
transpiration 2825
- cuticulaire 430
- par stomata 2649
transport de sédiments 2496
transporteur aérien 222
transports solides 2496
travaux de terrain 721
travertin 2831
treillis 2833
tremblement de terre 616
trémie 944
trémolite 2835
trépan 567, 572
- au diamant 496
treuil de forage 565
- de jaugeage 2011
- de levage 935
Trias 2836

tributaire 2837
tricône 2841
tripoli 2843
tritium 2844
trou 940
trouble 2851
trou d'aération 47
– d'échappement 47
– de forage 191, 940
– de puits 2997
– de vidange 304
tubage 253, 2236, 2237
– de protection 2298
– double 2656
– plein 183
– temporaire 2755
tube à mesure 2013
– Bourdon 198
– carottier 389
– de Pitot 2244
– sans soudure 2489
tuf 2850
– soudé 2314
tunnel de lave 1140
turbidité 2851
turboforeuse 2853
turbulence 2854
tuyeau 2236
– d'aspiration 2697
– de débit 518
– de drainage 559
– de refoulement 518
– en terre cuite 2788
– flexible 737

uniforme 2865
Unité Meinzer (USA) 2019
usine d'eau 2966
usure 120
utilisation de l'eau 2963
– des terres 1128
– jointe 356

valeur discontinue 522
– du pH 2223
– limite 1153
– maximale 2178
– moyenne 2005
vallée 2877
– antécédente 91
– anticlinale 92
– d'effondrement 2410
– enterrée 212
– structurale 2751
– subséquente 2675
– surimposée 2706
– synclinale 2739
– tributaire 2839
vanne 2881
– de contrôle 377
– de réglage 378
– maîtresse 1183
vanne-papillon 214
vanne principale 822
vapeur d'eau 2964
vaporisation 2882
variance 2884
variation saisonnière 2490
varve 2885
veine d'eau 893

vernier 2892
versant d'une vallée 2879
vésiculeux 2894
vidange 547
vides 2900
vigueur du relief 2386
viscosimètre 2896
viscosité 2897
vitesse 2889
– apparente 440
– ascensionnelle 2416
– dans les pores 2847
– Darcy 440
– d'avancement 2187
– de cisaillement 2530
– de décantation 2518
– de filtration 440
– de forage 580
– de gonflement 2736
– de terrain 720
– d'infiltration 2500
– du son 2611
– interstitielle 2847
– limite de sédimentation 2518
volcanisme 997, 2902
voltmètre 2907
volume de la phase solide 2605
– des pleins 2605
– des pores 2269
– spécifique 2621
– total des pores 2808

wollastonite 3022

xérophyte 3025

zéro de l'échelle 807
zircon 3031
zone au voisinage du sol 2602
– d'aération 3034
– d'appel 375
– de broyage 2526
– de départ 293
– de dispersion 524
– de la roche mère en voie
  d'altération 293
– de l'eau soutenue 2221
– de perte de boue 2775
– de pluie 3037
– de rétention 3034
– de saturation 3040
– des méandres 2002
– de transition 2820
– de transition saumâtre 2378
– d'évaporation 2602
– d'investigation 3035
– du gel annuel 84
– envahie 771, 1075
– failleuse 710
– fracturée d'un système de
  failles 2526
– inondable 748
– non-contaminée 2862
– phréatique 2221
– plastique de la lithosphère
  3038
– radiculaire 2435
– supérieure de la lithosphère
  3039

GERMAN

D

Abbildung, konforme 352
Abbinden des Zements 2515
Abdampfrückstand 2394
Abdeckung, mechanische 2015
Abdichtungszementbrühe 2488
Abfallbeseitigung 2919
Abfälle 2921
abfallender Kurvenast der
    Ganglinie 2354
Abfallstoffe 2921
Abfangen 1055
Abfluss 515, 2147, 2446
- , unterirdischer 2689
Abflussbeiwert 2447
Abflussfaktor 557
Abflussformel, rationale 2343
Abflussganglinie 517, 969
- , einfache 2559
Abflussgebiet 548
Abflusshydrograph 517
Abflusskurve 2342, 2632
abflussloses Becken 309
Abflusslosigkeit 1065
Abflussnetz 554
Abflussrückgang 2355
Abflusstafel 2635
Abgleiten 2571
Abgrund 9
Ablagerung, organogene 2136
Ablass 547
Ablasshahn 560
Ablassöffnung 304
Ablation 2
ableiten 535
Ableitung, richtungsgebundene
    513
Ablenkkeil 3012
Abrieb 120
Abrundung 2442
Absatz 2760
Abschiebung 2115
Abschleifung 2848
Absenkung 562
- , spezifische 2616
Absenkungsbereich 295
Absenkungsbetrag 562
Absenkungsfläche 107
Absenkungsganglinie 2792
Absenkungskurve 563
Absenkungsradius 2326
Absenkungstrichter 346
Absetzbecken 2516, 2577
Absetzfaktor 466
Absetzgeschwindigkeit 2518
Absolutdruck 7
absolute Atmosphere 4
- Feuchtigkeit 5
- Permeabilität 1071
- Porosität 6
Absonderung, säulenförmige 326
Absorption, selektive 2508
Absperrventil 283
Abstandsgeschwindigkeit 720
Abstandsgleiche 1088
Abtragung 451, 463, 668
Abtragungsfläche 670
Abtragungsvorgang 669
Abwasser 2261, 2519, 2922
Abwasserbehandlung 2520
Abwasserlast 2920

Abwasserreinigung 2520
Abwasserrückgewinnung 2949
Abweichung 87, 487
- von der Basislinie der SP
    Kurve 464
Ackerkrume 2608
adiabatisch 25
Adsorption 28
Advektion 29
aerobisch 32
Aggregat 35
aggressiv 36
Ähnlichkeit, dynamische 611
- , geometrische 835
- , kinematische 1111
Ähnlichkeitsbedingungen 2558
A-Horizont 37, 3036
Akkumulation 14, 33
- , fluviatile 12
akkumulierender Fluss 34
aktiver Gletscher 21
Aktivität, induzierte 1014
Aktivitätskoeffizient 23
Aktivwässer 22
Albedo 48
Algenbekämpfung 49
Algenkalkstein 50
Algonkium 51
Alkalimetall 53
Alkalinität 54
allochthon 55
alluviale Aufschüttungsebene
    60
- Gletscherablagerung 56
- Rinne 57
alluvialer Schuttfächer 58
Alluvium 62
amorphe Kieselsäure 66
Ampèremeter 65
Amphibol 68
Amplitude 69
analogische Lösung 71
Analoglösung 71
Analogmodell 70
- mit elektrisch leitender
    Schicht 343
Analyse, chemische 284
- , morphometrische 2078
- , statistische 2643
Andesit 73
Anfangsbedingungen 1034
Anfangsdruck 1035
Anfangsverluste 1033
Angaben 441
angeschwemmt 55
angreifend 36
Anhäufung 14
Anhydrit 82
anisotropisch 83
Anlandung 2255
Annahme, Dupuit'sche 608
Annulus 86
Anomalie 87
Anordnung 2166
- , gitterförmige 2834
- , richtungsmässige 2139
Anreicherung 2388
Ansatz 2477
Anschwellen 2735
Anschwellrate 2736

Anschwemmung 2554
Anstehendes 169
anstehendes Gestein 169
ansteigender Hang 11
Anstiegspunkt 2257
antezedenter Flusslauf 90
antezedentes Tal 91
Anwendungsmethode 2037
Anziehungskraft, molekulare
    2066
Apatit 94
Aquädukt 98
Äquivalent, chemisches 286
Äquivalenzgewicht pro
    Million 665
Aragonit 104
Arbeitsbühne 2444
Archaikum 105
Arealeruption 2534
arid 110
arithmetrisches Mittel 111
Arkatopege 385
Arkatotherme 2914
artesische Quelle 114
artesischer Brunnen 115
- Grundwasserleiter 113
Atmometer 118
Atmosphäre 119
- , absolute 4
- , physikalische 4
Atmosphärenüberdruck 804
Auffangbehälter 939
Auffangfläche 2350
Auffanggefäss 2362
Auffülltrichter 347
Aufgabebunker 944
aufgelassene Bohrung 1
aufgesetztes Tal 2706
auflösen 528
Aufnahme der Radioaktivität
    2324
Aufnahmefähigkeit 235, 1038
Aufschlämmen 642
Aufschluss 2146
Aufschlussbohrung 692
Aufschotterungsterrasse 722
Aufschüttung 12, 33
Aufschüttungsebene, alluviale
    60
Aufschüttungsterrasse 722
Aufspaltung der Abflussgang-
    linie 970
Auftrieb 211
Augit 122
Ausbeute 2368, 3026
- , sichere 2449
Ausdehnungsverbindung 690
Ausfällung 742
- , chemische 285
Ausfällungszement 898
Ausfällungszone 175, 3033
- , eisenhaltige 714
ausfliessen 516
Ausflockung 742
Ausfluss 515, 627, 2147
- , hydraulischer 952
Ausgangsmaterial 2171
ausgewaschener Kies 2150
Ausgleichbehälter 2381
Ausgleichskurve 27, 2380

Ausgleichung 429
ausgraben 687
Auskleidung 317
Auslass 2560
Auslaufquelle 885
Auslaugung 1142
Auslaugungszone 37, 3036
ausnutzbares Wasser 124
Ausräumen einer kleinen
   Bohrung 2348
ausschachten 504
Ausschlag 1110
aussenbürtig 689
Aussendurchmesser 696
Ausseruferungsgebiet 2153
Austauschfähigkeit 688
Austauschvermögen 688
Austrocknung 479
Ausuferung 743
Ausuferungsgebiet 748
autochthon 123
Azidität 15
azonales Bodenprofil 126

Bach 400
Bahngeschwindigkeit 2847
Bakterien, krankheitserregende
   2177
Bandmasspegel 2748
Barograph 139
Barometer 140
barometrischer Druck 142
- Wirkungsgrad 141
Barriere 143
Basalkonglomerat 146
Basalt 147
Basenaustausch 148
Basisbreite 155
Basislinie 152, 2523
Basiszeit 2791
Batholith 162
Baumgussform 2832
Becken 156
- , abflussloses 309
Beckeneigenschaften 157
Beckenform 161
Beckenumfang 160
Bedienungsbühne 2133
Bedingungen,
   Ghyben-Herzberg'sche 844
Beeinflussung, geologische 831
Begleitmineral 10
begrenzt durchlässiger Grund-
   wasserstauer 103
Belastung, externe 697
- , zulässige 2210
Belüftung 30
Belüftungsgrad 452
Benetzbarkeit 3008
benetzter Querschnitt 3009
- Umfang 3010
Benetzungsdauer 3011
benthonischer Schiefer 174
Beobachtungsbohrung 2121
Beobachtungsgebiet 691
Beobachtungsnetz, synoptisches
   2741
Bergfeuchte 243
Bergfussebene 2228
Bergrutsch 2427

Berieselungsanlage 2330
Beruhigungsschacht 2648
Berührungsfläche 366
Berührungspotential 367, 1102
beschreibende Gewässerkunde
   971
Bestandteil 361
Bestandteile, flüchtige 2901
Beton 338
Betriebsdruck 3023
Bettrauhigkeit 170
Bettrauhigkeitszahl 2441
Bewässerung 1081
Bewässerungsbedarf 610, 1082
bewegliche Elektrode 2082
Bezugsebene 442
Bezugskurve 2632
- der Brunnenfunktion w (u) 2855
Bezugsmarke 172
Bezugsniveau 442
Bezugspunkt 1197, 2376
B-Horizont 175, 3033
biegsamer Schlauch 737
Bifurkationsverhältnis 178
Bikarbonat 176
Bildung, lakustre 1117
Bimsstein 2303
Binnensee 1039, 1120
biochemischer Sauerstoffbedarf
   (B.S.B.) 179
Biotit 180
bläschenförmig 2894
Blattmeissel 545
bleibende Härte 2202
Block, pyroklastischer 2313
Blockbild 186, 2647
Blockdiagramm 186
Blocklava 188
Boden, salzhaltiger 918
Bodenaggregat 2589
Bodendecke 2590
Bodenfeuchte 2601
Bodenfeuchtedefizit 2064
Bodenfeuchtemessgerät 2592
Bodenfeuchtesaugspannung 2594
Bodenfrost 798
Bodenkrume 2590
Bodenmechanik 2591
bodennahe Zone 2602
Bodenoberfläche 2599
Bodenpartikel 2595
Bodenprobe 2597
Bodenprofil 2596
- , azonales 126
- , zonales 3032
Bodenquellung 2600
bodenständig 123
Bodenstruktur 2598
Bodenteilchen 2595
Bodentextur 2765
Bodenventil 774
Bodenverdunstung 678
Bodenwasser 2601
Bodenwassergehalt, vorherge-
   hender 89
Bodenwassergürtel 2602
Bohranlage 581
Bohrdruck 182
bohren 568
Bohren 571

Bohren mit Luftspülung 39
Bohrer 537
Bohrflüssigkeit 575
Bohrfortschritt 2187
Bohrgerüst 581
Bohrgeschwindigkeit 580
Bohrgestänge 584
Bohrhaken 577
Bohrkern 387
Bohrkernuntersuchung 388
Bohrklein 432
Bohrkopf 2737
Bohrkrone 572
Bohrlochsbehandlung 3004
- zur Erhöhung der Schüttung
   3002
Bohrlochsmund 2081
Bohrlochsohle 192
Bohrlochswand 2913
Bohrmannschaft 574
Bohrmast 1196
Bohrmeissel 572
Bohrmeister 576
Bohrprotokoll 570, 1164
Bohrschlamm 579
Bohrschmand 579
Bohrschwengel 2912
Bohrseil 573, 578
Bohrspitze 592
Bohrspülung 575, 580
Bohrstrang 583
Bohrtrommel 210
Bohrturbine 2853
Bohrturm 475, 581
Bohrung 191, 940
- , aufgelassene 1
- , endgültige 2204
- , erweiterte 2346
- , trockene 601
- , unverrohrte 2857
Bohrzeitprotokoll 582
Böschungswinkel 79
Bourdondruckdose 198
Brackwasser 199
Brackwasserzone im Grund-
   wasserleiter 2378
Brandung 2711
Brauchwasser 1021
Brechung, seismische 2505
Brechungswinkel 78
Breckzie 201
Bruch 782
Bruchbildung 784
Bruchfestigkeit 200
brüchig 794
Bruchstufe 709
Bruchtal 2410
Brückenbildung 203
Brückenkreis 202
Brunnen, artesischer 115
- , exzentrischer 618
- , frei fliessender artesischer
   756
- , gegrabener 605
- , gerammter 591
- , imaginärer 1000
- , nachgeräumter 2346
- , subartesischer 2682
- , unvollkommener 2172, 2749
- , versiegender 701

Brunnenabstand 3001
Brunnenaufzeichnung 2999
Brunnenausrichtung 2982
Brunnenbau 2985
Brunnenbeeinflussung 2993
Brunnendurchmesser 2988
Brunnenentwicklung 2987
Brunnenergiebigkeit 2983,
   3006
Brunnenergiebigkeitsmass 2614
Brunnenfeld 2989
Brunnenformel, Thiem'sche
   2776
Brunnenfunktion 2991
Brunnengleichung, Theis'sche
   2767
Brunnen in einem Grundwasser-
   stockwerk 2094
Brunnenkette 2998
Brunnenkopf 3003
Brunnenöffnung 2081
Brunnenpfeife 163
Brunnenprotokoll 2999
Brunnenschacht 2997
Brunnenschüttung 3006
Brunnenschutz, sanitärer 2467
Brunnenumrandung 2986
Brunnenwandung 2541
Brunnenwasser 3005

Caisson 223
Canyon 234
chaotische Struktur 281
chemische Analyse 284
- Ausfällung 285
- Mobilität 287
chemischer Sauerstoffbedarf
   288
chemisches Äquivalent 286
Chlor 292
Chlorung 291
C-Horizont 293
Colibakterium 322
Cryologie 420
Curie 426

Dach 244
Dachentwässerung 2434
Damm 1148
Dampfdruck 2883
Dämpfung 436
Dämpfungseffekt 437
Darcy 439
Darcy Geschwindigkeit 440
Darcysches Gesetz 438
Dargebot 3026
Daten 441
Dauerfrost 2200
Dauerkurve 609
Dauerlast 2203
Dauerlinie 609
- der Abflussmenge 755
Dauerquelle 2195
Dauerspende 2197, 2733
Deckschicht 2873
Deckschichten 2154
Dehydrationswasser 2945
Deich 505, 1148
Delle 561
Delta 456

Delta-Ablagerungen 457
dendritisch 460
Denudation 463
Desorptionskurve 482
Detritus 486
Devon 488
Diagenese 494
Diaklase 1100
Diamantbohren 495
Diamantbohrkrone 496
Diastrophismus 497
Diatomeenerde 498
Diatrema 2104
Dichte 461, 1192, 2615
dichteste Packung 2787
dichtester Wert 2058
Dichteströmung 462
Dichtung 818, 2165
Dichtungsmittel 2250
Diebszone 2775
dielektrische Konstante 499
- Verschiebung 500
Dielektrizitätskonstante 499
Differentialdruck 501
Diffusion 502
Diffusionskonstante 503
Diopsid 508
Diorit 509
direkter Oberflächenabfluss 5 4
diskontinuierlicher Wert 522
Diskontinuität 521
Diskordanz 81, 520, 2860
diskrete Grösse 522
Dispersion 523
- , hydrodynamische 963
Dispersionszone 524
Doline 538, 2563
Dolomit 539
doppelt wirkende Pumpe 540
Doppelverrohrung 2656
Dosiergerät 711
Dosierpumpe 2036
Dränagerohr 559, 2788
Drehbewegung 2437
Drehtisch 2439
Drehwaage 2804
Drehzahl 2116
Dreirollenmeissel 2841
Drillstemtest 585
Drosselventil 214, 2780
Druck 2289
- , barometrischer 142
- , hydrostatischer 986
- , osmotischer 2145
Druckabfall 2292
Druckaufbaukurve 2290
Druckaufbauverfahren 2369
Druckdose 2291
Druckfestigkeit 335
Druckfläche 2232
Druckgeber 2295
Druckhöhe 641, 922, 2293
- , piezometrische 2230
Druckluft 332
Druckluftpegel 206
Druckmesser 2229
Druckpotential 2231
Druckrohr 518
Druckschreiber 139
Druckstoss 2294
Druckunterschied 501

Druckverlust 923, 2292
Druckwelle 334
Drumlin 599
Dünensand 607
dunkler Glimmer 180
dünner Schuttmantel 61
Dupuit'sche Annahme 608
durchdringbar 2186
Durchfluss 515
Durchflussmessgerät 759
Durchgangsgeschwindigkeit
   440
durchgehender Fluss 372
Durchlass 423
Durchlassfähigkeit 382
durchlässig 2186, 2211
Durchlässigkeit, effektive 622
- , relative 2384
Durchlässigkeitsbeiwert 319
- , relativer 2869
Durchlässigkeitsziffer 319
- , ungesättigte 2869
Durchleitung 2822
Durchlöcherung 2198
durchsickern 2192
durchströmen 2192
durchtränkt 2940
Dürre 596
Düse 1095
Düsenmeissel 1096
Düsenstrahlpumpe 1097
dynamische Ähnlichkeit 611
Dynamitladung 612
Dynamometer 613

eckig 80
Effekt, elektrokinetischer 638
effektive Durchlässigkeit 622
- Porosität 624
effektiver Niederschlag 625
- Regen 626
effektive Rückhaltung 620
Effusion 630
Eichfluss 803
Eichkurve 228
Eichung 227
Eigenpotential 2510, 2626
Eigenschaften, elastische 631
Eimer 207
eindämmen 1009
Eindampfungsgestein 685
Eindellung 542
Eindringen 646, 1076
- , vollkommenes ---eines
   Brunnens 329
- von Meerwasser 2491
Eindringkapazität 1022
Eindringöffnung 2715
Eindringung 464, 1072
Eindringungskapazität 655
Eindringungsrate 2340
Eindringungstiefe 471, 1077
Einebnung 859
- , seitliche 1133
einfache Abflussganglinie 2559
Einfallen 323, 510
- , ursprüngliches 2140
einfallender Grundwasserleiter
   2790
Einfallswinkel 76

Einfassung 425
Einflussfaktoren 376
Einflussöffnung 1041
Einflusstrichter 346
eingedämmtes Wasser 2265
eingeführtes Wasser 1008
eingeleitete Materialfrachtung 2917
Eingreifen, fingerförmiges 1057
Einheit, geohydrologische 826
einheitlich 2865
Einheitsergiebigkeit 2824
Einheitshydrograph 2868
-, theoretischer 2742
Einheitskurve der Abfluss-
  ganglinie 2868
- der Abflussganglinie,
  synthetische 2742
Einmuldung 542
einpressen 1036
Einpresszement 269
Einschnürung 362
Einsickerfähigkeit 1025
Einsickerung 1023
-, künstliche 1015
einstürzen 261
eintreiben 588
Einwirkungsfläche 107
Einzelelektrodensonde 2072
Einzugsgebiet 257, 548, 1048,
  2955
Einzugsradius 556
Eis 995
eisenhaltig 715
eisenhaltige Ausfällungszone 714
Eisenoxyd 713
Eisenrost 713
Eiskappe 996
Eislakkolith 972, 2235
Eiszeit 847
elastische Eigenschaften 631
Elastizitätsmodul 3027
elektrisches Kernen 633
elektrochemisches Potential
  635
Elektrode, bewegliche 2082
Elektrodenabstand 636
Elektrofiltration 637
elektrokinetischer Effekt 638
Elektrolyt 639
Elektrolyttankanalog 342
Eluvialhorizont 37, 3036
Empfänger 2349
Emulsionsspalter 645
Endeffekt 647
endgültige Bohrung 2204
Endmoräne 2759
endogen 648
endogenes Wasser 1178
Energiebilanz 649
Energielinie 650, 652
Energieumsatz 653
Entalpie 654
Entgasung 817
Entlüftungsöffnung 47
Entmineralisierung 459
Entnahme, sichere 2449
Entnahmeanordnung 2306
Entnahmebreite 3014
Entnahmefläche 375

Entnahmegebiet 375
entnehmen 3021
Entropie 656
Entsalzung 476
entspringen 2628
entwässern 489
Entwässern 490
Entwässerungsanordnung 555
Entwässerungsgebiet 548
Entwässerungsgraben 551
Entwässerungsnetz 558
Entwässerungsstollen 553
Eozän 657
epigenetisches Tal 2706
Epilimnion 660
Epoche 661
Erdbeben 616
Erdbeschleunigung 879
Erdbohrer 121
Erdgas 2099
Erdgezeitenbewegung 617
Erdöllagerstätte 2126
Erdstrom 614
Erdung 888
Erdungsanschluss 891
Ergiebigkeit, spezifische 2614,
  2622
Erguss 630
Ergussgestein 629, 698
Ergusstafel 1139
Erhebung 2872
Erkaltung 354
erodierbar 667
Erosion 668
Erosionsbasis 150, 151
Erosionsfähigkeit 671
Erosionsfläche 670
Erosionskessel 2282
Erosionsrinne 913
Erosionsterrasse im Vorrumpf
  2657
Erosionsvorgang 669
Erschöpfung 465
Erschütterungswelle 2506
ersoffen 597
Erstarrungskluft 383
Erstarrungskruste 353
Erstarrungsprozess 354
erweiterte Bohrung 2346
Erweiterungsbohrung 2348
Erzschnur 2676
Eutrophierung 675
Evaporation 677
Evaporit 676
Evapotranspiration 686
-, mögliche 2279
-, potentielle 2279
exogen 689
Exploration, geophysikalische
  839
Explosion 693
externe Belastung 697
Extrusivgestein 698
exzentrischer Brunnen 618

Fächerschiessen 704
fahrbar 2846
Faktor, lithologischer 1156
fallendes Wasser 2687
Fallwasser, prismatisch
  gespeichertes 2296

Fallwasserspeicherung,
  keilförmige 2976
Falte 773
Fangglocke 171
Fanghaken 869
Fangkeile 2572
Fanglomerat 59
Fangwerkzeug 731
Fassungsvermögen 235
Fastebene 2185
Fäustel 2569
Fazies 699
Fazieswechsel 700
Fehlbohrung 601
feiner Kies 727
Feinsand 726, 728
Feinsieb 2043
Feinstsand 2893
Feldarbeit 721
Feldkapazität 716
Feldspat 712
Felduntersuchung 718
Feldversuch 719
Feldwert der Durchlässig-
  keitsziffer 717
Fels, gewachsener 2856
Felsboden 1158
Felspanzer 229
Felspanzerbildung 921
Felsterrasse 2431
Fernleitung 2239
Fernmessung 2752
festgelegte Grenze 734
Festkörpergerüst 2604
Festkörpervolumen 2605
Feuchte 949
Feuchteansammlung 2062
Feuchteäquivalent 2065
Feuchtegehalt, gravimetrischer
  877
-, volumetrischer 2909
Feuchtigkeit, absolute 5
Feuchtigkeitsgehalt 2063
Feuerstein 289
Filter 723
Filteranlage 725
Filtergeschwindigkeit 440
Filterkoeffizient 2498
Filterkorb 2699
Filterkuchen 724
Filterrohr 2486
Filterströmung 2193
fingerförmiges Eingreifen 1057
Firn 730
Fischschwanzmeissel 732
Flachbrunnen 2524
Flächenberieselung 2723
Flächenerguss 2534
Flächenerosion 2533
flächenhafter Grundwasser-
  austritt 2501
- Wasseraustritt 2722
Flächensickerung 2722
Flächenzentrum des Nieder-
  schlages 274
Flanke 735
Flaschenzug 185
Flaschenzugblock 2301
Flechtmuster 2833
Flexur 738

Flexur, monokline 2071
Fliessbewegung, sehr langsame 402
Fliesschicht 2068
Fliessdruck 757, 955
Fliessdruckmesser 613
fliessen 754
- in offenem Kanal 2131
- von gespanntem Grundwasser 348
Fliessgeschwindigkeit, kritische 412
Fliessgeschwindigkeitslog 767
Fliessrate 761
Fliesstest 764
Fliesswiderstand 763, 2397
Flossverdunstungskessel 741
Flotieren 753
flüchtige Bestandteile 2901
Fluoreszein 769
Fluss 2417, 2662
- , akkumulierender 34
- , durchgehender 372
- , intermittierender 1063
- , isolierter 1045
- , konsequenter 358
- , kurzfristig fliessender 659
- , natürlicher 2102
- , obsequenter 2120
- , perennierender 2196
- , radialer 2321
- , resequenter 2389
- , spezifischer 772
- , subsequenter 26, 2686
- , ungesättigter 2870
- , unterirdischer 2692
- , versinkender 1066
- , wasserabgebender 1032
- , wasseraufnehmender 628
- , wirbelfreier 1083
flussabwärts 541
flussaufwärts 2874
Flussbett 2418, 2663
Flussbettbeschaffenheit 278
Flussschleife 2419
Flussdichte 550
Flussgabelung 177
Flüssigkeit 766, 1155
- , homogene 942
Flüssigkeitsstandanzeiger mit Schwimmer 740
Flusskunde 2275
Flusslauf 2421, 2664
- , antezedenter 90
Flussmorast 2422
Flussmündungsgebiet 456
Flussniederung 193
Flussohle 2420
Flusspat 770
Flussprofil 2671
Flussterrasse 2424
Flussstrecke 2421
Flussstreckenhäufigkeit 2667
Flusssystem 2423
Flutwelle 752
fluviatile Akkumulation 12
Folgefluss 358
Förderdruck 519
Förderrate 2341
Förderseil 936

Formation, lakustre 1117
Formationsfaktor 776
Formationstemperatur 779
Formationswiderstandsfaktor 778
Form des Einzugsgebietes 161
Formfaktor 780
Formveränderung 450
Frachtung, natürliche 2101
Frachtungsfähigkeit 252
freie Oberflächenenergie 786
freies Grundwasser 2859
frei fliessender artesischer Brunnen 756
Fremdbelastung 697
Fremdwasser 1008
Frequenz 788
Frequenzanalyse 789
Frischwasser 791
Frischwasserlinse 793
Flügelmessgerät 428
Führungsschuh 912
Fumarole 800
funikuläres Wasser 801
Furchenquelle 280
Furtmessung 2911
Fussfläche 2182
Fussgranit 162
Fussplatte 154
Futterrohrverbinder 254

Gabbro 802
Galvanometer 809
Gammalog 810
Gang 506, 2888
- , unregelmässiger 2676
Ganglinie der Niederschlagsintensität 987
- des Wasserstandes 969
Gas 812
Gasabscheider 821
Gasausdehnungsmethode (Boyle-Mariotte) 816
Gasaustausch 815
Gasfernleitung 819
gasführend 813
Gasleitung 819
Gaspolster 814
Gassättigung 820
Gasspeicherung im Wasserträger 101
Geber 2817
Gebietsbilanz 662
Gebirgskette 2080
Gefäll 702, 2573
geflutete Zone 771, 1075
Gefrierprozess 354
Gefrierpunkt 787
Gefrierzone, jährliche 84
Gefrornis 2200
Gegendruck 129
Gegenstrom 396
Gegenstromspülung 2405
Gegenströmung 396
gegrabener Brunnen 605
Gehäuse 948
Gelände 2761
Geländeneigung 890, 2387
Geländeoberfläche 889
Geochemie 824

Geodäsie 825
Geohydrologie 827
geohydrologische Einheit 826
Geologie, tektonische 2679
geologische Beeinflussung 831
- Korrelation 832
geologischer Schnitt 829
geologisches Log 833
geologische Verhältnisse 830
geometrische Ähnlichkeit 835
geometrisches Mittel 834
Geomorphologie 837
Geophon 838
Geophysik 840
peophysikalische Exploration 839
geothermisch 841
geothermischer Gradient 842
gerammter Brunnen 591
Gerinne 768
Geröllfrachtung 2455
Gesamtabfluss 2666, 2810
Gesamthärte 2807
Gesamthöhe der Energielinie 651
Gesamtporenraum 2808
Gesamtporenvolumen 2808
Gesamtproduktion 424
Gesamtverdunstung 686
Gesamtwasserverbrauch 363
gesättigte Strömung 2469
Geschiebebelastung 364
Geschiebefracht 168
Geschiebefrachtung, hüpfende 2455
Geschiebelehm 194
Geschiebemergel 849, 2789
geschweisster Tuff 2314
Geschwindigkeit 2889
- , Darcy 440
Geschwindigkeitshöhe 2890
Geschwindigkeitslog 18
Geschwindigkeitspotential 2891
Gesetz, Darcysches 438
gespanntes Grundwasser 349
Gestalt, kugelförmige 2624
Gestängetest 585
Gestängeverbinder 2799
Gestein 2426
- , anstehendes 169
- , kavernöses 262
- , klastisches 298
- , kristallines 421
- , verfestigtes 359, 1019
Gesteinsbildung 494
Gesteinsfolge 2430
Gesteinsformation 2429
Gesteinskunde 2212
Gesteinstextur 2432
Gestell 785
gestörte Probe 531
Getriebepumpe 823
gewachsener Fels 2856
Gewässerkunde 977
- , beschreibende 971
Gewässernetz 554
Gewässerschutz 2263
Gewicht, spezifisches 2618, 2978

Gewichtszahl 2977
Gewindeverbinder 2778
Gewitter 2654
Geysir 843
Gezeitenschwankung 2785
Gezeitenstrom 2783
Gezeitenwirkungsgrad 2784
Ghyben-Herzberg'sche
  Bedingungen 844
Gipfel 2703
Gipfellinie 404
Gipfelpunkt 403
gitterförmige Anordnung 2834
Glazialablagerung 845
Glaziologie 854
gleichförmig 941
gleichförmige Strömung 2866
Gleichförmigkeitsziffer (nach
  Hazen) 2867
gleichmässig 2865
Gleichstrom 512
Gleitfrana 615
Gletscher 851
– , aktiver 21
Gletscherablagerung, alluviale
  56
Gletscherfurche 848
Gletschermilch 852
Gletscherschutt 846
Gletscherspalte 408
Gletscherzunge 853
Glimmer, dunkler 180
Glimmerschiefer 2040
Glückshaken 869
Gneiss 855
graben 504, 687
Graben 532, 858
Grabental 2410
Gradient 861
– , geothermischer 842
– , hydraulischer 954
Granat 811
Granodiorit 866
Grauwacke 886
Gravimeter 876
gravimetrischer Feuchtegehalt
  877
Greifbagger 297
Grenzbelastung 2673
Grenze, festgelegte 734
Grenzfläche 366, 1058
Grenzflächenspannung 1059
Grenzsaugfähigkeit 2696
Grenzschicht 196, 350
Grenzwert 1153
Grobkörnigkeit 313
Grobsand 312
Grobsplitt 419
Grösse, diskrete 522
– , skalare 2475
Grossspore 1176
grösster Reliefunterschied 1198
Grotte 260
Grube 2242
Grubenabflusswässer 2045
Grubenwasser 2049
Grubenwässer 2045
– , saure 17
Grundeis 72
Grundgestein 169

Grundgleichung, hydrologische
  976
Grundkomplex, kristalliner 145
Grundlast 153
Grundmoränengeschiebe 1162
Grundmoränetümpel 2734
Grundquelle 2681
Grundwasser 892
– , Fliessen von gespannten – – –
  348
– , freies 2859
– , gespanntes 349
– , künstliches 2360
– , schwebendes 2190, 2876
– , unechtes 1060
– , ungespanntes 2859
– , ursprüngliches 2097
– , vadoses 2876
– , wiederkehrendes 2402
Grundwasserabbau 2051
Grundwasserabfluss 910
– , unechter 2690
Grundwasserabsenkung 907
Grundwasserabsenkungskurve
  908
Grundwasserader 893
Grundwasseranreicherung,
  induzierte 1016
– , künstliche 2357
Grundwasseraustritt, flächenhafter 2501
– , natürlicher 2098
Grundwasserbarriere 894, 973
Grundwasserbecken 895
Grundwasserbestandsaufnahme
  903
Grundwasserdargebot, sicheres
  2449
Grundwassereinzugsgebiet 895
Grundwassererhebung 905
Grundwassererschliessung 896
Grundwasserfliessgeschwindig-
  keit, tatsächliche 720
Grundwasserfluss, ungespannter
  2858
– mit freier Oberfläche 765
Grundwassergleiche 1087
Grundwasser im Permafrost-
  bereich 1070
Grundwasserleiter 100
– , artesischer 113
– , einfallender 2790
– , küstennaher 314
– , leckender 1147
Grundwasserneubildung,
  künstliche 117
Grundwasseroberfläche 2219,
  2962
Grundwasserprovinz 906
Grundwasserreservoir 909
Grundwasserscheide 901, 902
Grundwassersohle 1171
Grundwasserspeicher 909
Grundwasserspende 900
– , künstliche 116
Grundwassersperre 102, 899
Grundwasserspiegel 904, 2962
– , schwebender 2191
Grundwasserspiegelabfall
  2216

Grundwasserspiegelanstieg
  2218
Grundwasserstandsmessgerät
  163
Grundwasserstauer 99
– , begrenzt durchlässiger 103
Grundwasserstockwerk 2093
Grundwasser über der Ge-
  frornis 2710
Grundwasserüberfall 897
Grundwasser unter der
  Gefrornis 2685
Grundwasserzement 898
Grundwasserzone 2221
Grünsand 887
gut sortierte Kornklasse 3000

Haarriss 2041
Haff 1118
Haftwasserzone 3034
Hahn 318
Halbwertszeit 916
Halteseil 915
Haltungsvermögen 2403
Hang 2573
– , ansteigender 11
Hangrutsch 1125
Härte 920
– , bleibende 2202
– , permanente 2202
– , temporäre 2756
– , vorübergehende 2756
Häufigkeit 788
Häufigkeitsanalyse 789
Häufigkeitsverteilung 790
häufigster Wert 2058
Hauptschieber 822, 1183
Häutchenwasser 2183
Hauteffekt 2566
Hebekappe 937
Hebekran 938
Hebevorrichtung 1093
Hebewerk 565, 935
Hebewinde 935
Hebung 2872
Heilquelle 2017
Hele-Shawmodell 929
hervorquellen 2628
heterogen 930
Hochebene 2246
Hochscholle 946
Höchstwert 2178
Hochwasser 743, 933
Hochwasserabfluss 932
Hochwasserberechnungs-
  grundlage 480
Hochwasserlängsschnitt 749
Hochwasserscheitel 745
Hochwasserschutz 744
Hochwasserspuren 747
Hochwasserweiterleitung 750
Höhe 640, 922, 1149
– des Salzgehaltes 2453
– des Wasserspiegels 2631
Höhenlinie 374
Höhenmarkierung 172
Höhenschichtlinie 374
Höhenverteilung 106
Höhle 260
Höhlenkunde 2623

Höhlenwasser 263
Hohlraum 2266
Hohlräume 2900
- , sekundäre 2492
homogen 941
homogene Flüssigkeit 942
Horizontalbrunnen 325
Hornblende 68, 945
Hornersche Wippe 2797
Hornstein 289
Horst 946
Horton-Zahl 947
hüpfende Geschiebefrachtung 2455
Hydratation 950
Hydraulik 960
hydraulische Leitfähigkeit 951
hydraulischer Ausfluss 952
- Gradient 954
hydraulische Rissbildung 953
- Rissbildung in Brunnen 2990
hydraulischer Radius 958
- Sprung 956
- Stoss 2936
hydraulisches Profil 957
hydrodynamische Dispersion 963
- Leitfähigkeit 962
Hydrogeochemie 967
Hydrogeologie 968
Hydrograph 969
Hydrographie 971
Hydrologie 977
- des Grundwassers 827
hydrologische Grundgleichung 976
hydrologischer Kreislauf 975
- Längsschnitt 2671
- Parameter 831
hydrologisches Jahr 2967
Hydrolyse 978
Hydrometeorologie 979
Hydrometrie 981
hydrometrische Messtelle 980
Hydrophyte 984
Hydrosphäre 985
hydrostatischer Druck 986
Hygrometer 988
hygroskopischer Kern 991
hygroskopisches Wasser 992
Hygroskopizität 989, 990
Hypolimnion 993
Hysteresis 994
- , kapillare 240

Illit 999
Illuvialhorizont 175, 3033
imaginärer Brunnen 1000
Imbibition 1001
Immissionsverfahren 2815
Impedanz 1003
Impuls 2069
Inbetriebsetzung eines Brunnens 2984
Indikator 2814
Indikatorhydrograph 282
Induktion 1017
Induktionslog 1018
induktiver Widerstand 1003
Industriediamant 1020

induzierte Aktivität 1014
- Grundwasseranreicherung 1016
Infiltrationsindex 1027
Infiltrationsstrecke 1026
Infiltrometer 1029
Infiltrometeruntersuchung 1030
Infusorienerde 498
Inhalt, organischer 2137
inkompressibel 1012
innenbürtig 648
Innendurchmesser 1042
Insolation 1043
Instabilitätserscheinung 1044
Integratorschaltung 1049
intermittierende Quelle 1062
intermittierender Fluss 1063
Interzeption 1055
Interzeptionsverlust 1056
Intrusion 1072
Intrusivgestein 1073
Inversion 1078
irreduzierbare Sättigung 1080
Isobathe 1084
Isochrone 1085
Isohyete 1086
Isolierhülle 1046
isolierter Fluss 1045
Isolierverbindung 1047
Isotachenebene 934
Isotherme 1090
Isotop 1092
- , radioaktives 2325
isotropisch 1092
Iterationsmethode 2039

Jahr, hydrologisches 2967
Jahresdurchschnitt 85
jahreszeitliche Schwankung 2490
jährliche Gefrierzone 84
Jura 1103
juveniles Wasser 1104

Kabel 3020
Kabelschuh 2436
Kaldera 226
Kalibermessgerät 230
Kalibermessung 231
Kalium 2276
Kalk, schwefelsaurer 82
kalkhaltig 224
kalkig 224
Kalkkruste 229
Kalkstein 1152
- , toniger 109
kalt 321
Kalzit 225
Kambrium 232
Kame 1105
Kamm 2409
Kanal 277
Känozoikum 272
kantig 80
Kaolin 1106
Kapazität, nutzbare 124
Kapillaranstieg 242
kapillare Hysteresis 240
kapillarer Verdrängungs-
vorgang 1001

Kapillarität 236
Kapillarkraft 238
Kapillarsaum 239
Kapillarwanderung 241
Kapillarwasser 243
Karbon 250
Karbonat 246
Karbonatgestein 248
Karst 1107
Karstgebiet 1108
Karsttrichter 538, 2563
Karte 1185
Kartierung, topographische 2718
kathodischer Schutz 258
Kausche 217, 2436
kavernöses Gestein 262
keilförmige Fallwasserspei-
cherung 2976
Kern, hygroskopischer 991
Kernbohren 392
Kernbohrkrone 390
Kernen, elektrisches 633
Kernfänger 391
Kernrohr 389
Kesselbrunnen 605
Kesselumrechnungskoeffizient 2170
Kettenpegel 275
Kies 870
- , ausgewaschener 2150
- , feiner 727
Kiesel 2181
Kieselerde 2550
Kieselgur 2843
Kieselsäure 2547
- , amorphe 66
Kieselstein 2181
Kiesfilter 875
Kiesgrube 874
Kiesmantel 871
Kiesschüttung 873
kinematische Ähnlichkeit 1111
Kissenlava 2233
Klärbecken 2517
klastisches Gestein 298
kleine Schlucht 2344
Kleinstpore 2042
Klemmenspannung 2148
Klimafaktor 307
Klinkenbergeffekt 1112
Kluft 397, 1100
Kluftfläche 1101
Kluftquelle 783
Klüftung 306
Knotenpunkt 2111
Kohlendioxyd 249
Kohlensäurequelle 247
Kolbenpumpe 2251
Kolk 2282
Kompressibilität 333
Kondensation 340
Kondensationskern 341
Kondensationswärme 926
konforme Abbildung 352
Konglomerat 355
Konkretion 339
Konkretionskruste 921
konsequenter Fluss 358
Konstante, dielektrische 499

Konstitutionswasser 2943, 2945
Kontaktlog 365
Kontaktwinkel 75
Kontinentalabsatz 371
Kontinentalschelf 370
Kontinuitätsgesetz 373
Kontinuitätsgleichung 373
Kontrollschieber 377
konvektiver Niederschlag 379
konvektive Strömung 462
Konvergenz 380
Konzentrationskurve 336
Konzentrationspunkt 337
Konzentrationszeit 2794
Korn 868
Körnchen 868
Korndurchmesser, wirksamer
  621
Korngestalt 863
Korngrösse 864
Korngrössenverteilung 865
körnig 867
Kornklasse, gut sortierte 3000
Kornpackung 862
Korrasion 393
Korrelation, geologische 832
Korrosionsverhütungsmittel
  394
korrosiv 395
korrosive Wässer 22
Kraft, osmotische 2144
Kraftmesser 613
Kraftpotential 775
krankheitserregende Bakterien
  2177
Kratersee 399
Kreide 276, 407
Kreiselpumpe 273
Kreislauf, hydrologischer 975
Kreuzmeissel 415
Kreuzschichtung 414
Kriechen 401
kristalliner Grundkomplex 145
kristallines Gestein 421
Kristallisationswasser 2944
kritische Fliessgeschwindigkeit
  412
- Wassertiefe 410
Kronenblock 418
Krustenbildung 1013
kugelförmige Gestalt 2624
Kugelschussapparat 914
Kugelventil 135
Kühlwasser 384
Kulminationspunkt 2636
künstliche Einsickerung 1015
- Grundwasseranreicherung
  2357
- Grundwasserneubildung 117
- Grundwasserspende 116
künstliches Grundwasser 2360
künstliche Wetterbeeinflussung
  2975
Kurbel 398
Kurvenast, abfallender --- der
  Ganglinie 2354
- , steigender 2415
- , unbeeinflusster 96
Kurvenschaar 703
kurzfristig fliessender Fluss 659

Küstenbereich 1160
Küstenebene 315
Küstenlinie 316
küstennaher Grundwasserleiter
  314
kutikuläre Transpiration 430

Laboratoriumsdaten 1114
Labor-Durchlässigkeits-
  beiwert 1113
Lage 1141
Lagebeschreibung 2801
Lagergang 2551
Lagerung 2166
Lagune 1118
Lakkolith 1115
lakustre 1116
- Bildung 1117
- Formation 1117
laminare Strömung 1121
Lamination 1122
Landerniedrigung 463
Landform 1123
Landkessel A (Standardgerät)
  2875
Landnutzung 1128
Landoberfläche 1127
Landrutsch 1125
landschaftsformender Vorgang
  836
Landverdunstungskessel 1124
- , versenkter 2705
Landvermessung 2729
Landverwendung 1128
Längsschitt, hydrologischer
  2671
Längsverwerfung 1168
latente Verdampfungswärme
  1130
Laterit 1136
Lateriterde 1137
Laterologaufnahme 1132
Lattenpegel 2630
Laufrad 1004
Laufzeit 2821
Lauge 204
Laugung 1142
Lavamatrix 2832
Lavaröhre 1140
Lavaschicht 1138
Lavatube 1140
Lawine 125
Leck 1143
leckender Grundwasserleiter
  1147
Lehm 1161
Leiter 344
Leitfähigkeit, hydraulische 951
- , hydrodynamische 962
- , spezifische 2617
Leithorizont 1188
Leitung 345
Leitvermögen 2823
lichte Maschenweite 2544
- Weite 1042
Lichtpunkt 1151
Limnologie 1154
lineare Streuung 2003
Linie gleiches Potentials
  664

Linie gleicher Eindring-
  kapazität 1089
Linse, undurchlässige 1007
Lithologie 1157
lithologischer Faktor 1156
Lithosphäre 1159
Litoral 1160
Loch 940
Log 1164
- , geologisches 833
Logauswertung 1167
Longitudinalwelle 1169
loses Material 1011
Löslichkeit 2607
Loslösung 2512
Löss 1163
Lösung, analogische 71
- , numerische 2118
Lösungshohlraum 2910
Lösungsmethode, numerische
  2117
Lösungszustand 2642
Luftabscheider 46
Luftauslassventil 45
luftbeeinflusste Zone 3034
Luftbildaufnahme 31
Luftdruck 44
Luftfeuchte, relative 2383
Lufthebeverfahren 42
Luftseil 43
Lufttrocken 40
Lysimeter 1175

Mäander 2001
Mäandergürtel 2002
Mächtigkeit 2774
Magma 1177
Magmagestein 998
magmatisches Wasser 1178
magnetische Suszeptibilität
  1180
Magnetit 1181
Magnetometerkartierung 1179
Mahlgestein 2096
Makropore 1176
Manometer 1184
Mar 2904
Markierung, radioaktive 2323
Marmor 1186
Masche 2029
Maschenweite 2030
- , lichte 2544
Massenabtrag 463
Massenerhaltung 1190
Massenflussmessgerät 1193
Massenkräfte 189
massige Textur 1194
Masstab 2478
Masstabbeiwert 2479
Mast 1196
Material, loses 1011
- , nicht zusammenhängendes
  1011
Materialfrachtung, eingeleitete
  2917
Maximalereignis 2000
maximale Schüttung 2806
mechanische Abdeckung 2015
Medianwert 2016
Medium, poröses 2272

Meereshöhe, mittlere 2004
Meeresspiegel 2487
Meerwasser 1187, 2124
Meinzereinheit (USA) 2019
Meissel, stumpfer 606
Meisselkörper 2798
Meisselschneide 290
Meisselspiel 181
Melioration 2363
Membranmodell 2023
Membranpotential 2024
Mengenlinie 1191
Meniskus 2025
Mergel 109, 1189
Mesophyte 2031
Mesozoikum 2032
Messband 2748
Messchacht 806
Messelektrode 2278
Messflügel 2438
Messgerinne 2009
Messkabel 1165
Messkreis 2007
Messlänge einer Anordnung
  2609
Messlatte 2012, 2630
Messpule 2008
Messrinne 2010
Messtank 805
Messtation 808
Messtelle 695
- , hydrometrische 980
Messung 2006
Messwagen 1166
Messwarte 808
Messwehr 2014
Messwinde 2011
Messzylinder 2013
metamorphes Wasser 2033
meteorisches Wasser 2034
Meteorologie 2035
Methode, numerische
  (Lösungs-) 2117
- der endlichen Differenzen
  729
Mikrolog 365
Mikropore 2042
Mikrosieb 2043
Mineralien 2047
Mineralöl 2046
Mineralquelle 2048
Minimalereignis 2050
Miozän 2052
mischbar 2053
Mischlänge 2056
Mischverhältnis 2057
Mitnehmerstange 1109
mit Schichteinschaltungen
  versehen 1051
Mittel, arithmetisches 111
- , geometrisches 834
mittelkörniger Sand 2018
Mittelwert 2005
mittlere Meereshöhe 2004
mit Zwischenmitteln versehen
  1051
Mobilität, chemische 287
- der Ionen 1079
Modell 2059
Modellverfahren 2060

Modellversuch 2061
mögliche Evapotranspiration
  2279
Molekulardiffusion 2067
molekulare Anziehungskraft
  2066
Monel-Metall 2070
monoklinale Flexur 2071
monomolekulare Schicht 2073
Montmorillonit 2074
Moor 2075
Moräne 2076
Moränenablagerung 2077
Moränenschutt 2077
Morast 2316
morphometrische Analyse 2078
Mulde 2740, 2845
Muldenquelle 468
Muldental 2739
mulmig 794
multiple Reflexionen 2095
Mündung 644, 674
- eines Entwässerungsgebietes
  159
Mure 2089
Muschelkalk 386
Mutterboden 2802
Mutterlauge 2079
Mylonit 2096

Nachfall 264
Nachfolgefluss 2686
Nachfolgetal 2675
Nachfrage 458
nachgeräumter Brunnen 2346
Nachschneider 2347
nahtloses Rohr 2489
Natrium 2588
natürliche Frachtung 2101
natürlicher Fluss 2102
- Grundwasseraustritt 2098
natürliches Wasser 2103
Nebenfluss 2837, 2838
Neigung 860
Neigungsmesser 1010
Nennlast 2203
Nettoeinstrahlung 2105
Netz 2106
Netzpunkt 2111
Neutralitätspunkt 2107
Neutronenlog 2108
Neutronenquelle 2109
nicht bodenständig 55
- mischbar 1002
nicht zusammenhängendes
  Material 1011
Niederschlag 2285
- , effektiver 625
- , konvektiver 379
- , orographischer 2142
- , zykonaler 434
Niederschlagberechnungs-
  grundlage 481
Niederschläge auf Wasser-
  flächen 279
Niederschlagsbeobachtungsnetz
  2332
Niederschlagsfall
  2654
Niederschlagsfülle 13

Niederschlagsgebiet 549
Niederschlagshöhe 472
Niederschlagsmesser 2112,
  2288
Niederschlagssammler 2652
Niederschlagsschreiber 2366
Niederschlagssumme 13
Niederschlagsüberschuss
  2287
Niederschlags-Verdunstungs-
  verhältnis 2286
Niedrigwasser 1174
Niedrigwasserabfluss 1173
Niveau, piezometrisches 2232
Nonius 2892
Normale 2113
normale Verwerfung 2115
- Wassertiefe 2114
Nullhöhe 3029
Nullpunkteinstellung 3028
numerische Lösung 2118
- (Lösungs-) Methode 2117
nutzbare Kapazität 124
Nutzwasser 1021

Oase 2119
obere Permafrostgrenze 2201
- Zone der Gesteinshülle 3039
Oberfläche, spezifische
Oberflächenabfluss 2159, 2446,
  2721
- , direkter 514
Oberflächenabsenkung 1126
Oberflächenenergie, freie 786
Oberflächenfilm 2717
Oberflächenhaftwasser,
  zusammenhängendes 801
Oberflächenrückhaltung 2714,
  2720
Oberflächenspannung 2724
Oberflächenspeicherung 2714
Oberflächenverkleinerung 2712
Oberflächenwasser 2725
Oberflächenwasservorräte
  2726
oberirdisch 3
Oberkarbon 2188
Oberlauf 924
obsequenter Fluss 2120
Obsidian 2122
ofentrocken 2152
offenes System 2132
Ölbohrung 2127
Ölfeldwässer 2125
Oligozän 2128
Olivin 2129
oolithisch 2130
Optimierung 2134
Ordnungsstufe eines Flusses
  2670
Ordovizium 2135
organischer Inhalt 2137
organische Verunreinigung 2138
organogene Ablagerung 2136
Orientierung 2139
orographischer Niederschlag
  2142
Orthogonalität 2143
Ortstein 229
Oser 673

osmotische Kraft 2144
osmotischer Druck 2145
Oszillograph 2367
Ozean 2123

Packer 2165
Packung 2166
- , dichteste 2787
- , poröseste 1170
Paläozän 2168
Paläozoikum 2169
Parameter, hydrologischer 831
Partialdruck 2173
Partikel 2174
Passtück 24
Pediment 2182
Pegel 469, 2012
Pegelnullpunkt 807
Pendulärregime 2184
perennierende Quelle 2195
perennierender Fluss 2196
Perforation 2198
Perforiergerät 2996
Periode 2199
periodisch fliessender Strom
    1063
Perm 2209
Permafrost 2200
Permafrostgrenze, obere 2201
permanente Härte 2202
permanenter Welkepunkt 2205
Permeabilität, absolute 1071
- , quergerichtete 2829
- , relative 2384
Permeabilitätsbarriere 2206
Permeabilitätstensor 2207
Permeameter 2208
Petrographie 2212
Pflanzendecke 2887
pflanzennutzbares Wasser 124
Pflanzenverdunstung 2825
Pflanzenverdunstungsmesser
    2227
Pfütze 2300
Photoelektronenverstärker-
    röhre 2215
Photogeologie 2213
Photogrammetrie 2214
Phreatophyte 2222
pH-Wert 2223
Phyllit 2224
physikalische Atmosphäre 4
- Untersuchung 2225
Physiographie 2226
piezometrische Druckhöhe 2230
piezometrisches Niveau 2232
Pipeline 2239
Pitot'sche Röhre 2244
Planimeter 2245
plastische Verformung 401
- Zone der Gesteinshülle 3038
Plateau 2246
plättchenförmig 2247
Plattenschiefer 2568
Pleistozän 2248
Pliozän 2249
Pluton 162
plutonisches Wasser 2252
Podsolboden 2254
Poise 2258

Polarisierung 2259
Pore 2266
Porendruck 2268
Poreneintrittsradius 2267
Poreneis 1068
Porenfliessgeschwindigkeit
    2847
Porengehalt 2271
Porenluftgehalt 38
Porenraum 1067, 2269
- , relativer 2899
- , ursprünglicher 2141
Porensaugsaum 239
Porensaugwasser 243
Porensaugwirkung 236
Porenwasser, ursprüngliches
    357
Porenwasserdruck 2268
Porenwinkelwasser 1069
Porenwinkelwasserregime 2184
poröses Medium 2272
poröseste Packung 1170
Porosimeter 2270
Porosität 2271
- , absolute 6
- , effektive 624
- , sekundäre 2493
- , totale 2809
- , wirksame 623
Potamologie 2275
Potential 2277
- , elektrochemisches 635
Potentialelektrode 2278
Potentialströmung 2280
potentielle Evapotranspiration
    2279
Potentiometer 2281
Präkambrium 2284
Pressluft 332
Presslufthammer 41
prismatisch gespeichertes
    Fallwasser 2296
Probe, gestörte 531
Probenahme 2460
- aus der Bohrlochswand 1131
Profil, hydraulisches 957
- , seismisches 2503
Psychrometer 2299
Pufferlösung 208
Pulsgenerator 2302
Pumpanlage 2309
Pumpe, doppelt wirkende 540
Pumpenauskleidung 2310
Pumpenförderung 2304
Pumpenkammer 2305
Pumpensumpf 2704
Pumpstation 2307
Pumpversuch 2308
Punktquelle 507
Pyknometer 2311
Pyrit 2312
pyroklastischer Block 2313
Pyroxen 2315

Quartär 2317
Quarz 2318
Quecksilberinjektionsverfahren
    2028
Quecksilbermanometer 2027
Quecksilbersäule 2026

Quelle 781, 2627
- , artesische 114
- , intermittierende 1062
- , perennierende 2195
- , subaquatische 2681
Quellen 2735
Quellgebiet 924
Quellpunkt 2612
Quellstube 2613
quergerichtete Permeabilität
    2829
Querschnitt 417
- , benetzter 3009
Querverwerfung 416

radialer Fluss 2321
radioaktive Markierung 2323
radioaktiver Tracer 2323
radioaktives Isotop 2325
Radius, hydraulischer 958
Rahmen 785
Rammbär 595
Ramme 593
Rammspitze 592
Randbedingungen 195
Randwinkel 75
rationale Abflussformel 2343
Rauhigkeit 2440
Rauhigkeitsbeiwert 2441
Räumer 2347
Raumgewicht 209
Redoxpotential 2371
Reduzierstück 2372
Reduzierverbindung 2373
Reflektion, seismische 2504
Reflexionen, multiple 2095
Reflexionswinkel 77
Refraktion, seismische 2505
Regelation 2377
Regelventil 378
Regen 2327
- , effektiver 626
Regenbildung 777
Regenfall 2654
Regengleiche 1086
Regenhöhe 473
Regenintensität 2329, 2333
Regenmesser 2331
Regensimulator 2330
Regenstärke 2329
Regenstrich 3037
Regenüberschuss 2328
Regime 762
Registriergerät 2364
Registriertrommel 2365
Registrierwalze 2365
Reibungsbeiwert 795
Reibungskraft 2898
Reibungsverlust 796
- im Brunnen 2995
Reihenbildung von Bohrungen
    2982
reiner Sand 305
Reinigung verklebter Zufluss-
    flächen 446
Rekristallisation 2370
relative Durchlässigkeit 2384
- Luftfeuchte 2383
- Permeabilität
    2384

relativer Durchlässigkeitsbei-
   wert 2869
- Porenraum 2899
relative Streuung 320
Relief 2385
Reliefenergie 702, 2386, 2387
Reliefunterschied, grösster
   1198
Remanenzerscheinung 994
resequenter Fluss 2389
Rest 2394
Restabsenkung 2393
Rhyolith 2408
richtungsgebundene Ableitung
   513
richtungsmässige Anordnung
   2139
Rieselgrabenverfahren 533
Riff 2375
Ringraum 86
Rinne 768, 913, 2664
- , alluviale 57
Rinnsal 2425, 2840
Ripplemarke 2412
Riss 397
Rissbildung, hydraulische 953
- in Brunnen, hydraulische
   2990
Rohr 2236
- , nahtloses 2489
Röhre, Pitot'sche 2244
Rohrförderseil 255
Rohrschneider 2994
Rohrverbinder 2238
Rohrzange 2241
Rohwasser 2345
Rollenmeissel 2433
rostfreier Stahl 2637
Rotarybohren mit hydrau-
   lischem Antrieb 959
Rotaryverfahren mit Gegen-
   spülung 2407
Rücken 2409
Rückfluss 127, 2404
Rückgangskonstante 2353
Rückgangskurve 2354
Rückgewinnung 2363
Rückhaltevermögen 2403, 2650
Rückhaltung 484
- , effektive 620
Rückspülungsmethode 130
Rückstand 2394
Rückstau 132
Rückstaukurve 133
Rückstauwasser 132
Rückzugsmoräne 2352
ruhige Strecke 2320
- Strömung 2816
Rumpfebene 2185
Rundhöcker 599
Rundnischenquelle 2849
Rüschelzone 2526
Rutschschere 1094
Rutschspiegel 2570

Saline 2451
Salzdom 2456
Salzfestigkeit 2458
Salzgeschwindigkeitsverfahren
   634
Salzgestein 676, 685

salzhaltiger Boden 918
Salzpfanne 52
Salzsäure 961
Salzsee 2457
Salzstock 2456
Salzwasser 2452, 2459
Sammelbehälter 2390
Sammelbrunnen 325
Sammelgefäss 207
Sammelleitung 324
Sand 2461
- , mittelkörniger 2018
- , reiner 305
- , toniger 300, 2525
Sandabscheider 477, 2465
Sandbank am Gleithang 2255
Sandboden 2379
Sandkastenmodell 2463
Sandlöffel 134
Sandmodell 2463
Sandpumpe 134, 2464, 2576
Sandr 56
Sandrebene 2151
Sandstein 2466
sanitärer Brunnenschutz 2467
Saprolith 2468
Sattel 93
Satteltal 92
Sättigung, irreduzierbare 1080
Sättigungsdefizit 2470
Sättigungsdruck 2473
Sättigungsgrad 454
Sättigungspunkt 2472
Sättigungsregime 2474
Sättigungsverteilung 2471
Sättigungszone 3040
Säuerling 247
Sauerstoff 2163
Sauerstoffbedarf 2164
- , biochemischer (B.S.B.) 179
- , chemischer 288
Saugheber 2564
Saughebewirkung 2565
Saughöhe 1150, 2694, 2695
Saugleitung 2697
Saugpumpe 2698
Saugraum 1040
Saugsaum 239
Saugwirkung des Bodenwassers
   2593
säulenförmige Absonderung 326
Säulenklüftung 326
Säurebehandlung von Brunnen 16
Säuregrad 15
saure Grubenwässer 17
Schacht 2521
Schachtbrunnen 605
Schallerzeuger 2610
Schallgeschwindigkeit 2611
Schallhärte 19
Schauer 2654
Schaufelrad 1004
Scheibe 2532
Scheide 536
scheinbarer spezifischer
   Widerstand 95
Scheitelung, untere 2636
Schenkel 735
Scherfestigkeit 2529
Schergeschwindigkeit 2530
Scherintensität 2528

Scherung 2527
Scherungswelle 2830
Scherwelle 2531
Schicht 165, 1141, 2660
- , monomolekulare 2073
- , undurchlässige 350
Schichteinschaltungen, mit
--- versehen 1051
Schichtenfolge 2513, 2693
Schichtflexur 2071
Schichtfuge 166, 2175
Schichtlücke 2860
Schichtmächtigkeit 2774
Schichtneigungsmessung 511
Schichtprofil 828
Schichtquelle 197, 368
Schichtströmung 1121
Schichtstufe 422
Schichtung 1122, 2658
- nach dem Salzgehalt 2454
Schichtungsebene 167
Schieber 822
Schiefer 2480, 2568
- , benthonischer 174
Schieferung 2481
Schiessen 2337
Schild 2535
Schillkalk 386
Schirmelektrode 911
Schlacke 2567
- , vulkanische 2567
Schlagbohrer 294
Schlagbohrverfahren 2194
Schlagbrunnen 591
Schlagbrunnenspitze 592
Schlamm 2083
Schlammstrom 2089
Schlauch 737
- , biegsamer 737
Schleppkraft 252
Schlucht 857
- , kleine 2344
Schluckbohrung 527
Schluckfähigkeit 1038
Schluff 2553
Schlund 9
Schlüsselloch 413
Schmandlöffel 134, 2576
Schmelzen 2020
Schmelzpunkt 2021
Schmelztuff 2314
Schmelzwässer 2022
Schmelzwasserablagerung
   2149
Schmutzstoff 2260
Schmutzwasser 2261
Schnee 2578
Schneeausstecher 2585
Schneedecke 2579
Schneedichte 2580
Schneegrenze 2583
Schneeniederschlagsmesser
   2582
Schneepegel 2586
Schneeprobenehmer 2585
Schneeschmelze 2584
Schneetiefe 474
Schneewehe 2581
Schneide 431
Schnitt, geologischer 829

Schnittpunkt 1054
Schockpunkt 2536
Schöpfseil 2462
Schotterfüllung 872
Schreiber 2364
Schreibpegel 2959
Schreibregenmesser 2366
Schreibspur 2189
Schrotbohren 2539
Schuppe 2476
Schürfbohrung 692
Schürfloch 2764
Schusspunkt 2540
Schutt 444, 486
Schuttfächer 2747
- , alluvialer 58
Schüttgewicht 209
Schuttkegel 2746
Schuttmantel, dünner 61
Schüttung 2983
- , maximale 2806
Schutz, kathodischer 258
Schutzhülle 1046
Schutzverrohrung 2298
Schwankung, jahreszeitliche 2490
- des Grundwasserspiegels 2217
Schwebefrachtung 2730
schwebender Grundwasser-spiegel 2191
schwebendes Grundwasser 2190, 2876
- Wasser 2732
Schwebstoff 2731
Schwebstoffbelastung 2730
Schwefelkies 2312
Schwefelsäure 2701
schwefelsaurer Kalk 82
Schwefelwasserstoff 966
Schweissverbindung 2981
Schwelle 2552
Schwellensättigungswert 2779
Schwereanomalie 880
Schwerekomponente 881
Schweremesser 876
Schweremessmethode 884
Schwerewasser 878
Schwerkraft 883
Schwerkraftentwässerung 882
Schwerstange 569, 2562
Schwimmer 739
Schwimmerschacht 806
Schwimmerschreibpegel 740
Schwimmsand 2319
Schwingungsweite 69
Sedimentablagerung 2494
Sedimentation 2495
Sedimentfrachtung 2496
Sedimenttransport 2496
See 1120
Seehöhe 2487
Seeverdunstung 2391
sehr langsame Fliessbewegung 402
seigere Sprunghöhe 2782
Seihverlust 233
Seil 3020
Seilbahn 222
Seilbohren 216

Seilpegel 3019
Seilschlagbohren 221
Seilschlagbohrer 220
Seiltrommel 218
seismische Brechung 2505
- Reflextion 2504
- Refraktion 2505
seismisches Profil 2503
seismische Welle 2506
Seismometer 2507
Seitenerosion 137
Seitenmoräne 1135
Seitental 2839
seitliche Einebnung 1133
seitlicher Zufluss 1134
sekundäre Hohlräume 2492
- Porosität 2493
Selbstreinigungskraft 2509
Selektivabsorption 2508
selektive Absorption 2508
Senkbrunnen 2361
Senke 2561, 2845
Senkkasten 223
Senkschacht 2359
Serpentin 2514
sichere Ausbeute 2449
- Entnahme 2449
sicheres Grundwasserdargebot 2449
Sicherheitsventil 2448
Sicherheitswert der Entnahme 2450
Sickerbeckenmethode 158
Sickerfläche 2502
Sickergeschwindigkeit 2500
Sickerquelle 2501
Sickerrate 2500
Sickerschacht 2539
Sickerstrecke 2502
Sickerströmung 2193, 2497
Sickerung 2497
Sickerwasser 1028
Sickerweg 2499
Sieb 2484, 2542
Siebanalyse 2543
Siebanlage 2485
Siebblech 2575
Siebrohr 2486, 2574
Siebrückstand 2545
Silberjodid 2557
Silikat 2550
Silikatgestein 2546
Siliziumbronze 2549
Siliziumdioxyd 2550
Siliziummessing 2548
Silur 2556
Siphon 2564
Skalare 2475
skalare Grösse 2475
Skalennullpunkt 807
Sohlschicht 1171
Solifluktion 2606
Solquelle 2451
Sonde 940, 2297
Sonnenbestrahlung 1043
Sonnenstrahlung 2603
Spaltbarkeit 306
Spalte 409, 733
Spannungsmesser 2281, 2907
Speicherfähigkeit 2650

Speicherkoeffizient 2651
Speichersee 2390
Speicherungsbeiwert 2651
Speichervermögen 2650
Spende 761
spenden 516
spezifische Absenkung 2616
- Ergiebigkeit 2614, 2622
- Leitfähigkeit 2617
- Oberfläche 2620
spezifischer elektrischer
 .Widerstand 632
- Fluss 772
- Widerstand 2398
spezifisches Gewicht 2618, 2978
- Volumen 2621
- Wasserhaltungsvermögen 2619
Spiegel 1149
Spillseil 259
Spitze 2178
Spitzenabfluss 2179
Spitzensegment 405
Spitzenwert 2178
Spitzenwertanzeiger 406
Spleiss 219
Sprengkapsel 184, 485
Sprengstoff 694
Sprengung 693
Springbrunnen 781
Springquelle 843
Sprödbruch 205
Sprung 706
- , hydraulischer 956
Sprunghöhe, seigere 2782
Sprungschicht 2771
Spülbohrung 1098
spülen 2411
Spülkopf 1037
Spülkopfkrümmer 856
Spülungsauslass 2091
Spülungsfiltrat 2088
Spülungskreislauf 2085
Spülungspumpe 2092
Spülungssäule 2086
Spülungsverlust 2090
Spülungszusatz 2084
Spülwasser 131
Spurenbestandteil 2812
Spurenelement 2812, 2813
Stahl, nichtrostender 2637
Stalagmit 2639
Stalaktit 2638
Stammabfluss 2646
Standanzeiger 2634
Standardabweichung 2640
Standardbohrgerät 2641
Standardgerät 2112
Standrohr 2713
statistische Analyse 2643
Staudamm 435
Staudruckmesser 2244
stauen 1009
Staukurve 133
Stauquelle 144
Stausee 2390, 2393
Stauseeverdunstung 2391
Stechpegel 943
Stehendwasser 443

Steigdauer 2795
steigender Kurvenast 2415
steigendes Wasser 751
Steiggeschwindigkeit 2416
Steigrohr 2413, 2414
Steigung 860
steil 2645
Steilabfall 672
Steilufer 931
Stein 2426
Steinboden 1158
Steinfall 2427
Steinpackung 2428
Steinsalz 917
stetige Strömung 2644
Steuerventil 378
Stichprobe 2335
Stickstoff 2110
Stielgang 2104
Stirnfluss 2120
Stoffübertragung 1195
stomatäre Transpiration 2649
Stopfbüchse 2167, 2680
Stöpseln eines Brunnens 2727
Störgeräusch 128
Störung 530
Störungszone 710
Stoss, hydraulischer 2936
Stossdämpfung 67
Stosswelle 2537
Strahl 1095
Strahlenverseuchung 2322
Strand 164
Stratigraphie 2659
Strecke, ruhige 2320
Streichen 2674
Streuströme 2661
Streuung 2884
- , lineare 2003
- , relative 320
Strom 2417, 2667
- , periodisch fliessender 1063
- , unbeeinflusster 2102
Stromelektrode 427
Stromentwicklung 2665
Stromfaden 2672
Stromgeschwindigkeitsmesser
  428
Stromlinie 2669
Strommesser 65
Stromnetz 2423
Stromschnelle 2336
Stromtal, verdecktes 212
Strom- und Potentiallinien-
  netz 760
Strömung, gesättigte 2469
- , gleichförmige 2866
- , konvektive 462
- , laminare 1121
- , ruhige 2816
- , stetige 2644
- , unbeeinflusste 2895
- , unstetige 2871
- in der belüfteten Zone 2870
Strömungsnetz 760
Strömungspotential 2668
Strömungswiderstand 544
Strudel 3013
Struktur, chaotische 281
Strukturdom 2677

Strukturfaktor 2678
Strukturgeologie 2679
Stufe 672
stumpfer Meissel 606
Sturm 2654
Sturzflut 736
subaquatische Quelle 2681
subartesischer Brunnen 2682
Sublimation 2683
subsequenter Fluss 26, 2686
subsequentes Tal 2675
Suchgerät 1144
Sulfat 2700
Summenganglinie 758, 1191
Summenkurve 1191, 2702
Sumpf 190, 2704
Superposition 2707
Süsswasser 791
Süsswasserbarriere 792
Suszeptibilität, magnetische
  1180
Syenit 2738
synoptisches Beobachtungs-
  netz 2741
synthetische Einheitskurve der
  Abflussganglinie 2742
System, offenes 2132
Szintallationszähler 2482

Tafelberg 2743
Tagebau 2719
täglich 534
Tal 2877
- , antezedentes 91
- , aufgesetztes 2706
- , epigenetisches 2706
- , subsequentes 2675
- , tektonisches 2751
Talhang 2879
Talk 2745
Talquelle 2880
Talschutt 2878
Talsperre 435
Talweg 2766
tatsächliche Grundwasser-
  fliessgeschwindigkeit 720
Taubildung 491
Tauchkolbenpumpe 2243, 2251
Tauchpumpe 2684
Taupunkt 492
Teich 2264
Teilchen 2174
Teil pro Million 2176
tektonisch 2750
tektonische Geologie 2679
tektonisches Tal 2751
Temperaturgradient, verti-
  kaler 1129
Temperaturlog 2754
Temperaturschichtung 2770
Temperaturumkehr 1078
Temperaturwirksamkeit 2753
temporäre Härte 2756
Tensorgrösse 2758
Terrasse 2760
Tertiär 2762
Testbohrung 2763
Textur, massige 1194
Theis'sche Brunnengleichung
  2767

theoretischer Einheitshydro-
  graph 2742
Thermalquelle 2769
Thermoelement 2772
Thermometer 2773
Thiem'sche Brunnenformel
  2776
Thixotropie 2777
Tidefluss 2786
Tiefbohrung 448
Tiefenanzeiger 469
Tiefenlinie 1084
Tiefenschurf 2483
Tiefscholle 858
Tobel 2344
Ton 299, 302
Tongestein 2555
tonhaltig 108
toniger Kalkstein 109
- Sand 300, 2525
Tonmineral 301
Tonpfropfen 303
Tonrohr 2788
Topographie 2801
topographische Kartierung 2718
- Wasserscheide 2800
Torf 2180
Torsion 2803
Torsionswaage 2804
Tortuosität 2805
totale Porosität 2809
Totalisator 2652
Tracer, radioaktiver 2323
Tracerverfahren 2815
Tragseil 251
Transgression 2818
Transpiration 2825
- , kutikuläre 430
- , stomatäre 2649
Transpirationshöhe 2826
Transpirationskoeffizient 2827
Transportfähigkeit 252, 382
Transportvorgang 2828
Transversalwelle 2531
Travertin 2831
Treibkappe 589
Treibsand 566
Treibschelle 590
Treibspitze 592
Treibstange 594
Tremolit 2835
Trennung 2512
Trias 2836
Trinkbarkeit 2273
Trinkwasser 586, 2274
Tripelpunkt 2842
Tritium 2844
trocken 110
Trockenbatterie 600
trockene Bohrung 601
Trockeneis 602
Trockenheit 596
Trockenofen 603
Trockenpflanze 3025
Trockenriss 2087
Trockenrückstand 604
Trockenschrank 603
Trockenwetterkurve 149
Trockenwetterlinie 2356
Trocknen 479

Trocknungsrate 2339
Trocknungsriss 483
Trog 2845
Trommel 598
Tropfenabfang 1055, 1056
Tropfendurchfall 2781
Tropfstein 587
Trübung 2851
Tuff 2850
- , geschweisster 2314
Turbinenpumpe 2852
Turbulenz 2854
Turmalin 2811

Überbohren 2918
Überdruck 2161
Überfallwehr 2625
Überflusswehr 2158
Übergang 2819
Übergangszone 2820
Übergreifen der Brunnensenk-
    flächen 2993
Überlagerungsdruck 2155
Überlast 2160
Überlauf 2156
überlaufen 2157
Übersättigung 2708
Überschiebung 2162
Überschwemmung 743, 1074
Überschwemmungsgebiet 748
Überschwemmungsmethode 746
über Tage 3
Übertageausrüstung 2716
Überwasserspiegelzone 3034
Überzug 317
Ufer 136, 643, 2538
Uferböschung 643
Uferdamm 2100
Ufererosion 137
Uferfiltrierung 138
Uferspeicherung 138
Umbiegung 173
Umfang, benetzter 3010
Umgehungsleitung 215
Umrechnungsfaktor 381
Umrechnungszahl 381
unbeeinflusster Kurvenast 96
unbeeinflusster Strom 2102
unbeeinflusste Strömung 2895
unbehandeltes Wasser 2345
unberührte Zone 2862
Undichtigkeit 1143
Undichtigkeitsfaktor 1145
Undichtigkeitszahl 1146
undurchlässig 1005, 1006
undurchlässige Linse 1007
- Schicht 350
unechter Grundwasserabfluss
    1060, 2690
ungesättigte Durchlässigkeits-
    ziffer 2869
ungesättigter Fluss 2870
ungespannter Grundwasserfluss
    2858
ungespanntes Grundwasser
    2859
ungleichförmig 930
unregelmässiger Gang 2676
unstetige Strömung 2871
untere Scheitelung 2636

Untergrund 2688
Untergrundsperre 899
unterirdisch 2691
unterirdischer Abfluss 2689
- Fluss 2692
unterirdische Wässer 2864
Unterkarbon 2055
Unterlauf 1172, 2744
Unterlegscheibe 2916
Untersetzung 2374
Unterströmung 2863
untersuchte Zone 3035
Untersuchung, physikalische
    2225
Untersuchungsbohrung 2763
Unterwasser 2744
Unterwasserpumpe 2684
Unterwasserseil 3007
Unterwasserspiegelzone 3040
Unterwasserturbinenpumpe
    449
unverrohrte Bohrung 2857
unvolkommener Brunnen 2172,
    2749
Urgebirge 145
ursprünglicher Porenraum 2141
ursprüngliches Einfallen 2140
- Grundwasser 2097
- Porenwasser 357

vadoses Grundwasser 2876
Vektorfeld 2886
Ventil 2881
Venturikanal 411
verästelt 460
Verbindung 1099
Verbrauch 458
Verbrauchsrate 2338
Verbundwirtschaft 356
Verdampfung 2882
Verdampfungswärme 927
- , latente 1130
verdecktes Stromtal 212
Verdichtung 327
Verdrängung 525
- mit einem Lösungsmittel
    2054
Verdrängungspumpe 526
Verdrängungsvorgang,
    kapillarer 1001
Verdrehung 2803
Verdrillung 2803
Verdunstung 677
Verdunstungshöhe 470
Verdunstungskessel 681
Verdunstungsmesser 118
Verdunstungsrückstand 2394
Verdunstungsunterdrückung
    683
Verdunstungsverlust 679
Verdunstungsverminderung 682
Verdunstungsvermögen 684
Verdunstungswaage (nach
    Wild) 2924
Verfahren imaginärer Ab-
    bildungen in der komplexen
    Ebene 2038
verfestigtes Gestein 359, 1019
Verfestigung 360
Verfestigungsgrad 453

Verformung 450
- , plastische 401
Verfrachtung 2828
verfügbares Wasser (für die
    Verdunstung) 680
Vergletscherung 850
Verhältnisse, geologische 830
Verhärtung 919
Verjüngung 2382
Verkittung 267
verkleben 308
Verleihung 97
Verlustzone 2775
Vermessung 2728, 2729
Vermessungskunde 825
Verriegelung 187
Verrohrung 253, 2237
- , vorläufige 2755
Verrohrungsschuh 256
Verschiebung, dielektrische
    500
Verschleissfestigkeit 2973
Verschlickung 2554
Verschmutzung 369, 2262
Versenkbrunnen 527
versenkter Landverdunstungs-
    kessel 2705
Versickerungsbecken 1024
Versickerungsbrunnen 8, 2361
Versickerungsbrunnenkette
    2358
Versickerungschacht 2359
versiegen 2445
versiegender Brunnen 701
versinkender Fluss 1066
Versorgungsnetz 2709
Verspätung 2793
Versuchsbecken 691
Versuchsbohrung 2763
Versuchswerte 1114
verstopfen 308
Verteilerrohr 2240
Verteilung 523
- der Niederschlagsintensität
    2655
Verteilungskurve 529
Vertiefung 467
vertikaler Temperaturgradient
    1129
verunreinigtes Wasser 2261
Verunreinigung 2260, 2262
- , organische 2138
Verwerfung 706
- , normale 2115
Verwerfungsebene 708
Verwerfungslinie 707
Verwerfungsquelle 2861
Verwerfungsstufe 709
Verwerfungszone 710
Verwitterung 2974
Verzahnung 1057
Verzögerung 455, 1119, 2793
Verzweigungsverhältnis 178
Viskosimeter 2896
Viskosität 2897
volkommenes Eindringen eines
    Brunnens 329
Vollanalyse 330
Vollbohrverfahren 799
Vollverrohrung 183

Voltmeter 2907
Volumen, spezifisches 2621
Volumenflussmessgerät 2908
volumetrischer Feuchtegehalt
  2909
Vorbohrer 2629
Vorbohrmeissel 2234
Vordringen 646
Vorfluter 2351
Vorgang, landschaftsformender
  836
Vorgebirge 797
vorhergehender Bodenwasser-
  gehalt 89
vorläufige Verrohrung 2755
Vorratsverminderung 465
Vorrichtung zur Durch-
  lässigkeitsmessung 2208
Vorschubgeschwindigkeit 2187
vorübergehende Härte 2756
Vorwetterbeiwert 88
Vulkanasche 2903
vulkanische Schlacke 2567
vulkanisches Wasser 2906
Vulkanismus (im engeren
  Sinne) 2902
Vulkanismus (im weiteren
  Sinne) 997
Vulkanschlot 2905
Vulkansee 2904

wabenförmig 64
Wadi 2915
wahrnehmbare Wärme 2511
Wallberg 673
Walze 598
Wanderung 2044
Wärme, wahrnehmbare 2511
Wärmeaustausch 925
Wärmeinhalt 654
Wärmeleitfähigkeit 2768
Wärmeschichtung 2770
Wärmeumsatz 928
Warve 2885
Wasser 2923
- , ausnutzbares 124
- , eingedämmtes 2265
- , eingeführtes 1008
- , endogenes 1178
- , fallendes 2687
- , funikuläres 801
- , hygroskopisches 992
- , juveniles 1104
Wässer, korrosive 22
Wasser, magmatisches 1178
- , metamorphes 2033
- , meteorisches 2034
- , natürliches 2103
- , pflanzennutzbares 124
- , plutonisches 2252
- , schwebendes 2732
- , steigendes 751
- , unbehandeltes 2345
Wässer, unterirdische 2864
Wasser, verfügbares (für die
  Verdunstung) 680
- , verunreinigtes 2261
- , vulkanisches 2906
Wasserabgabe durch Ver-
  dunstung 678

wasserabgebender Fluss 1032
Wasserabscheider 2954
wasserabstossend 983
wasseranziehend 982
Wasseranziehungskraft 990
Wasseraufnahmefähigkeit 2650
wasseraufnehmender Fluss 628
Wasseraustritt, flächenhafter
  2722
Wasserbedarf 2933, 2950
Wasserbeschaffenheit 2948
Wasserbewirtschaftung 2929
Wasserbilanz 2927
Wasserdampf 2964
Wasserdarbietung 2960
Wasserdurchtränkung 2941
Wassereinbruch 2937
Wasserergiebigkeit 2968
Wasserfassung 2928
wasserführend 2925
Wasserführung im Hauptfluss-
  lauf 1182
Wassergehalt 2930
Wassergewinnung 2928
Wassergüte 2948
wasserhaltig 2925
Wasserhaltungsvermögen,
  spezifisches 2619
Wasserhammer 2936
Wasserhärte 920
Wasserhaushalt 974
Wasserhebung 2947
Wasser in der luftbeeinflussten
  Zone 2732
Wasserkrankheit 2926
Wasserkreislauf 2932
Wasserlauf 2931
Wasserleitung 2946
wasserlöslich 2957
Wassermangel 2956
Wassermessung 2935
Wassermutung durch Wünschel-
  rutengänger 543
Wassernutzung 2963
Wasserpflanze 984
Wasserprobe 2953
Wasserrecht 2938
Wasserrückgewinnung 2949
Wasserrückhaltevermögen 2619
Wasserschatz 2951
Wasserscheide 536, 552, 2955
- , topographische 2800
Wasserspeicherung an der
  Bodenoberfläche 2253, 2720
- in Senken 2653
Wasserspende 2968
Wasserspiegel 2939
Wasserspiegelgefälle 2961
Wasserstand 2631, 2958
Wasserstandsanzeiger 2634
Wasserstandsganglinie 2633
- im Brunnenschacht 2992
Wasserstoffbrückenbindung 964
Wasserstoffexponent 2223
Wasserstoffionenkonzentration
  965
Wassertiefe, kritische 410
- , normale 2114
Wassertiefenmessgerät 705
Wasseruhr 2942

Wasserversorgung 2960
Wasservorräte 2951
Wasserweg 2965
Wasserwerk 2966
Wasserwert des Schnees 2934
Wasserwirtschaft 2952
Wechsel 2406
Wechselstrom 63
Wehr 2625, 2979
Wehrbeiwert 2980
Weite, lichte 1042
weiterleiten 2443
Weiterleitung 2822
welken 3015
Welkepunkt 3016
- , permanenter 2205
Welle 2522
- , seismische 2506
Wellenausbreitung 2971
Wellenfront 2969
Wellengeschwindigkeit 2972
Wellenweg 2970
Weltmeer 2123
Wendepunkt 2256
Werkbühne 2133
Wert, dichtester 2058
- , diskontinuierlicher 522
- , häufigster 2058
Wetterbeeinflussung, künst-
  liche 2975
Wetterkunde 2035
Wichte 2978
Widerstand, induktiver 1003
- scheinbarer spezifischer 95
- , spezifischer 2398
- , spezifischer elektrischer 632
Widerstand-Elektrodenab-
  standskurve 2400
Widerstandsbeiwert 546
Widerstands-Kapazitätsnetz
  2395
Widerstandslog 2399
Widerstandsmessung 2401
Widerstandsthermometer 2396
Wiederauffüllung 2357
Wiederaufwältigung 3024
Wiederherstellung 2363
wiederkehrendes Grundwasser
  2402
Windablagerung 658
Winde 245, 1093
Windfaktor 3017
Windfeld 3018
Windmesser 74
Wippe 2797
- , Hornersche 2797
Wirbel 619, 3013
wirbelfreier Fluss 1083
wirksame Porosität 623
wirksamer Korndurchmesser
  621
Wirkungsgrad, barometrischer
  141
Wolke 310
Wolkenbruch 213, 311
Wollastonit 3022
Wünschelrute 537
Wünschelrutenmutung 543
Wurzelwerk 2587
Wurzelzone 2435

Wüste 478

Zähigkeit 2897
Zahnradpumpe 823
Zeitalter 666
Zeitdauer bis zum Anfangs-
    einsatz 112
Zeitgleiche 1085
Zeitzähler 2796
Zement 265
Zementabdichtung 270
Zementation 267
Zementationsgrad 453
Zementbrühe 271
Zementhaftung 268
zementieren 266
Zentralwert 2016
Zerfallsprodukt 445
zersetzen 447
Zerstreuung 523
Zeta-Potential 3030
Ziehbrunnen 564
Zirkon 3031
Zisterne 296
zonales Bodenprofil 3032
Zone, bodennahe 2602
- , geflutete 771, 1075
- , luftbeeinflusste 3034
- , unberührte 2862
- , untersuchte 3035
- der Gesteinshülle, obere 3039
- der Gesteinshülle, plastische
    3038
- des angewitterten Ausgangs-
    gesteins 293
- des unverwitterten Ausgangs-
    materials 493
Zufallsverteilung 2334
Zufluss 1031
- , seitlicher 1134
Zugfestigkeit 2757
zulässige Belastung 2210
Zusammenfluss 351
zusammenhängendes Ober-
    flächenhaftwasser 801
Zusammensetzung 331
Zuschusswasser 328
Zustandsgleichung 663
Zwickelwasser 1069
Zwischenfluss 1050
Zwischengebirgszone 1064
Zwischenkornspannung 1061
Zwischenmittel 1052, 1053
Zwischenmitteln, mit ---
    versehen 1051
Zwischenraum 1067
Zyklus 433
zykonaler Niederschlag 434